AN INTRODUCTION TO
ALGEBRAIC
STRUCTURES

HOLDEN-DAY SERIES IN MATHEMATICS
Earl E. Coddington and Andrew M. Gleason, Editors

AN INTRODUCTION TO

ALGEBRAIC
STRUCTURES

Azriel Rosenfeld

University of Maryland

HOLDEN-DAY

San Francisco, Cambridge, London, Amsterdam

To the memory of
my mother

FOREWORD

This book has two central themes. First, it separates out the universal-algebra parts of "group theory" and develops them in a broader context. This is not, as a rule, more difficult than deriving them for groups (or groups with operators), and it has the advantage that their generality is more apparent. Here the treatment begins with the mapping theorems (**18**)† and with the Jordan–Hölder and Krull–Schmidt theorems for modular lattices (**14–15**). The former have as immediate corollaries the isomorphism theorems for groupoids (**26**), while the latter are easily extended into the Jordan–Hölder and Krull–Schmidt theorems for groupoids and groupoids with idempotent elements (**28–29, 39**). All of these results then generalize trivially to universal algebras (**56**), of which groups with operators are a very special case (**63–65**). The concepts of dimension and rank are also defined here for ordered sets and lattices (**10, 12**), and later extended to Abelian groups (**51**) and vector spaces (**67**).

Second, the book emphasizes the essential unity of the elementary "theories" of groups, Abelian groups, rings, fields, and vector spaces by developing them in the context of a central, general problem—namely, that of describing the algebraic structures which satisfy "finiteness conditions": prime, monogenic, finite, finitely generated (**42 ff.**). This leads naturally to such topics as Cauchy's and Sylow's theorems (**46**); simple and "semisimple" groups (**47–48**) and Hamiltonian groups (**55**); finitely generated Abelian groups (**50, 52**); simple and finite field extensions, Galois fields and Galois theory (**70–73**); and the Wedderburn theorems on simple and semisimple rings (**74–75**).

An attempt has been made to make the book relatively self-contained, even to the extent of deriving, rather than assuming, needed results about natural numbers (**4–5**) and cardinal numbers (**20–21**), as well as Zorn's lemma (**9**).

† Boldface numbers in parentheses refer to sections.

These sections can be skimmed or skipped if desired. On the other hand, the sections on relations and functions (**2–3**) should be read carefully.

Some of the results presented here are new, or at least have not appeared previously in book form. Among these are parts of the theory of normal subsets and subgroupoids (**27–28**) and its specialization to groups (**38**), as well as the theorems on prime semigroups (**44**), prime semirings (**69**), and lattice-finite rings (**76**).

Most of the readers of this book will have had some degree of prior exposure to algebraic structures. At many points in the book it has been found desirable to step aside from the formal development and make remarks which assume such prior knowledge, or which informally introduce or comment on parts of the formal material. These "asides" have been indented in order to set them off from the body of the book.

The exercises have been interspersed throughout the text, rather than being grouped at the ends of sections. This was done because most of them are actually propositions or lemmas which form an integral part of the main development, and which are often used (and referred to) later on, but whose proofs are left to the reader. The exercises vary in degree of difficulty from trivial to hard, with the majority being relatively easy. The reader is strongly advised to solve them as he goes along.

Credit is due to the many students at Yeshiva University and the University of Maryland who were subjected to much of the material of this book, in various formative stages, during 1958–60 and 1963–5. Special thanks to Messrs. Peter A. Kolmus and John L. Pfaltz, who reviewed many sections of the book as part of a reading course. Mr. Kolmus also carefully checked most of the first half of the book and proposed a number of improvements; in particular, he developed the proof of the main theorem in Section 15 (Lemmas 1–3 and Theorem 1). Thanks also to Professor Victor B. Schneider and Mr. James W. Snively, Jr., who participated in a review of the final draft. Last, first, and always, deepest appreciation to the author's wife for her continuing patience and encouragement, without which this book, and so much else, could never have been possible.

Suggestions for further reading

N. Bourbaki, *Algèbre*. Hermann, Paris, 1951–9. (English translation, Addison-Wesley, Reading, Mass. (in preparation).)

P. M. Cohn, *Universal Algebra*. Harper and Row, New York, 1965.

S. Lang, *Algebra*. Addison-Wesley, Reading, Mass., 1965.

E. Schenkman, *Group Theory*. Van Nostrand, Princeton, N.J., 1965.

TABLE OF CONTENTS

AN INTRODUCTION TO
ALGEBRAIC
STRUCTURES

I

SETS, FUNCTIONS, AND NUMBERS

In this and the next three chapters we set the stage for our study of algebraic structures by developing certain basic properties of sets, functions, equivalence relations, order relations, natural numbers, and cardinal numbers that will be needed in later chapters.

1. SETS

This section reviews the fundamentals of the "algebra of sets"—the concepts and basic properties of set, element of a set, subset, union, intersection, and relative complement. We make no distinction here between "sets" and "classes"; our set theory is strictly naïve.

SETS AND THEIR ELEMENTS

We take "**set**" and "**is an element of**" as undefined concepts; "$x \in S$" means "x is an element of S." One often says, equivalently, that "x is in S," or that "S contains x." We write "$x \notin S$" for "x is not in S."

Sets are often defined by listing their elements inside a pair of braces. For example, $\{a\}$ means "the set whose only element is a"; $\{a, b\}$ means "the set whose elements are a and b"; and so on. Here a and b are supposed to be different from one another; $\{a, a\}$ means the same thing as $\{a\}$.

We write $a = b$ ("a equals b") for "a and b are the same," and $a \neq b$ ("a is unequal to b") for "a and b are different." Since a set is defined by specifying its elements, the sets A and B are equal if and only if they have the same elements—that is, if and only if $x \in A$ implies $x \in B$ and vice versa.

1

Evidently $\{a\} = \{b\}$ if and only if $a = b$; and for all sets A, B, C we have

(1) $A = A$
(2) $A = B$ implies $B = A$
(3) $A = B$ and $B = C$ imply $A = C$.

In words: Equality is **reflexive**, **symmetric**, and **transitive**.

Another important way of defining a set is by *describing* its elements. When doing this, we usually use the notation $\{x \mid x$ has a specified property$\}$ (read: "the set of x such that x has a specified property"). For example,

$$\{x \mid x \text{ is a chapter of this book}\}$$

defines the set of chapters of this book.

> There are usually many different ways of describing a given set. For example, the following all define the same set (the concepts involved will be introduced formally later on):
>
> $\{2, 4\}$
> $\{x \mid x \in \mathbf{N}; \; x \le 4; \; x \ne 1, 3\}$
> $\{x \mid x = 2y \text{ for some } y \in \mathbf{N}; \; x < 5\}$
> $\{2x \mid x \in \mathbf{N}, \; x < 3\}$.

A property which does not apply to anything ("x is the hundredth chapter of this book," "x is blue and not blue," etc.) defines a set which has no elements. Such a set is called **empty**. Evidently all empty sets are equal, so that we can speak of "the" empty set; this set is denoted by $\varnothing$.

INCLUSION; SUBSETS

We say that the set A is **contained** in the set B if every element of A is also an element of B. If A is contained in B, we write $A \subseteq B$, and say that A is a **subset** of B. The concept of "containedness" of sets in one another is usually called **inclusion**. The following properties of inclusion are left as exercises:

Exercise 1. *For all sets A, B, C we have*

(a) $A \subseteq A$
(b) *If $A \subseteq B$ and $B \subseteq A$, then $A = B$*
(c) *If $A \subseteq B$ and $B \subseteq C$, then $A \subseteq C$.*

In words: Inclusion is **reflexive**, **weakly antisymmetric**, and **transitive**.

Exercise 2. *For any set S we have*

(a) $\varnothing \subseteq S$
(b) $S \subseteq \varnothing$ *if and only if $S = \varnothing$.*

Exercise 3. $\{x\} \subseteq S$ *if and only if $x \in S$.*

If $A \subseteq B$, we can also say that B **contains** A (notation: $B \supseteq A$). If $A \subseteq B$ but $A \neq B$, we say that A is a **proper** subset of B (or that A is properly contained in B, or that B properly contains A), and write $A \subset B$ (or $B \supset A$).

Exercise 4. *Prove that $\supseteq$ is reflexive, weakly antisymmetric, and transitive.*

Exercise 5. *Prove that $\subset$ is* **irreflexive** *(that is, $A \subset A$ is always false),* **antisymmetric** *(that is, $A \subset B$ and $B \subset A$ are never both true), and transitive.*

UNION, INTERSECTION, RELATIVE COMPLEMENT

If A and B are sets, we define the **union** of A and B as

$$\{x \mid x \in A \quad \text{or} \quad x \in B \quad \text{(or both)}\}$$

and the **intersection** of A and B as

$$\{x \mid x \in A \quad \text{and} \quad x \in B\}.$$

These sets are denoted by $A \cup B$ and $A \cap B$, respectively. Example: The union of $\{a, b\}$ and $\{b, c\}$ is $\{a, b, c\}$, and their intersection is $\{b\}$.

Exercise 6. *For all sets A, B, C we have*

(a) $A \cup A = A \cap A = A$
(b) $A \cup B = B \cup A$ *and* $A \cap B = B \cap A$
(c) $A \cup (B \cup C) = (A \cup B) \cup C$ *and* $A \cap (B \cap C) = (A \cap B) \cap C$
(d) $A \cup (B \cap C) = (A \cup B) \cap (A \cup C)$ *and*
    $A \cap (B \cup C) = (A \cap B) \cup (A \cap C)$.

In words: Union and intersection are **idempotent,** **commutative,** *and* **associative,** *and each of them* **distributes** *over the other.*

Exercise 7. *If $A' \subseteq A$ and $B' \subseteq B$, then $A' \cup B' \subseteq A \cup B$ and $A' \cap B' \subseteq A \cap B$.*

Exercise 8. *For all sets A and B we have $A \cap B \subseteq A \subseteq A \cup B$. Moreover, $A \cap B = A$ if and only if $A \subseteq B$, and $A \cup B = A$ if and only if $B \subseteq A$.*

Exercise 9. *For any set A we have $A \cup \varnothing = A$ and $A \cap \varnothing = \varnothing$. In words: $\varnothing$ is an* **identity** *for union, and is* **absorbent** *for intersection. Moreover, $A \cup B = \varnothing$ implies $A = B = \varnothing$.*

If $A \cap B = \varnothing$, we say that A and B are **disjoint** (or that A is disjoint from B).

If A and B are sets, the **relative complement of B in A** is defined as

$$\{x \mid x \in A \quad \text{but} \quad x \notin B\}$$

and is denoted by $A - B$. For example, $\{a, b\} - \{b, c\} = \{a\}$.

Exercise 10. *For all sets A, B, C we have*

(a) $A - B \subseteq A$

(b) $A - B = A$ *if and only if A and B are disjoint*

(c) $A - B$ *and B are disjoint, and their union is* $A \cup B$

(d) $A - B = \varnothing$ *if and only if* $A \subseteq B$

(e) $A - B = A - (A \cap B)$; $A \cap B = A - (A - B)$

(f) $(A \cup B) - C = (A - C) \cup (B - C)$

(g) $(A \cap B) - C = (A - C) \cap (B - C) = (A \cap B) - (A \cap C) = A \cap (B - C)$

(h) $A - (B \cup C) = (A - B) \cap (A - C) = (A - B) - C$

(i) $A - (B \cap C) = (A - B) \cup (A - C)$.

We can state (f–g) in words as: Relative complement distributes over both union and intersection from the right; intersection distributes over relative complement.

SETS OF SETS

The elements of a set can themselves be sets. For example, if A and B are sets, we can define the set $\{A, B\}$ which has A and B as its elements. Note that $\{A, B\}$ is not the same as the union of A and B; the elements of A and B are *not* elements of $\{A, B\}$. Similarly, the set $\{A\}$ is not the same as the set A. In particular, note that the set $\varnothing$ is empty, but the set $\{\varnothing\}$ is not, since it has the set $\varnothing$ as an element.

Let $\mathscr{S}$ be a nonempty set of sets. We define the union of the sets in $\mathscr{S}$ by

$$\bigcup_{S \in \mathscr{S}} S = \{x \mid x \in S \text{ for some (that is, for at least one) } S \in \mathscr{S}\}$$

and their intersection by

$$\bigcap_{S \in \mathscr{S}} S = \{x \mid x \in S \text{ for all } S \in \mathscr{S}\}.$$

Note that the definitions of union and intersection given earlier are just the special cases in which $\mathscr{S} = \{A, B\}$. If $\mathscr{S} = \{S\}$, we evidently have $\bigcup_{S \in \mathscr{S}} S = \bigcap_{S \in \mathscr{S}} S = S$. We shall denote the union of the sets in $\{A, B, C\}$ by $A \cup B \cup C$ ("the union of A, B, and C"), and similarly for intersection.

Exercise 11. *If $\mathscr{S}' \subseteq \mathscr{S}$, then*

$$\bigcup_{S \in \mathscr{S}'} S \subseteq \bigcup_{S \in \mathscr{S}} S$$

and

$$\bigcap_{S \in \mathscr{S}'} S \supseteq \bigcap_{S \in \mathscr{S}} S.$$

Exercise 12. *If $\mathscr{S} = \mathscr{A} \cup \mathscr{B}$, then*

$$\bigcup_{S \in \mathscr{S}} S = \left(\bigcup_{S \in \mathscr{A}} S\right) \cup \left(\bigcup_{S \in \mathscr{B}} S\right)$$

and

$$\bigcap_{S \in \mathscr{S}} S = (\bigcap_{S \in \mathscr{A}} S) \cap (\bigcap_{S \in \mathscr{B}} S).$$

Similarly, if $\mathscr{T} = \mathscr{A} \cap \mathscr{B}$, then

$$\bigcup_{S \in \mathscr{T}} S \subseteq (\bigcup_{S \in \mathscr{A}} S) \cap (\bigcup_{S \in \mathscr{B}} S)$$

and

$$\bigcap_{S \in \mathscr{T}} S \supseteq (\bigcap_{S \in \mathscr{A}} S) \cup (\bigcap_{S \in \mathscr{B}} S).$$

Give examples showing that the inclusions cannot be replaced by equalities.

We shall often be concerned with sets whose elements are subsets of a given set. In particular, if S is any set, we can consider the set of *all* subsets of S, that is, $\{A \mid A \subseteq S\}$; this set will be denoted by $\mathscr{P}_S$ (mnemonic: the set of "parts" of S). For example, we have $\mathscr{P}_\varnothing = \{\varnothing\}$; $\mathscr{P}_{\{x\}} = \{\varnothing, \{x\}\}$; $\mathscr{P}_{\{x,y\}} = \{\varnothing, \{x\}, \{y\}, \{x, y\}\}$.

Exercise 13. *Prove that the following statements about the nonempty set of sets $\mathscr{S}$ are equivalent:*

   (a) *For all A, B in $\mathscr{S}$, either $A = B$ or $A \cap B = \varnothing$*

   (b) *For all $A \in \mathscr{S}$, we have $A \cap (\bigcup_{S \in \mathscr{S} - \{A\}} S) = \varnothing$*

   (c) *For all $x \in \bigcup_{S \in \mathscr{S}} S$, the set $\{A \mid A \in \mathscr{S}; x \in A\}$ has only a single element.*

[If (a–c) hold, we say that the sets in $\mathscr{S}$ are **disjoint**.]

Exercise 14. $(\bigcup_{S \in \mathscr{S}} S) \cap T = \bigcup_{S \cap T \in \{S \cap T \mid S \in \mathscr{S}\}} (S \cap T);$

             $(\bigcap_{S \in \mathscr{S}} S) \cup T = \bigcap_{S \cup T \in \{S \cup T \mid S \in \mathscr{S}\}} (S \cup T).$

In particular, if each $S \in \mathscr{S}$ is disjoint from T, so is $\bigcup_{S \in \mathscr{S}} S$.

Exercise 15. $A - B$, $B - A$, *and $A \cap B$ are disjoint, and their union is $A \cup B$.*

2. RELATIONS

ORDERED PAIRS

Up to this point it has made no difference in what order the elements of a set are arranged; $\{x, y\}$ and $\{y, x\}$ are equal, since they have the same elements. If we want to single out x as "first" and y as "second," we must consider something other than the set $\{x, y\}$. For example, we can consider the set

$$\{\{x\}, \{x, y\}\}.$$

If $x \neq y$, the roles played by x and y in this set are different, since only x is an element of both of its elements. This set is called the **ordered pair** (x, y); x is called its *first term*, and y its *second term*. Note that, even if $x = y$, the ordered pair $(x, x) = \{\{x\}\}$ is not the same as the set $\{x\}$; thus both terms of an ordered pair can be the same. Evidently, if $x \neq y$ we have $(x, y) \neq (y, x)$.

PRODUCT SETS

We define the **product** of the sets A and B as

$$A \times B = \{(a, b) \mid a \in A, b \in B\},$$

in other words, as the set of ordered pairs which have their first terms in A and their second terms in B. Here A and B need not be distinct; we can also consider the product of a set with itself, $A \times A = \{(x, y) \mid x, y \text{ in } A\}$. Note that if $A \neq B$ we have $A \times B \neq B \times A$.

> In analytic geometry, when we assign ordered pairs of numbers to points of the plane as coordinates, we are treating the plane as the product of two lines. In fact, products of sets are sometimes called *Cartesian products* in honor of Descartes, the father of analytic geometry.

Examples:

(a) $\varnothing \times S = S \times \varnothing = \varnothing$ for all S; conversely, if $A \times B = \varnothing$, then $A = \varnothing$ or $B = \varnothing$

(b) $\{a\} \times \{b\} = \{(a, b)\}$

(c) If $A \subseteq C$ and $B \subseteq D$, then $A \times B \subseteq C \times D$

(d) $\times$ distributes over union, intersection, and relative complement—in other words, for all A, B, C we have $A \times (B \cup C) = (A \times B) \cup (A \times C)$ and $(B \cup C) \times A = (B \times A) \cup (C \times A)$, and similarly for $\cap$ and $-$.

> We have defined "product" here only for a pair of sets. The definition can be generalized to an arbitrary set of sets (see Section 19), but first we must use the two-set case to define the concepts of *relation* and *function*.

RELATIONS

By a **relation** between the sets A and B is meant any subset of the product set $A \times B$.

> Intuitively, a relationship between elements of A and elements of B is defined by specifying which elements of A stand in the relationship to which elements of B—in other words, by specifying the set of pairs (a, b), where $a \in A$, $b \in B$, for which the relationship holds. Since specifying the relationship is equivalent to specifying the set of pairs, we can—and do—say, formally, that the relationship *is* the set of pairs.

In particular, if $B = A$, a relation between A and B is called a relation on A.

Examples:

(a) Since $\varnothing$ is a subset of $A \times B$, it can be regarded as a relation between A and B. When speaking of $\varnothing$ as a relation, we call it the **empty** relation (*no* elements of A and B are related).

(b) $A \times B$ itself is called the **trivial** relation between A and B (every element of A is related to every element of B).

(c) $I_A = \{(x, x) \mid x \in A\}$ is called the **equality** relation on A (two elements are related if and only if they are the same).

(d) Let $\mathscr{S}$ be any set of sets; then

$$\{(A, B) \mid A, B \text{ in } \mathscr{S}; \quad A \subseteq B\}$$

is called the **inclusion** relation on $\mathscr{S}$, and is denoted by $\subseteq_{\mathscr{S}}$. [The subscripts may be omitted here and in Example (c) if there is no danger of confusion as to what set is meant.] We can similarly define relations on $\mathscr{S}$ in terms of $\supseteq$, $\subset$, and $\supset$. Note that for any $\mathscr{S}$, $\subseteq_{\mathscr{S}}$ contains $I_{\mathscr{S}}$.

(e) Let R be a relation between A and B, and let A', B' be subsets of A, B, respectively; then $R \cap (A' \times B')$ is a relation between A' and B'. In particular, let R be a relation on S, and let $S' \subseteq S$; then $R \cap (S' \times S')$ is a relation on S', and is called the **restriction** of R to S'.

INVERSE RELATIONS

If R is a relation between A and B, then

$$\{(b, a) \mid (a, b) \in R\}$$

is a relation between B and A. This relation is called the **inverse** of R, and is denoted by R^{-1}.

Examples:

(a) $\varnothing^{-1} = \varnothing$

(b) $(A \times B)^{-1} = B \times A$

(c) $(I_A)^{-1} = I_A$

(d) $(\subseteq_{\mathscr{S}})^{-1} = \supseteq_{\mathscr{S}}$

(e) $(R \cap (A' \times B'))^{-1} = R^{-1} \cap (B' \times A')$.

Exercise 1. *For any relations Q, R we have*

(a) $(R^{-1})^{-1} = R$

(b) $Q^{-1} = R^{-1}$ *if and only if* $Q = R$

(c) $Q^{-1} \subseteq R^{-1}$ *if and only if* $Q \subseteq R$.

COMPOSITION OF RELATIONS

Let Q be a relation between A and B, and R a relation between B and C; then

$$\{(a, c) \mid (a, b) \in Q \quad \text{and} \quad (b, c) \in R \quad \text{for some} \quad b \in B\}$$

is a relation between A and C. We call this relation the **composite** of Q and R, and denote it by $Q \circ R$. Note that if Q and R are both relations on the same set S, then $Q \circ R$ is also a relation on S.

Examples:
  (a) For any relation R between A and B we have $\varnothing \circ R = R \circ \varnothing = \varnothing$.
      [Note that when we write $\varnothing \circ R$, we are regarding $\varnothing$ as the empty relation between some set and A; when we write $R \circ \varnothing$, we are regarding $\varnothing$ as the empty relation between B and some set.] In words: $\varnothing$ is **absorbent** for composition of relations.
  (b) $(A \times B) \circ (B \times C) = A \times C$, provided that $B \neq \varnothing$.
  (c) For any relation R between A and B we have $I_A \circ R = R \circ I_B = R$. In particular, if R is any relation on A, we have $I_A \circ R = R \circ I_A = R$. In words: I_A is an **identity** for composition of relations on A.
  (d) $R \cap (A' \times B') = I_{A'} \circ R \circ I_{B'}$.

Exercise 2. *Prove that composition of relations is* **associative**—*in other words, that if P, Q, R are relations between A and B, B and C, C and D, respectively, then $(P \circ Q) \circ R = P \circ (Q \circ R)$.*

Exercise 3. $(Q \circ R)^{-1} = R^{-1} \circ Q^{-1}$. [Note the reversal of order!]

Exercise 4. If $Q' \subseteq Q$ and $R' \subseteq R$, then $Q' \circ R' \subseteq Q \circ R$.

3. FUNCTIONS

Three special types of relations—functions, order relations, and equivalences—play central roles in mathematics. In this section we introduce functions; order relations will be introduced in the next chapter; and equivalences will be introduced in Chapter IV, where we will also study further the properties of functions.

A relation F between S and T is called a **function** from S into T if for each $s \in S$ there is *exactly one* $t \in T$ such that $(s, t) \in F$.

In an arbitrary relation between S and T, there can be elements of S which are not the first term of any pair, or which are the first term of many different pairs. Our formal definition of "function" is consistent with the intuitive concept of a function from S into T as a rule which assigns to *each* element of S a *unique* element of T.

This unique t is denoted by $F(s)$, and is called the **image** of s under F; we say that F "takes s into t." The set S is called the **domain** of F, and we say that F

"is defined on S." The element s in the expression $F(s)$ is sometimes referred to as the **argument** of F, and $F(s)$ as the **value** of F at s.

> The following examples of functions are intended, not to illustrate the concept of a function, which is surely familiar enough, but rather as exercises in handling the formalism of functions regarded as sets of ordered pairs.

Examples:

(a) The equality relation I_A is a function from A into A. When we speak of I_A as a function, we call it the **identity function** on A. [As for the other examples of relations given in Section 2, it is easily verified that the empty relation between A and B is a function if and only if $A = \varnothing$; the trivial relation $A \times B$ is a function if and only if $A = \varnothing$ or B has only a single element; and $\subseteq_{\mathscr{S}}$ is a function if and only if it is equal to $I_{\mathscr{S}}$.]

(b) More generally, let S be any set, and S' any subset of S. Then $I_{S'}$, regarded as a subset of $S' \times S$, is a function from S' into S; it is called the **embedding** function of S' in S. Like the identity function on S', this function takes every element of S' into itself.

(c) Let F be a function from S into T, and let S' be any subset of S; then $F \cap (S' \times T)$ is a function from S' into T, and is called the **restriction** of F to S'.

> Note that when we defined the restriction of a *relation* to a subset in Section 2, we restricted both terms of the ordered pairs in it, not just their first terms. Thus the two definitions disagree if F is a function from S into S. When we are talking about functions, "restriction" will always mean restriction of the first terms, as defined in this section. Readily, the restriction of F to S' is just $I_{S'} \circ F$.

(d) Let S, T be sets, and t any element of T; then the relation

$$F_t = \{(s, t) \mid s \in S\} = S \times \{t\}$$

is a function from S into T. Such a function is called a **constant** function.

(e) Let F be a function from S into T, and for any $S' \subseteq S$, let

$$\tilde{F}(S') = \{F(s) \mid s \in S'\}.$$

Then

$$\{(S', \tilde{F}(S')) \mid S' \subseteq S\}$$

is a function from $\mathscr{P}_S$ into $\mathscr{P}_T$. Note that $\tilde{F}(\varnothing) = \varnothing$, and that $\tilde{F}(\{x\}) = \{F(x)\}$ for all $x \in S$. From now on we shall usually omit the tilde, since it will be clear from the notation used for the argument whether F or $\tilde{F}$ is meant. Thus, we shall refer to "$F(S')$" as the image of S' "under F."

(f) Let S be a set, and F a function from $\mathscr{P}_S - \{\varnothing\}$ into S such that $F(A) \in A$ for all nonempty $A \subseteq S$. Such an F is called a **choice function** on S. We shall occasionally need to assume the existence of a choice function on a given set S; the assumption that such a function exists for any S is known as the **axiom of choice**.

Exercise 1. *Let F, G be functions defined on S; then $F = G$ if and only if $F(x) = G(x)$ for all $x \in S$.* [In other words, a function on S can be defined by specifying its value for each $x \in S$.]

Exercise 2. *Let F be a function defined on S, and let A, B be subsets of S such that $A \subseteq B$; then $F(A) \subseteq F(B)$.*

Exercise 3. *Let F be a function defined on S, and let $\mathscr{A}$ be a set of subsets of S; then*

$$F(\textstyle\bigcup_{A\in\mathscr{A}} A) = \bigcup_{\mathscr{A}} F(A) \quad and \quad F(\bigcap_{A\in\mathscr{A}} A) \subseteq \bigcap_{\mathscr{A}} F(A).$$

Here $\bigcup_{\mathscr{A}} F(A)$ is short for $\bigcup_{F(A)\in\{F(A)\,\mid\,A\in\mathscr{A}\}} F(A)$, and similarly for $\bigcap$; we shall use this abbreviated notation from now on.

Show by example that the $\subseteq$ cannot be replaced by $=$. Verify also that for all subsets A, B we have $F(A - B) \supseteq F(A) - F(B)$.

Exercise 4. *Let F be a function from A into B, and G a function from C into D; then $F \cup G'$ is a function from $A \cup C$ into $B \cup D$, where G' is the restriction of G to $C - A$.*

INVERSES AND COMPOSITES OF FUNCTIONS

If F is a function from S into T, the inverse relation F^{-1} is not necessarily a function, since for a given $t \in T$ there may be many, or no, elements of S such that $(t, s) \in F^{-1}$. The set of such elements of S—that is, the set $\{s \mid F(s) = t\}$—is called the **preimage** of t under F, and is denoted by $F^{-1}(t)$.

Exercise 5. *Let F be a function from S into T, and for any $T' \subseteq T$, let $F^{-1}(T') = \{s \mid F(s) \in T'\}$.*

As in Example (e) above, we should put a tilde above the F^{-1} to distinguish it from the inverse relation F^{-1}; but here too we shall usually omit the tilde, and shall refer to $F^{-1}(T')$ as the preimage of T' "under F."

Prove that $\{(T', F^{-1}(T')) \mid T' \subseteq T\}$ *is a function from* $\mathscr{P}_T$ *into* $\mathscr{P}_S$. [Note that $F^{-1}(\{t\})$ is the same thing as $F^{-1}(t)$.]

Exercise 6. *With notation as in Exercise 5, prove also:*
   (a) *If* A, B *are subsets of* T *and* $A \subseteq B$, *then* $F^{-1}(A) \subseteq F^{-1}(B)$.
   (b) *If* $\mathscr{A}$ *is a set of subsets of* T, *then* $F^{-1}(\bigcup_{\mathscr{A}} A) = \bigcup_{\mathscr{A}} F^{-1}(A)$ *and* $F^{-1}(\bigcap_{\mathscr{A}} A) = \bigcap_{\mathscr{A}} F^{-1}(A)$.

Proposition 1. *A composite of functions is a function.*

Proof: Let F be a function from A into B, and G a function from B into C. Then the composite relation $F \circ G$ is the set of pairs $(a, c) \in A \times C$ such that, for some $b \in B$, we have $(a, b) \in F$ and $(b, c) \in G$. But this means that $b = F(a)$ and $c = G(b)$; hence for any $a \in A$ there is exactly one element c of C, namely $G(F(a))$, such that $(a, c) \in F \circ G$, which proves that $F \circ G$ is a function. $\;\;/\!/$

Note that $F \circ G$ takes x into $G(F(x))$—*not* into $F(G(x))$!

Proposition 2. *For any function* F *defined on* S *we have* $F^{-1} \circ F = I_{F(S)}$.

Proof: Since F^{-1} is a subset of $F(S) \times S$, and F a subset of $S \times F(S)$, the composite relation $F^{-1} \circ F$ is a subset of $F(S) \times F(S)$, and consists of the pairs (x, y) such that $(x, s) \in F^{-1}$ and $(s, y) \in F$ for some $s \in S$. But this means that $x = F(s)$ [since $(s, x) \in F$] and $y = F(s)$, so that $x = y$, proving $F^{-1} \circ F \subseteq I_{F(S)}$. Conversely, for all $F(s) \in F(S)$ we have $(F(s), s) \in F^{-1}$ and $(s, F(s)) \in F$, so that $(F(s), F(s)) \in F^{-1} \circ F$, proving that $I_{F(S)} \subseteq F^{-1} \circ F$. These two inclusions prove the required equality. $\;\;/\!/$

Exercise 7. *The relation* R *between* S *and* T *is a function if and only if* $R \circ R^{-1} \supseteq I_S$ *and* $R^{-1} \circ R \subseteq I_T$.

Exercise 8. *Let* F *be a function defined on* S, *and* R *a relation between* $F(S)$ *and* S *such that* $R \circ F \subseteq I_{F(S)}$; *then* $R \subseteq F^{-1}$.

ONTO AND ONE-TO-ONE FUNCTIONS

A function F from S into T is called **onto** if for each $t \in T$ there is *at least* one $s \in S$ such that $t = F(s)$. It is called **one-to-one** if for each $t \in T$ there is *at most* one such $s \in S$. If F is both one-to-one and onto, it is called a **one-to-one correspondence** of S with T (or between S and T).

> An onto function is sometimes called **surjective**, a one-to-one function **injective**, and a one-to-one correspondence **bijective**.

If there exists a one-to-one correspondence of S with T, we say that S is in one-to-one correspondence with T (notation: $S \sim T$), or that S and T are in one-to-one correspondence with each other. A one-to-one correspondence of a set S with itself is called a **permutation** of S.

Examples:

(a) I_S is a permutation of S. In particular, the empty function $\varnothing$ is a permutation of the empty set.

(b) The embedding function of S' in S is a one-to-one function of S' into S. More generally, if F is any one-to-one function defined on S, and S' is any subset of S, then the restriction of F to S' is one-to-one.

(c) Any function F defined on S is a function from S onto $F(S)$. In particular, any one-to-one function defined on S is a one-to-one correspondence of S with $F(S)$.

Exercise 9. *In Exercise 4, if B and D are disjoint, and F, G are each one-to-one, so is $F \cup G'$.*

Exercise 10. *A function is one-to-one if and only if it takes proper subsets into proper subsets (that is, $A \subset B$ implies $F(A) \subset F(B)$ for all subsets A, B of the domain of F).*

Exercise 11. *The following statements about the function F defined on S are equivalent:*

(a) *F is one-to-one*

(b) *$A \cap B = \varnothing$ implies $F(A) \cap F(B) = \varnothing$ for all $A, B \subseteq S$*

(c) *$F(A \cap B) = F(A) \cap F(B)$ for all $A, B \subseteq S$.*

Exercise 12. *F is one-to-one if and only if $\tilde{F}$ is one-to-one, and similarly for onto.*

Exercise 13. *F is one-to-one if and only if F^{-1} (Exercise 5) is onto, and vice versa.*

Exercise 14. *For any function F defined on S, the restriction of F^{-1} to $F(S)$ is one-to-one.*

Exercise 15. *If F and G are both one-to-one or both onto, so is $F \circ G$.*

Proposition 3. *Let F be a function defined on S; then $F(S)$ is in one-to-one correspondence with a subset of S.*

Proof: Let G be a choice function on S; then readily

$$\{(y, G(F^{-1}(y))) \mid y \in F(S)\}$$

is a one-to-one correspondence of $F(S)$ with the subset

$$S' = \{G(F^{-1}(y)) \mid y \in F(S)\}. \quad /\!/$$

Note that $S' = S$ if and only if $F^{-1}(y)$ has only a single element for each $y \in F(S)$—or, equivalently, if and only if F^{-1} is a function.

Proposition 4. *The following statements about the function F, defined on the set S, are equivalent:*

(1) *F is a one-to-one correspondence of S with F(S)*
(2) F^{-1} *is a one-to-one correspondence of F(S) with S*
(3) F^{-1} *is a function from F(S) into S.*

Proof: If (1) holds, there is exactly one ordered pair in F having any given element of S as first term, and exactly one having any given element of $F(S)$ as second term. Hence the same must be true for F^{-1} (with "first" and "second" interchanged), so that F^{-1} is a one-to-one correspondence, proving (2), and conversely. If (3) holds, the fact that F is a function gives F^{-1} the one-to-one and onto properties; thus (3) implies (2), while the converse implication is trivial. //

Proposition 5. *The function F defined on S is one-to-one if and only if $F \circ F^{-1} = I_S$.*

Proof: If F is one-to-one, x is the sole element of $F^{-1}(F(x))$, and conversely. //

The following converse to Proposition 5 provides a method, which will be used repeatedly in later chapters, of establishing one-to-one correspondences between sets.

Proposition 6. *Let F be a function from S into T, and G a function from T into S. If $F \circ G = I_S$, then F is one-to-one and G is onto, and the restriction of G to F(S) is F^{-1}.*

Proof: If $F \circ G = I_S$, for all $x \in S$ we have $G(F(x)) = x$. In particular, any $x \in S$ is in $G(F(S))$, so that $S \subseteq G(F(S)) \subseteq G(T)$, proving G onto. Moreover, if $F(a) = F(b)$, we have $a = G(F(a)) = G(F(b)) = b$, so that F is one-to-one. Finally, let G' be the restriction of G to $F(S)$; then readily $F \circ G'$ must still be all of I_S. We thus have $F^{-1} = F^{-1} \circ I_S = F^{-1} \circ (F \circ G') = (F^{-1} \circ F) \circ G' = I_{F(S)} \circ G' = G'$. //

Corollary. *If $F \circ G = I_S$ and $G \circ F = I_T$, then F and G are one-to-one correspondences, and each of them is the inverse of the other.*

4. NATURAL NUMBERS

In this section we outline a formal definition of the natural numbers ("positive integers"). It would be easy enough to take for granted all of the properties of natural numbers which will be needed in later chapters, but it is of interest to see how these properties can be derived from a few basic assumptions.

We assume that there exists a set **N** with the following properties:

(a) There is an element $1 \in \mathbf{N}$, and a one-to-one correspondence F of **N** with $\mathbf{N} - \{1\}$, such that

(b) If S is a subset of **N** which contains 1, and if $x \in S$ implies $F(x) \in S$ for all $x \in \mathbf{N}$, then $S = \mathbf{N}$.

N will be called the set of **natural numbers**.

> Our definition of **N** is nothing more than a rewording of the familiar Peano postulates for the natural numbers; the function F is Peano's successor function. When we stipulate that F is a one-to-one correspondence of **N** with $\mathbf{N} - \{1\}$, we are saying that
>
> > (a′) Every element of **N** has a unique successor, since F is a function
> >
> > (a″) No two elements have the same successor, since F is one-to-one
> >
> > (a‴) Every element but 1 has a predecessor, since F is onto $\mathbf{N} - \{1\}$.
>
> [As we shall see later (Theorems 5.1 and 20.1), the assumption that there exists $1 \in \mathbf{N}$ such that $\mathbf{N} \sim \mathbf{N} - \{1\}$ is tantamount to assuming that **N** is infinite.] Our (b) is, of course, just the principle of mathematical induction.

ADDITION

Our formal treatment of the natural numbers is based on

Theorem 1. *For every $m \in \mathbf{N}$ there exists a unique function F_m from* **N** *into* **N** *such that*

(α) $F_m(1) = F(m)$

(β) $F_m(F(k)) = F(F_m(k))$ *for all $k \in \mathbf{N}$.*

> [Note that (β) is equivalent to $F \circ F_m = F_m \circ F$.]

Proof: Let S be the set of $m \in \mathbf{N}$ for which such an F_m exists. Then $1 \in S$, since taking $F_1 = F$ evidently satisfies (α-β). If $n \in S$, let $F_{F(n)} = F_n \circ F$; then by (α) we have $F_{F(n)}(1) = F(F_n(1)) = F(F(n))$, while by ($\beta$), $F \circ F_{F(n)} = F \circ (F_n \circ F) = (F \circ F_n) \circ F = (F_n \circ F) \circ F = F_{F(n)} \circ F$, so that $F_{F(n)}$ satisfies (α-β)—in other words, $F(n)$ is also in S. Thus by induction, S is all of **N**, that is, F_m exists for all $m \in \mathbf{N}$.

To prove that F_m is unique for each m, let G_m be any function satisfying (α-β), and let T be the set of $n \in \mathbf{N}$ such that $G_m(n) = F_m(n)$. By (α) we have $G_m(1) = F(m) = F_m(1)$, so that $1 \in T$. Moreover, if $k \in T$, then by (β)

we have $G_m(F(k)) = F(G_m(k)) = F(F_m(k)) = F_m(F(k))$, so that $F(k) \in T$. Hence $T = \mathbf{N}$, that is, $G_m(n) = F_m(n)$ for all $n \in \mathbf{N}$, so that $G_m = F_m$. $/\!/$

From now on we shall denote $F(n)$ by $n + 1$, and $F_m(n)$ by $n + m$ (read "n plus m"). Applying F_m to n is called **addition** of m to n; $n + m$ is called the **sum** of n and m, and n, m are called the **terms** of the sum. In this "additive" notation, assumptions (α-β) become $1 + m = m + 1$ and $(k + 1) + m = (k + m) + 1$, respectively. Since $F_{F(n)}(k) = F(F_n(k))$, we also have $k + (n + 1) = (k + n) + 1$. Hereafter, we shall also employ the usual notation for particular natural numbers, namely $F(1) = 2$, $F(2) = 3$, and so on, as well as the usual names "one," "two," "three," and so on.

For many purposes it is useful to "adjoin" an additional element,† denoted by 0 ("zero"), to $\mathbf{N}$, and to extend the functions F_m to $\mathbf{N} \cup \{0\}$ by defining $F_m(0) = m$; in particular, $F(0) = 1$. We shall denote $\mathbf{N} \cup \{0\}$ by $\mathbf{N}°$, and call it the set of **nonnegative integers**. For uniformity, we denote the identity function $I_{\mathbf{N}°}$ by F_0, and denote $F_0(n)$ by $n + 0$; thus $n + 0 = n$ for all $n \in \mathbf{N}°$—in other words, 0 is an **identity** for addition.

We develop some important properties of addition in the following group of propositions:

Proposition 1. F_m is one-to-one—in other words, $r + m = s + m$ implies $r = s$ for all r, s in $\mathbf{N}°$.

Proof: This is certainly true for the identity function F_0, and for $F_1 = F$ by definition; while if it is true for F_m, it is also true for $F_{m+1} = F_m \circ F$ (Exercise 3.15). $/\!/$

Proposition 1 is called the **law of cancellation** for addition. Since F_m is one-to-one, F_m^{-1} is a function defined on $F_m(\mathbf{N}°)$. We shall denote $F_m^{-1}(n)$ by $n - m$ (read: "n minus m"). Applying F_m^{-1} to n is called **subtraction** of m from n; $n - m$ is called the **difference** of n and m. Note in particular that $n - 0 = F_0^{-1}(n) = F_0(n) = n$; that $n - n = F_n^{-1}(n) = F_n^{-1}(F_n(0)) = I_{\mathbf{N}°}(0) = 0$, for all $n \in \mathbf{N}°$; that $(n + m) - m = F_m^{-1}(F_m(n)) = n$, so that if $r = n + m$, then $n = r - m$; and that $F^{-1}(n) = n - 1$ is defined for all $n \in \mathbf{N}$.

Proposition 2. $n + m = m + n$ for all m, n in $\mathbf{N}°$ (in words: addition is commutative).

Proof: This is true for $n = 0$ by definition, and for $n = 1$ by (α). If it is true for n, then we have $m + (n + 1) = (m + n) + 1 = (n + m) + 1 = (n + 1) + m$ by (β), so that it is also true for $n + 1$. $/\!/$

Exercise 1. *Prove that addition is* **associative**—*in other words, that* $(r + s) + t = r + (s + t)$ *for all* r, s, t *in* $\mathbf{N}°$. [*Hint:* Use induction on t.]

_____

† Given any set, an element not in it must exist; see Exercise 20.4.

Proposition 3. *For all $m \in \mathbf{N}^\circ$ we have $m \notin F_m(\mathbf{N})$.*

Proof: By definition we have $0 \notin F_0(\mathbf{N}) = \mathbf{N}$ and $1 \notin F_1(\mathbf{N}) = F(\mathbf{N}) = \mathbf{N} - \{1\}$. Suppose that $n \notin F_n(\mathbf{N})$, but $n + 1 \in F_{n+1}(\mathbf{N}) = F(F_n(\mathbf{N}))$, say $n + 1 = (k + n) + 1$; then we would have $n = k + n$ in $F_n(\mathbf{N})$, contradiction.   //

Proposition 4. *For all $m \in \mathbf{N}^\circ$ we have $F_{m+1}(\mathbf{N}) = F_m(\mathbf{N}) - \{m + 1\}$.*

Proof: For all $k \in \mathbf{N}$ we have $k + (m + 1) = (k + 1) + m \in F_m(\mathbf{N})$, so that $F_{m+1}(\mathbf{N}) \subseteq F_m(\mathbf{N})$; while by Proposition 3, $m + 1 \notin F_{m+1}(\mathbf{N})$, so that $F_{m+1}(\mathbf{N}) \subseteq F_m(\mathbf{N}) - \{m + 1\}$. Conversely, if x is in $F_m(\mathbf{N}) - \{m + 1\}$, say $x = y + m$, we must have $y \neq 1$. Hence y is in $F(\mathbf{N})$, say $y = z + 1$, so that $x = (z + 1) + m = z + (m + 1)$ is in $F_{m+1}(\mathbf{N})$.   //

Corollary. $F_{m+1}(\mathbf{N}^\circ) = F_m(\mathbf{N}^\circ) - \{m\}$ *for all $m \in \mathbf{N}^\circ$.*

Exercise 2. *Prove that each $F_m(\mathbf{N}^\circ)$ is an* **ideal** *under addition—in other words, that for all $r \in F_m(\mathbf{N}^\circ)$ and all $n \in \mathbf{N}^\circ$, we have $r + n \in F_m(\mathbf{N}^\circ)$.*

Exercise 3. *Prove that $m + n = 0$ if and only if $m = n = 0$.* [Hint: Show that $0 \notin F_m(\mathbf{N}^\circ)$ for all $m \in \mathbf{N}$.]

THE NATURAL NUMBERS "THROUGH m"

The set $F_m(\mathbf{N})$ is called the set of natural numbers *beyond* m; the set $\mathbf{N}_m = \mathbf{N} - F_m(\mathbf{N})$ is called the set of natural numbers *through* m. We shall often denote $\mathbf{N}_m$ by $\{1, \ldots, m\}$; in justification of this notation, see Propositions 5–6. Analogously, we define $\mathbf{N}_m{}^\circ = \mathbf{N}^\circ - F_m(\mathbf{N}) = \mathbf{N}_m \cup \{0\} = \{0, \ldots, m\}$. The following propositions give some properties of the sets $\mathbf{N}_m$; the statements and proofs of their analogs for the sets $\mathbf{N}_m{}^\circ$ are left to the reader.

Proposition 5. $\mathbf{N}_1 = \{1\}$; $\mathbf{N}_{m+1} = \mathbf{N}_m \cup \{m + 1\}$ *for all $m \in \mathbf{N}$.*

Proof: The definitions and Proposition 4.   //

Corollary 1. $\mathbf{N}_m \subset \mathbf{N}_{m+1}$ for all $m \in \mathbf{N}$.

Corollary 2. $1 \in \mathbf{N}_m$ for all $m \in \mathbf{N}$.

Proposition 6. $m \in \mathbf{N}_m$, *and $m + 1 \notin \mathbf{N}_m$, for all $m \in \mathbf{N}$.*

Proof: The definitions and Proposition 3.   //

Proposition 7. $\mathbf{N}_r \cup F_r(\mathbf{N}_s) = \mathbf{N}_{r+s}$ *for all r, s in $\mathbf{N}$.*

Proof: This is true for $s = 1$ by Proposition 5. If it holds for s, then

$$\begin{aligned}
\mathbf{N}_r \cup F_r(\mathbf{N}_{s+1}) &= \mathbf{N}_r \cup F_r(\mathbf{N}_s \cup \{s + 1\}) = \mathbf{N}_r \cup F_r(\mathbf{N}_s) \cup \{F_r(s + 1)\} \\
&= \mathbf{N}_{r+s} \cup \{F_r(s + 1)\} = \mathbf{N}_{r+s} \cup \{(s + 1) + r\} \\
&= \mathbf{N}_{r+s} \cup \{(r + s) + 1\} = \mathbf{N}_{(r+s)+1} = \mathbf{N}_{r+(s+1)},
\end{aligned}$$

proving it for $s + 1$.   //

Note that

$$\mathbf{N}_r \cap F_r(\mathbf{N}_s) \subseteq \mathbf{N}_r \cap F_r(\mathbf{N}) = \mathbf{N}_r \cap (\mathbf{N} - \mathbf{N}_r) = \varnothing.$$

Proposition 8. $r \in \mathbf{N}_s$ *if and only if* $r = s$ *or* $\mathbf{N}_r \subset \mathbf{N}_s$.

Proof: Since $r \in \mathbf{N}_r$, if $r \notin \mathbf{N}_s$ we cannot have $\mathbf{N}_r \subseteq \mathbf{N}_s$, which proves "if." "Only if" is trivial for $s = 1$; if it holds for s, and r is in $\mathbf{N}_{s+1} = \mathbf{N}_s \cup \{s + 1\}$, then either $r = s + 1$, or else r is in $\mathbf{N}_s$, in which case by induction hypothesis $\mathbf{N}_r \subseteq \mathbf{N}_s \subset \mathbf{N}_{s+1}$, proving "only if" for $s + 1$. $\quad //$

Proposition 9. *If* $r \in \mathbf{N}_s$ *and* $r + 1 \notin \mathbf{N}_s$, *then* $r = s$.

Proof: If $r \in \mathbf{N}_s$ we have $r + 1 = F(r) \in F(\mathbf{N}_s) \subseteq \mathbf{N}_{s+1}$ (Proposition 7) $= \mathbf{N}_s \cup \{s + 1\}$; thus if $r + 1 \notin \mathbf{N}_s$ we must have $r + 1 = s + 1$, so that $r = s$. $\quad //$

Corollary. *If* $\mathbf{N}_r = \mathbf{N}_s$, *then* $r = s$.

Proof: Propositions 6 and 9. $\quad //$

Proposition 10. $r \notin \mathbf{N}_s$ *if and only if* $\mathbf{N}_s \subset \mathbf{N}_r$.

Proof: "If" follows immediately from Proposition 8. "Only if" is vacuously true for $r = 1$; if it holds for r, and we have $r + 1 \notin \mathbf{N}_s$, then either $r \notin \mathbf{N}_s$ —so that $\mathbf{N}_s \subset \mathbf{N}_r \subset \mathbf{N}_{r+1}$, as desired—or else the hypothesis of Proposition 9 holds, so that $\mathbf{N}_s = \mathbf{N}_r \subset \mathbf{N}_{r+1}$ in any case. $\quad //$

Corollary. *For all* r, s *in* $\mathbf{N}$, *exactly one of the following holds:* $\mathbf{N}_r \subset \mathbf{N}_s$; $\mathbf{N}_s \subset \mathbf{N}_r$; $r = s$.

If $\mathbf{N}_r \subset \mathbf{N}_s$, we say that r is *less than* s (notation: $r < s$). We abbreviate "$r < s$ or $r = s$" by $r \leq s$ (read: "r is not greater than s"). If $r < s$, we also sometimes say that s is *greater than* r (notation: $s > r$). Similarly, we can write $s \geq r$ (read: "s is not less than r") instead of $r \leq s$; it is evidently equivalent to "$s > r$ or $s = r$."

By Proposition 8, $r \leq s$ is equivalent to $r \in \mathbf{N}_s$; thus for all $m \in \mathbf{N}$ we have $N_m = \{x \mid x \in \mathbf{N}; x \leq m\}$. In fact, by Corollary 2 to Proposition 5 we can also write $N_m = \{x \mid x \in \mathbf{N}; 1 \leq x \leq m\}$. We shall usually write "$1 \leq i \leq m$" instead of "$i \in \mathbf{N}_m$", and "$0 \leq i \leq m$" for "$i \in \mathbf{N}_m{}^\circ$".

Proposition 11. *Let* $\leq$ *denote the relation* $\{(r, s) \mid r \leq s\}$ *on* $\mathbf{N}$; *then* $\leq$ *is* **reflexive, weakly antisymmetric,** *and* **transitive**—*in other words, for all* r, s, t *in* $\mathbf{N}$ *we have* $r \leq r$; $r \leq s$ *and* $s \leq r$ *imply* $r = s$; $r \leq s$ *and* $s \leq t$ *imply* $r \leq t$.

Proof: By the Corollary to Proposition 9, $r \leq s$ is equivalent to $\mathbf{N}_r \subseteq \mathbf{N}_s$; hence these properties of $\leq$ follow from the corresponding properties of $\subseteq$. $\quad //$

Proposition 12. *For all* r, s *in* $\mathbf{N}$ *we have* $r \leq s$ *or* $s \leq r$.

Proof: The Corollary to Proposition 10. $\quad //$

Exercise 4. *Let $<$ denote the relation $\{(r, s) \mid r < s\}$ on $\mathbf{N}$; then*

(a) *$<$ is* **irreflexive**, **antisymmetric**, *and* **transitive**—*that is, for all r, s, t in $\mathbf{N}$ we have $r < r$ false; $r < s$ and $s < r$ not both true; $r < s$ and $s < t$ imply $r < t$.*

(b) *For all r, s in $\mathbf{N}$, exactly one of the following is true: $r < s$; $r > s$; $r = s$.*

Proposition 13. *$r \leq s$ if and only if $s = r + k$ for some $k \in \mathbf{N}^{\circ}$.*

Proof: $\mathbf{N}_r \subset \mathbf{N}_s$ is equivalent to $s \notin \mathbf{N}_r$, that is, to $s \in F_r(\mathbf{N})$, say $s = k + r = r + k$ with $k \neq 0$. //

Corollary. *$r < s$ if and only if $s = r + k$ for some $k \in \mathbf{N}$.*

Proposition 14. *If $a \leq c$ and $b \leq d$, then $a + b \leq c + d$. In fact, if $a < c$ and $b \leq d$, or $a \leq c$ and $b < d$, then $a + b < c + d$.*

Proof: Let $c = a + h$, $d = b + k$; then $c + d = (a + h) + (b + k) = (a + b) + (h + k)$, where $h + k = 0$ if and only if $h = k = 0$. //

Similarly, if $a \leq c$ and $b \geq d$, then $a - b \leq c - d$ (if they are defined); and if either $\leq$ in the hypothesis is replaced by $<$, so is that in the conclusion.

Corollary. *If $a + b = c + d$, and $a < c$, then $b > d$.*

Exercise 5. *If S is a subset of $\mathbf{N}$ which contains 1, and if $\mathbf{N}_m \subseteq S$ implies $m + 1 \in S$ for all $m \in \mathbf{N}$, then $S = \mathbf{N}$.* [Hint: Let T be the set of $m \in \mathbf{N}$ such that $\mathbf{N}_m \subseteq S$, and use induction.]

SEQUENCES AND n-TUPLES

A function from $\mathbf{N}$ into the set A is called a **sequence** of elements of A. We shall usually denote such a function by an expression of the form $(a_i)_\mathbf{N}$, where a_i is the image of $i \in \mathbf{N}$; a_i is called the *ith term* of the sequence. Similarly, a function from $\mathbf{N}_m$ into A is called an **m-tuple** of elements of A, and is denoted by $(a_1, \ldots, a_m)$. The set of all m-tuples of elements of A will be denoted by A^m (read "A to the m"); this set is called the mth Cartesian **power** of A (see Section 19).

There is a natural one-to-one correspondence between A^1 and A, namely $\{(a_1, (a_1)) \mid a_1 \in A\}$; and a natural one-to-one correspondence between A^2 and $A \times A$—in fact, we are using the same notation (a_1, a_2) for the ordered 2-tuple and the ordered pair. For the sake of brevity we shall say "pair" instead of "2-tuple," "triple" instead of "3-tuple," and so on; "first term" instead of "1th term," "second term" instead of "2th term," and so on.

One often needs to prove the existence of a sequence or n-tuple which satisfies certain conditions. Our concluding theorem establishes the existence of a unique sequence having a given first term and satisfying a given "recurrence relation" in which the $(i + 1)$st term is defined in terms of the ith term for each $i \in \mathbf{N}$.

Theorem 2. *For each $m \in \mathbf{N}$, let H_m be a function from the set A into itself, and let x be any element of A. Then there exists a unique sequence $(a_i)_\mathbf{N}$ of elements of A such that $a_1 = x$, and $a_{k+1} = H_k(a_k)$ for each $k \in \mathbf{N}$.*

Proof: We show first that for each $n \in \mathbf{N}$ there exists an n-tuple $(a_1, \ldots, a_n)$ of elements of A such that

$$(\gamma_n) \quad a_1 = x; \; a_{k+1} = H_k(a_k) \text{ for each } k \text{ such that } k + 1 \in \mathbf{N}_n.$$

In fact, let S be the set of $n \in \mathbf{N}$ for which such an n-tuple G_n exists. Evidently $1 \in S$, since $G_1 = \{(1, x)\}$ clearly satisfies (γ_1). Moreover, if $G_n = (a_1, \ldots, a_n)$ satisfies (γ_n), then $G_{n+1} = G_n \cup \{(n + 1, H_n(a_n))\}$ satisfies (γ_{n+1}); thus by induction, $S = \mathbf{N}$.

We verify next that G_n is unique for each $n \in \mathbf{N}$. This is clear for $n = 1$; suppose it true for n, and let G_{n+1}, G_{n+1}^* be two $(n + 1)$-tuples satisfying (γ_{n+1}). Readily, the restrictions of G_{n+1} and G_{n+1}^* to $\mathbf{N}_n$ are n-tuples which satisfy (γ_n); hence these restrictions must be equal. We then have $G_{n+1}^*(n + 1) = H_n(G_{n+1}^*(n)) = H_n(G_{n+1}(n)) = G_{n+1}(n + 1)$, so that $G_{n+1}^* = G_{n+1}$.

The sequence $G = (G_i(i))_\mathbf{N}$ is then readily as required by the theorem, and is unique by an easy induction argument. //

> Note that in the course of proving Theorem 2 we have also shown the existence of a unique n-tuple having a given first term and satisfying a given "recurrence relation."

As an immediate application of these results, let $F = (n_1, \ldots, n_m)$ be any m-tuple of elements of $\mathbf{N}°$. Then there exists a unique m-tuple $(s_1, \ldots, s_m)$ of elements of $\mathbf{N}°$ such that $s_1 = n_1$, and $s_{k+1} = s_k + n_{k+1}$ for each $k \in \mathbf{N}_{m-1}$. We denote s_k by $\sum_{i=1}^{k} n_i$; it is called the sum of $(n_1, \ldots, n_k)$. This sum can also be written as $\sum_{i \in \mathbf{N}_k} n_i$, as $\sum_{i \in \mathbf{N}_k} F(i)$, or as $n_1 + \cdots + n_k$.

Exercise 6. *Let $m_i \le n_i$ for each $i \in \mathbf{N}_k$; then $\sum_{i=1}^{k} m_i \le \sum_{i=1}^{k} n_i$, and if $m_j < n_j$ for some $j \in \mathbf{N}_k$, then $\sum_{i=1}^{k} m_i < \sum_{i=1}^{k} n_i$.*

Exercise 7. *Let G be any permutation of $\mathbf{N}_k$; then $\sum_{i=1}^{k} n_i = \sum_{i=1}^{k} n_{G(i)}$.* [Hint: See Theorem 33.2.]

> If $F = (a_1, \ldots, a_n)$ is an n-tuple of elements of A, and G is a permutation of $\mathbf{N}_n$, then $G \circ F$ is an n-tuple of elements of A, and the set of its terms is the same as that of

F, since $F(G(\mathbf{N}_n)) = F(\mathbf{N}_n)$. As in Exercise 7, we denote $G \circ F$ by $(a_{G(1)}, \ldots, a_{G(n)})$.

By Exercise 7, the sum of an n-tuple does not depend on the order of its terms. In particular, let H be a function from S into $\mathbf{N}^\circ$, and let K be a one-to-one correspondence of $\mathbf{N}_n$ with $T \subseteq S$; then $K \circ H$ is an n-tuple of elements of $\mathbf{N}^\circ$, and the sum of this n-tuple depends only on H and T, but not on K. We can thus speak of "the sum of the $H(t)$'s," and denote it by $\sum_{t\in T} H(t)$.

5. FINITE SETS

We are now in a position to introduce formally the concepts of "finite set" and "infinite set," and to establish their basic properties.

Theorem 1. *The following statements about the nonempty set S are equivalent:*

(1) $S \sim \mathbf{N}_m$ *for some* $m \in \mathbf{N}$
(2) $S \nsim S'$ *for all proper subsets S' of S*
(3) $S' \nsim \mathbf{N}$ *for all subsets S' of S.*

> Here $\nsim$ means "is not in one-to-one correspondence with."

Proof: To prove that (1) implies (2), it suffices by Exercises 3.10 and 3.15 to show that $\mathbf{N}_m$ is not in one-to-one correspondence with any proper subset of itself. This is certainly true for $m = 1$, since $\mathbf{N}_1 = \{1\}$ has only $\varnothing$ as a proper subset. Suppose it true for $\mathbf{N}_k$, and suppose that there existed a one-to-one correspondence G of $\mathbf{N}_{k+1}$ with a proper subset of itself. We consider two cases:

(a) If $k + 1 \in G(\mathbf{N}_{k+1})$, say $k + 1 = G(r)$, let $G(k + 1) = s$, and let $G' = G - \{(r, k + 1)\} - \{(k + 1, s)\} \cup \{(r, s)\} \cup \{(k + 1, k + 1)\}$. Then G' is readily still a one-to-one correspondence of $\mathbf{N}_{k+1}$ with $G(\mathbf{N}_{k+1})$, and $G'(k + 1) = k + 1$. Hence $G' - \{(k + 1, k + 1)\}$ is a one-to-one correspondence of $\mathbf{N}_{k+1} - \{k + 1\} = \mathbf{N}_k$ with $G(\mathbf{N}_{k+1}) - \{k + 1\}$, which is a proper subset of $\mathbf{N}_k$ [for, if it were all of $\mathbf{N}_k$, we would have $G(\mathbf{N}_{k+1}) = G(\mathbf{N}_{k+1}) - \{k + 1\} \cup \{k + 1\} = \mathbf{N}_k \cup \{k + 1\} = \mathbf{N}_{k+1}$, contradicting the definition of G]; and this is impossible by the induction hypothesis.

(b) If $k + 1 \notin G(\mathbf{N}_{k+1})$, we have $G(\mathbf{N}_{k+1}) \subseteq \mathbf{N}_k$. Hence $G - \{(k + 1, G(k + 1))\}$ is a one-to-one correspondence of $\mathbf{N}_{k+1} - \{k + 1\} = \mathbf{N}_k$ with $G(\mathbf{N}_{k+1}) - \{G(k + 1)\}$, which is a proper subset of $\mathbf{N}_k$, contradicting the induction hypothesis.

To see that (2) implies (3), suppose that S had a subset A which was in one-to-one correspondence with $\mathbf{N}$, say $G(\mathbf{N}) = A$. Let $F_A = G^{-1} \circ F \circ G$, where F is the successor function on $\mathbf{N}$; then F_A is readily a one-to-one correspondence of A with $A - \{G(1)\}$. It follows (Exercise 3.9) that $F_A \cup I_{S-A}$ is a one-to-one correspondence of S with its proper subset $S - \{G(1)\}$, contradicting (2).

Finally, we prove that (3) implies (1). Suppose that S is not in one-to-one correspondence with any $\mathbf{N}_m$, and let G be a choice function on S. By Theorem 4.2, there exists a sequence $(S_i)_\mathbf{N}$ of subsets of S ($=$ elements of $\mathscr{P}_S$) such that $S_1 = S - \{G(S)\}$, and

$$\begin{aligned} S_{k+1} &= S_k - \{G(S_k)\} & &\text{if} \quad S_k \neq \varnothing \\ &= \varnothing & &\text{if} \quad S_k = \varnothing. \end{aligned}$$

Suppose that $S_n = \varnothing$ for some $n \in \mathbf{N}$. If $n = 1$, we have $S = \{G(S)\} \sim \mathbf{N}_1$, contradiction. Otherwise, it is easily seen (using induction) that $S = \{G(S)\} \cup \{G(S_k) \mid k \in \mathbf{N}_{n-1}\}$, which readily $\sim \mathbf{N}_n$, since the $G(S_k)$'s must all be different; contradiction. Hence $S_k \neq \varnothing$ for all $k \in \mathbf{N}$, and it is easily verified that $\{(k, G(S_k)) \mid k \in \mathbf{N}\}$ is a one-to-one correspondence of $\mathbf{N}$ with the subset $\{G(S_k) \mid k \in \mathbf{N}\}$ of S. $/\!/$

A set which is empty or which has the properties of the theorem is called **finite**; a set which is not finite is called **infinite**. Clearly a set which is in one-to-one correspondence with a finite (infinite) set is itself finite (infinite).

Corollary 1. *Every $\mathbf{N}_m$ is finite; $\mathbf{N}$ is infinite.*

Corollary 2. *If $\mathbf{N}_r \sim \mathbf{N}_s$, then $r = s$.*

Proof: If not, then by the corollary to Proposition 4.10, either $\mathbf{N}_r \subset \mathbf{N}_s$ or $\mathbf{N}_s \subset \mathbf{N}_r$; but no $\mathbf{N}_m$ can be in one-to-one correspondence with a proper subset of itself. $/\!/$

By Corollary 2, if $S \neq \varnothing$ is finite, we have $S \sim \mathbf{N}_m$ for some *unique* $m \in \mathbf{N}$. We say that such an S has m *elements*, and call m the *number of elements* of S. To extend this terminology to the empty set, we say that 0 is the number of elements of $\varnothing$. A set with n elements, where $n \neq 0$, is often denoted by an expression of the form $\{x_1, \ldots, x_n\}$.

Corollary 3. *Any infinite set contains an m-element subset for every $m \in \mathbf{N}$; any n-element set contains an m-element subset for every $m \leq n$.*

Proof: $\mathbf{N}_m \subset \mathbf{N}$ for all m; $\mathbf{N}_m \subseteq \mathbf{N}_n$ if $m \leq n$. $/\!/$

SUBSETS, IMAGES, AND UNIONS OF FINITE SETS

Proposition 1. *Any subset of a finite set is finite.*

Proof: Use (3) of Theorem 1. $/\!/$

Note that Proposition 1 can be restated as: Any set which has an infinite subset is itself infinite.

Proposition 2. *Any image of a finite set is finite.*

Proof: By Proposition 3.3, any $F(S)$ is in one-to-one correspondence with a subset of S.   //

A stronger version of Propositions 1–2 is provided by

Proposition 3. *If S has n elements, any subset or image set of S has m elements for some $m \leq n$. Moreover, if the subset is proper, or the function is not one-to-one, then $m < n$.*

Proof: Suppose that the subset S' had r elements, where $r > n$. Let G, H be one-to-one correspondences of $\mathbf{N}_r$ with S' and of S with $\mathbf{N}_n$, respectively; then $G \circ H$ is readily a one-to-one correspondence of $\mathbf{N}_r$ with its proper subset $H(S') \subseteq \mathbf{N}_n \subset \mathbf{N}_r$, which is impossible. The same proof shows that $r = n$ is impossible unless $S' = S$. For the last part, use Proposition 3.3 and the remark following it.   //

Corollary. *If A and B each have n elements, a function from A into B is one-to-one if and only if it is onto.*

Proof: If F is one-to-one, $F(A)$ has n elements, so must be all of B. Conversely, if $F(A) = B$, it has n elements, so that F must be one-to-one by the last part of the proposition.   //

Proposition 4. *If A and B are finite, so is $A \cup B$; in fact, if A has r elements and B has s elements, then $A \cup B$ has t elements for some $t \leq r + s$.*

Proof: Let G, H be one-to-one correspondences of A, B with $\mathbf{N}_r, \mathbf{N}_s$, respectively, and let G' be the restriction of G to $A - B$; then by Proposition 4.7 and Exercise 3.9, $G' \cup (H \circ F_r)$ is a one-to-one correspondence of $A \cup B$ with a subset of $\mathbf{N}_{r+s}$.   //

Corollary 1. *If A and B are disjoint, then $t = r + s$.*

Proof: $G' = G$, and $G \cup (H \circ F_r)$ is evidently onto.   //

Corollary 2. *Let $T \subset S$, where T has m elements and S has n elements; then $S - T$ has $n - m$ elements.*

Proposition 5. *A finite union of finite sets is finite.*

Proof: Let $\mathscr{A}$ be a finite set of sets, say $\mathscr{A} \sim \mathbf{N}_m$, where the elements of $\mathscr{A}$ are all finite sets. If $m = 1$, say $\mathscr{A} = \{A\}$, then $\bigcup_{A \in \mathscr{A}} A = A$ is finite. Otherwise, let $S \in \mathscr{A}$, so that S is finite. Now $\mathscr{A} - \{S\} \sim \mathbf{N}_{m-1}$, so that by induction hypothesis $\bigcup_{A \in \mathscr{A} - \{S\}} A$ is finite. Hence by Proposition 4, $\bigcup_{A \in \mathscr{A}} A = (\bigcup_{A \in \mathscr{A} - \{S\}} A) \cup S$ is also finite.   //

If $\mathscr{A} = \{A_1, \ldots, A_m\}$, we can (compare Exercise 3.3) denote $\bigcup_{A \in \mathscr{A}} A$ by $\bigcup_{i \in \mathbf{N}_m} A_i$, or (more commonly) by $\bigcup_{i=1}^m A_i$, and similarly for $\bigcap$. It is now straightforward to prove

Proposition 6. *Let A_i have n_i elements, $1 \le i \le m$; then $\bigcup_{i=1}^m A_i$ has at most $\sum_{i=1}^m n_i$ elements, and has exactly that many if the A's are disjoint.*

PRODUCTS AND POWERS OF FINITE SETS

Proposition 7. *If A and B are finite, so is $A \times B$.*

Proof: For each $a \in A$, let $B_a = \{(a, x) \mid x \in B\}$. Clearly $\{(x, (a, x)) \mid x \in B\}$ is a one-to-one correspondence of B with B_a, so that B_a is finite. Let $\mathscr{A} = \{B_a \mid a \in A\}$; then evidently $\{(a, B_a) \mid a \in A\}$ is a one-to-one correspondence of A with $\mathscr{A}$, so that $\mathscr{A}$ is also finite. Thus $A \times B = \bigcup_{a \in A} B_a$ is a finite union of finite sets, and so is finite by Proposition 5. //

By Proposition 7, for all m, n in $\mathbf{N}^\circ$, $\mathbf{N}_m \times \mathbf{N}_n$ is finite (where $\mathbf{N}_0$ means $\varnothing$). The number of elements of $\mathbf{N}_m \times \mathbf{N}_n$ is denoted by mn, and is called the **product** of m and n; we say that m and n are **factors** of mn. Evidently, for any $m \in \mathbf{N}^\circ$, $G_m = \{(n, mn) \mid n \in \mathbf{N}^\circ\}$ is a function from $\mathbf{N}^\circ$ into $\mathbf{N}^\circ$; applying G_m to n is called **multiplication** of n by m. It is easy to prove the following stronger version of Proposition 7:

Proposition 8. *If A has m elements and B has n elements, then $A \times B$ has mn elements.*

The following exercises summarize useful properties of multiplication:

Exercise 1. *For all r, s, t, u, v in $\mathbf{N}^\circ$ we have*
(a) $rs = sr$
(b) $0r = 0$; $1r = r$
(c) $r(s + t) = rs + rt$ [Hint: If B and C are disjoint, so are $A \times B$ and $A \times C$]; $r(s - t) = rs - rt$
(d) $r(st) = (rs)t$ [Hint: Part (c) and induction on t]
(e) $rs = 0$ implies $r = 0$ or $s = 0$
Corollary: $rs = rt$ implies $r = 0$ or $s = t$
(f) $r \le rs$ unless $s = 0$; $r = rs$ if and only if $r = 0$ or $s = 1$
(g) If $r \le u$ and $s \le v$, then $rs \le uv$; if either of the first two $\le$'s is $<$, so is the third, provided $uv \ne 0$.

In words: (a) *Multiplication is* **commutative**; (b) 0 *is* **absorbent**, *and* 1 *an* **identity**, *for multiplication:* (c) *multiplication* **distributes over** *addition and subtraction;* (d) *it is* **associative**; (e) *restricted to* $\mathbf{N}$, *it obeys the* **law of cancellation**.

Exercise 2. *Let r, s be elements of $\mathbf{N}^\circ$. If $s = kr$ for some $k \in \mathbf{N}^\circ$, we say that s is a* **multiple** *of r, and that r* **divides** *s (or "is a divisor of s"); notation:*

$r|s$). *Prove that "divides" is* **reflexive, weakly antisymmetric,** *and* **transitive**— *in other words, that for all r, s, t in* $\mathbf{N}^\circ$ *we have*

(a) $r|r$
(b) $r|s$ *and* $s|r$ *imply* $r = s$
(c) $r|s$ *and* $s|t$ *imply* $r|t$.

Verify also that $0|s$ *if and only if* $s = 0$, *that* $s|1$ *if and only if* $s = 1$, *and that* $1|s$ *and* $s|0$ *for all* $s \in \mathbf{N}^\circ$. *Finally, prove that if* $r|a$ *and* $r|b$, *then* $r \mid a + b$ *and* $r \mid a - b$ (*if the latter is defined*).

Exercise 3. *Let* $(a_i)_\mathbf{N}$ *be the sequence of natural numbers defined by* $a_1 = m$; $a_{n+1} = a_n + m$. *The set of terms of this sequence will be denoted by* $m\mathbf{N}$. *Prove that* $n \in m\mathbf{N}$ *if and only if* $n \neq 0$ *and* $m|n$.

Exercise 4. $p \in \mathbf{N}$ *is called* **prime** *if* $p \neq 1$ *and its only divisors are* 1 *and itself. Prove that* 2 *and* 3 *are prime.*

Exercise 5. *By Exercise 1(e), if* $s = kr$ *and* $r \neq 0$, *then* k *is uniquely determined by* r *and* s. *We denote this unique* k *by* s/r (*or* $\frac{s}{r}$; *read "s over r"*), *and call it the* **quotient** *of* s *by* r. (*The process of combining* s *and* r *to obtain* s/r *is called* **division** *of* s *by* r.) *Prove that for all* r, s, t *in* $\mathbf{N}^\circ$ *such that the indicated quotients exist, we have*

(a) $0/r = 0$; $r/1 = r$
(b) $(r + s)/t = (r/t) + (s/t)$
(c) $(rs)/t = r(s/t)$
(d) $r/(st) = (r/s)/t$.

Exercise 6. *For all* $a \in \mathbf{N}^\circ$ *and all* $b \in \mathbf{N}$ *there exist* q, r *in* $\mathbf{N}^\circ$ *such that* $a = qb + r$ *and* $r < b$. [*Hint: If* $a < b$, *take* $q = 0$, $r = a$. *Otherwise, note that not every multiple of* b *can be* $\leq a$—*for example,* $a \leq ab < (a + 1)b$ *by Exercise 1(f); hence (use induction!) there must exist* $q \in \mathbf{N}$ *such that* $qb \leq a$ *but* $a < (q + 1)b$.] *We call* r *the* **remainder** *left by* a *upon division by* b. *Prove that* q *and* r *are uniquely determined by* a *and* b.

Exercise 7. *Let* $\{A_1, \ldots, A_m\}$ *be a set of disjoint sets each of which has* n *elements; then* $\bigcup_{i=1}^m A_i$ *has* mn *elements—in other words,* $\sum_{i=1}^m n = mn$ (*"multiplication is repeated addition"*). [*Hint: Proposition 6 and the proof of Proposition 7.*]

Proposition 9. *If* S *is finite, so is* S^n *for any* $n \in \mathbf{N}$.

Proof: This is clear for $n = 1$, since $S^1 \sim S$. Moreover, S^{m+1} is readily in one-to-one correspondence with $S^m \times S$; thus if S^m is finite, so is S^{m+1} by Proposition 7. $\|$

The number of elements of $\mathbf{N}_m{}^n$ is denoted by m^n (read "m to the n," or more fully, "m to the nth power"); in the expression m^n, m is called the **base**, and n the **exponent**. The process of combining m and n to obtain m^n is called **exponentiation**.

Proposition 10. *If S has m elements, S^n has m^n elements.*

Exercise 8. *For all r, s, t in* **N** *we have*
  (a) $0^t = 0$, $1^t = 1$, $r^1 = r$
  (b) $(rs)^t = r^t s^t$
  (c) $r^{s+t} = r^s r^t$
  (d) $r^{st} = (r^s)^t$.

Exercise 9. *Let the sequence $(a_i)_N$ of elements of* **N** *be defined by $a_1 = 1$; $a_{n+1} = na_n$. The nth term of this sequence is called n* **factorial**, *and is denoted by $n!$. Prove that if S and T each have n elements, the number of one-to-one correspondences of S with T is $n!$. Corollary: If S has n elements, the number of permutations of S is $n!$.*

Exercise 10. *Let S, T have m, n elements, respectively, where $0 \le m \le n$; prove that the number of one-to-one functions from S into T is $n!/(n - m)!$, where we define $0! = 1$. Corollary: The number of m-element subsets of T is* $\dfrac{n!}{m!\,(n - m)!}$. $\left[\text{This number is usually denoted by } \binom{n}{m}.\right]$

Proposition 11. *If S has n elements, $\mathscr{P}_S$ has 2^n elements.*

Proof: Given $A \subseteq S$, define $F_A = \{(x, 1) \mid x \in A\} \cup \{(x, 2) \mid x \in S - A\}$; thus F_A is a function from S into $\mathbf{N}_2$. Conversely, given such a function F, define $A_F = \{x \mid F(x) = 1\}$, so that A_F is a subset of S. Then readily (use the corollary to Proposition 3.6), $\{(A, F_A) \mid A \subseteq S\}$ is a one-to-one correspondence of $\mathscr{P}_S$ with the set of functions from S into $\mathbf{N}_2$; and since S has n elements, this set of functions is readily in one-to-one correspondence with $\mathbf{N}_2{}^n$. //

Corollary. *S is finite if and only if $\mathscr{P}_S$ is finite.*

Proof: If S is infinite, $\mathscr{P}_S$ has the infinite subset $\{\{x\} \mid x \in S\}$. //

Proposition 12. *We can never have $S \sim \mathscr{P}_S$.*

Proof: Suppose that G were a one-to-one correspondence of S with $\mathscr{P}_S$; let $S^* = \{x \mid x \in S; x \notin G(x)\}$. Since G is onto, there exists $x^* \in S$ such that $G(x^*) = S^*$. If $x^* \in S^*$, then by definition of S^* we must have $x^* \notin G(x^*) = S^*$, contradiction; while if $x^* \notin S^*$, we must have $x^* \in G(x^*) = S^*$, contradiction. //

Corollary. *There exists an infinite set—namely, $\mathscr{P}_N$—which is not in one-to-one correspondence with* **N**.

A set which is in one-to-one correspondence with **N** is called **denumerable** (or, more fully: **denumerably infinite**).

II

ORDERED SETS

6. ORDER RELATIONS

The relation R on the set S is called an **order relation** if it is **reflexive, weakly antisymmetric**, and **transitive**—in other words, if for all x, y, z in S we have

(1) $(x, x) \in R$

(2) $(x, y) \in R$ and $(y, x) \in R$ imply $x = y$

(3) $(x, y) \in R$ and $(y, z) \in R$ imply $(x, z) \in R$.

[Note that these properties can also be written concisely as (1) $I_S \subseteq R$; (2) $R \cap R^{-1} \subseteq I_S$; (3) $R \circ R \subseteq R$.] If R is an order relation on S, we say that S is an **ordered set** under R. If there is no doubt as to which R is meant, we omit the "under R."

Examples:

(a) $S = \mathscr{P}_T$, where T is any set; R is $\subseteq_S$. [More generally: S is any set of sets; R is $\subseteq_S$ (Exercise 1.1).]

(b) $S = \mathbf{N}$ or $\mathbf{N}°$; R is $\leq$ (Proposition 4.11).

(c) $S = \mathbf{N}$ or $\mathbf{N}°$; R is "divides" (Exercise 5.2).

(d) The restriction of an order relation to a subset is an order relation on the subset.

(e) $\varnothing$ cannot be an order relation unless $S = \varnothing$, nor can $S \times S$ unless S has at most one element; but I_S is always an order relation on S.

(f) Any intersection of order relations is an order relation.

(g) The inverse of an order relation is an order relation.

Exercise 1. *Is a composite of order relations always an order relation?*

If R also obeys the **law of dichotomy**—that is, $(x, y) \in R$ or $(y, x) \in R$ for all x, y in S (or more concisely: $R \cup R^{-1} = S \times S$)—it is called a **total order relation**. If R is total, the ordered set S is called a **chain** ("under R" understood).

Examples:

(a) $\subseteq$ is not total unless T has at most one element.

(b) $\leq$ is total (Proposition 4.12).

(c) | is not total (Exercise 5.4).

(d) Any restriction of a total order relation is total.

(e) I_S is not total unless S has at most one element.

(f) The inverse of a total order relation is total.

Note that even if R is not total, its restriction to a subset $A \subseteq S$ may be total (trivial example: $A = \{a\}$). If this is the case, we say that A is a chain of the ordered set S. By Example (d), any subset of a chain is a chain.

Exercise 2. *Let P, Q be relations on S such that P is reflexive and Q obeys the law of dichotomy; then $P \circ Q$ and $Q \circ P$ obey the law of dichotomy.*

It is often useful to represent an order relation by a diagram in which elements of the ordered set are denoted by dots, and pairs of elements belonging to the relation are joined by lines, with the first element of a pair placed lower down than the second. For example, $\subseteq$ on $\mathscr{P}_{\{x,y\}}$ is represented by the diagram

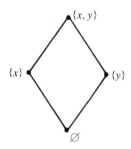

while $\subseteq$ on $\mathscr{P}_{\{x,y,z\}}$ is represented by

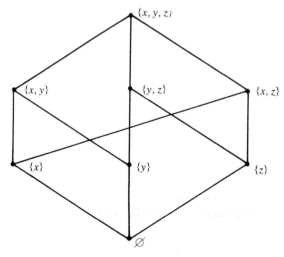

From now on we shall use the notation $\leq$ to represent an arbitrary order relation, writing "$x \leq y$" in place of "$(x, y) \in R$." It will always be clear from the context which relation is intended. Some other useful notational conventions: We write "$x \leq y \leq z$" as an abbreviation for "$x \leq y$ and $y \leq z$." If A, B are subsets of the ordered set, we write "$A \leq B$" as an abbreviation for "$a \leq b$ for all $a \in A$ and all $b \in B$"; in particular, "$A \leq x$" means "$a \leq x$ for all $a \in A$." The inverse relation of $\leq$ will be denoted by $\geq$, and the relation "$\leq$ but $\neq$" (that is, $R - I_S$) will be denoted by $<$.

Exercise 3. *If $\leq$ is any order relation on S, prove that $<$ satisfies*

(a) **Irreflexivity:** *Not $x < x$*
(b) **Antisymmetry:** *Not both $x < y$ and $y < x$*
(c) **Transitivity:** *$x < y$ and $y < z$ imply $x < z$*

*—in fact, $x < y$ and $y \leq z$, or $x \leq y$ and $y < z$, also imply $x < z$ for all x, y, z in S. Such a relation is called a **strict order relation** on S. Prove further that if $\leq$ is total, then $<$ also satisfies*

(d) **Trichotomy:** *$x < y$ or $y < x$ or $x = y$.*

[More concisely, representing $<$ by Q: (a) $I_S \cap Q = \varnothing$; (b) $Q \cap Q^{-1} = \varnothing$; (c) $Q \circ Q \subseteq Q$; (d) $Q \cup Q^{-1} \cup I_S = S \times S$.] Conversely, prove that if Q is a strict order relation on S, then $Q \cup I_S$ is an order relation, and if Q also satisfies the law of trichotomy, then $Q \cup I_S$ is total.

Exercise 4. *Let A, B be chains of S such that $A \leq B$; then $A \cup B$ is a chain of S.*

ORDER PRESERVING FUNCTIONS

Let P, Q be order relations on the sets A, B, respectively, and let F be a function from A into B. We call F **order preserving** ("with respect to P and Q" understood) if $(x, y) \in P$ implies $(F(x), F(y)) \in Q$ for all x, y in A. If F is a one-to-one correspondence, and both F and F^{-1} are order preserving, we call F an **order isomorphism**, and say that A and B are **order isomorphic** ("with respect to P and Q" understood).

Examples:

(a) Any function is $\subseteq$-preserving; any one-to-one correspondence is an $\subseteq$-isomorphism (Exercise 3.2 and Proposition 3.4).
(b) For any $m \in \mathbf{N}^\circ$, the function $F_m = \{(n, m + n) \mid n \in \mathbf{N}^\circ\}$ is an $\leq$-isomorphism of $\mathbf{N}^\circ$ with $F_m(\mathbf{N}^\circ)$ (Proposition 4.14).
(c) For any $m \in \mathbf{N}$, the function $G_m = \{(n, mn) \mid n \in \mathbf{N}\}$ is both an $\leq$-isomorphism (Exercise 5.1(g)) and an $|$-isomorphism of $\mathbf{N}$ with $m\mathbf{N}$.
(d) Any restriction of an order-preserving function is order preserving, and similarly for an order isomorphism.

(e) The identity function is an order isomorphism with respect to any order relation, and any constant function is order preserving with respect to any order relations.

(f) Any function from A into B is order preserving with respect to I_A and I_B, and is an order isomorphism if it is a one-to-one correspondence.

(g) If a function is order preserving (an order isomorphism) with respect to P and Q, it is the same with respect to P^{-1} and Q^{-1}.

(h) The inverse of an order isomorphism is an order isomorphism (fill in "with respect to ..."!).

(i) A composite of order-preserving functions (order isomorphisms) is order preserving (an order isomorphism; fill in "with respect to ..."!).

Exercise 5. *An order-preserving function takes chains into chains. Moreover, an order preserving function defined on a chain is an order isomorphism if and only if it is one-to-one.*

Exercise 6. *If F is a one-to-one order preserving function defined on A, then $x < y$ implies $F(x) < F(y)$ for all x, y in A. Conversely, if A is a chain and F is a function defined on A such that $x < y$ implies $F(x) < F(y)$ for all x, y in A, then F is one-to-one order preserving (whence, by Exercise 5, an order isomorphism).*

7. BOUNDS; GREATEST AND LEAST ELEMENTS

Let $\leq$ be an order relation on S, and let A be a subset of S. We say that $x \in S$ is an **upper bound** for A ("with respect to $\leq$" understood) if $a \leq x$ for all $a \in A$; that $x \in S$ is a **lower bound** for A, if $x \leq a$ for all $a \in A$. Note that if $A = \varnothing$, any $x \in S$ is both an upper and a lower bound for A. Evidently an upper bound with respect to $\leq$ is the same thing as a lower bound with respect to $\geq$, and vice versa.

A subset need not have any upper or lower bounds. For example, let $S = \mathscr{P}_T - \{\varnothing\}$, where T is any set; then if $x \neq y$, the subset $\{\{x\}, \{y\}\}$ has no lower bound with respect to $\subseteq$. A more familiar example: $\mathbf{N}$ has no upper bound with respect to $\leq$.

Exercise 1. *An upper bound for A is an upper bound for any subset of A, and analogously for lower bounds.* (*)†

Exercise 2. *An order preserving function takes upper bounds into upper bounds.* (*)

---

† An asterisk in parentheses (*) at the end of an exercise, proposition, or theorem in this or the next chapter means that a "dual" statement, with "upper" replaced by "lower" and so on, is also valid [**Exercise:** Supply it!].

An upper or lower bound for A can be an element of A. For example, any $x \in S$ is both an upper and a lower bound for $\{x\}$; any $\mathbf{N}_m$ has the lower bound 1 and the upper bound m. A bound for A which is not an element of A is called **strict**.

Proposition 1. *At most one element of A can be an upper bound for A.* (*)

Proof: If x, y, both in A, are both upper bounds for A, we have in particular $x \leq y$ and $y \leq x$, so that $x = y$. $\parallel$

By virtue of Proposition 1, if $x \in A$ is an upper (lower) bound for A, we can call x the **greatest (least) element** of A. (We may sometimes say "largest" or "smallest" instead of "greatest" and "least.") If S itself has greatest and least elements, they are often denoted by 1 and 0, respectively; thus $0 \leq x \leq 1$ for all $x \in S$.

Examples:
- (a) For $\subseteq$ on $\mathscr{P}_T$, $\varnothing$ is the least element and T the greatest element.
- (b) For $\leq$ or $\mid$ on $\mathbf{N}$, 1 is the least element, and there is no greatest element. (What happens in the cases of $\leq$ and $\mid$ on $\mathbf{N}^\circ$?) For $\leq$ on $\mathbf{N}$, any $\mathbf{N}_m$ has 1 as least element and m as greatest element.

Exercise 3. *Let $x \in B \subseteq A$ be the greatest element of A; then x is the greatest element of B.*

Exercise 4. *An order preserving function takes greatest elements into greatest elements.* (*)

Exercise 5. *Let S be an ordered set, and let a, b be elements of S such that $a \leq b$; then the set $\{x \mid a \leq x \leq b\}$ is called the* **interval** *$[a, b]$. Verify that $[a, b]$ has least element a and greatest element b, and that $[a, b] = [c, d]$ if and only if $a = c$ and $b = d$.*

Exercise 6. *The subset A of an ordered set is called a* **segment** *if $a \in A$, $b \leq a$ imply $b \in A$. For example, for any y, the sets $\{x \mid x \leq y\}$ and $\{x \mid x < y\}$ are segments. Verify that a lower bound of a nonempty segment must be its least element.*

The least element of the set of upper bounds for A, if it exists, is called the **least upper bound** of A, and is denoted by sup A. Similarly, the greatest element of the set of lower bounds for A is called the **greatest lower bound** of A, and is denoted by inf A.

Examples:
- (a) If S has the greatest element 1, then sup $S = \inf \varnothing = 1$. If S has the least element 0, then inf $S = \sup \varnothing = 0$.
- (b) sup $\{x\} = \inf \{x\} = x$ for all $x \in S$.

(c) For $\subseteq$ on $\mathscr{P}_T$, we have sup $\mathscr{A} = \bigcup_{\mathscr{A}} A$ and inf $\mathscr{A} = \bigcap_{\mathscr{A}} A$ for any nonempty $\mathscr{A} \subseteq \mathscr{P}_T$; while inf $\varnothing = T$, sup $\varnothing = \varnothing$.

Proposition 2. *If A has the greatest element x, then $x = $ sup A. Conversely, if* sup A *is in A, it is the greatest element of A.* (*)

Proof: The converse follows immediately from the definition of greatest element, since the sup is an upper bound. For the direct part, note that the greatest element is an upper bound, and since it is in A it must be $\leq$ any other upper bound. //

Exercise 7. *If $A \subseteq B$, then* sup A *(if it exists) $\leq$ any upper bound for B (in particular,* sup $A \leq$ sup B, *if it exists). Moreover, if* sup A *is an upper bound for B, then it is* sup B. (*)

Exercise 8. *The following statements are equivalent:*

(a) $x \leq y$
(b) sup $\{x, y\} = y$
(c) inf $\{x, y\} = x$.

8. MAXIMAL AND MINIMAL ELEMENTS

Even if a subset A of an ordered set has no greatest element, it may have "maximal" elements—that is, elements such that nothing in A is "strictly greater" than any of them. For example, if $x \neq y$, then $A = \{\{x\}, \{y\}\}$ has no greatest element with respect to $\subseteq$, but it has both $\{x\}$ and $\{y\}$ as maximal elements, since no element of A properly contains either of them.

We call $x \in A$ a **maximal element** of A if there exists no $y \in A$ such that $x < y$—or, equivalently, if $x \leq y$ implies $x = y$ for all $y \in A$. Similarly, we call x a **minimal element** of A if there is no $y \in A$ such that $y < x$. We shall sometimes say "maximal in" instead of "a maximal element of." Note that by the above example, a maximal element need not be unique, and an element can be both maximal and minimal.

Exercise 1. *The greatest element of A, if it exists, is maximal, and in fact is the sole maximal element of A.* (*)

Exercise 2. *If A is a chain, it can have at most one maximal element, and this element, if it exists, is the greatest element of A.* (*)

Exercise 3. *If $x \in B \subseteq A$ is maximal in A, it is maximal in B.* (*)

Exercise 4. *An order isomorphism takes maximal elements into maximal elements.* (*)

As we have seen by example, even a set with only two elements need not have an upper bound or a greatest element. For maximal elements, on the other hand, we have

Proposition 1. *Every nonempty finite ordered set has a maximal element.* (*)

Proof: If $A = \{x\}$, x is maximal; suppose the proposition is true for sets with n elements, and let A have $n + 1$ elements. Let $x \in A$; if x is maximal, we are done. If not, $A - \{x\}$ has n elements, so has a maximal element y. If $y \leq x$, readily this makes x maximal in A, contradiction. Otherwise, y itself is maximal in A, since if $y \leq z$ we must have $z \neq x$, so that $z = y$ by the maximality of y in $A - \{x\}$.   //

Corollary 1. *Every nonempty finite chain has a greatest element.* (*)

Proof: The proposition and Exercise 2.   //

Corollary 2. *Every nonempty finite chain has a sup.* (*)

We can say much more than this about finite chains; in fact, we can apply Corollary 1 to prove

Proposition 2. *Any chain with m elements is order isomorphic to* $\mathbf{N}_m$ *under* $\leq$.

Proof: This is trivial for $m = 1$; suppose it true for m, and let A have $m + 1$ elements. Let x be the greatest element of A (Corollary 1 to Proposition 1); then $A - \{x\}$ has m elements, so that there exists an order isomorphism G of $A - \{x\}$ with $\mathbf{N}_m$. Let $H = G \cup \{(x, m + 1)\}$; then readily H is an order isomorphism of A with $\mathbf{N}_{m+1}$.   //

Exercise 5. *Prove that there is only one order isomorphism of a given m-element chain with* $\mathbf{N}_m$. [Hint: If the restriction of H to $A - \{x\}$ is unique, so is H.]

Finite chains will be studied further in Section 10.

We next consider chains which are order isomorphic to $\mathbf{N}$ itself. A chain which is order isomorphic to $\mathbf{N}$ under $\leq$ is called an **ascending chain**; a chain which is order isomorphic to $\mathbf{N}$ under $\geq$ is called a **descending chain**.

Proposition 3. *Let* $(a_i)_\mathbf{N}$ *be a sequence of elements of an ordered set such that* $a_m < a_{m+1}$ *for all* $m \in \mathbf{N}$; *then* $\{(r, a_r) \mid r \in \mathbf{N}\}$ *is an order isomorphism, so that the set of terms of* $(a_i)_\mathbf{N}$ *is an ascending chain.* (*)

Proof: It follows easily by induction on k that $a_m < a_{m+k}$ for all m, k in $\mathbf{N}$. Thus (Proposition 4.13) $m < n$ implies $a_m < a_n$, so that (Exercise 6.6) the sequence is an order isomorphism.   //

THE MAXIMUM AND MINIMUM CONDITIONS

Theorem 1. *The following statements about the ordered set S are equivalent:*

(1) *No subset of S is an ascending chain*

(2) *Every nonempty subset of S has a maximal element.* (*)

Proof: If (1) holds, and A is a nonempty subset of S which has no maximal element, let F be a choice function on A, and let $F(A) = a_1$. Since a_1 is not maximal, the set $A_1 = \{x \mid x \in A; a_1 < x\}$ is nonempty; let $F(A_1) = a_2$. Since a_2 is not maximal, the set $A_2 = \{x \mid x \in A; a_2 < x\}$ is still nonempty; let $F(A_2) = a_3$. By Theorem 4.2, this procedure defines a sequence of elements of A, and by Proposition 3, this sequence is an ascending chain, contradicting (1).

Conversely, if (2) holds, in particular any ascending chain $A = G(\mathbf{N})$ must have a maximal element, say $G(m)$; but since G is an order isomorphism, by Exercise 6.6 we must have $G(m) < G(m + 1)$, contradiction.   //

Property (1) of Theorem 1 is called the **ascending chain condition**; property (2) is called the **maximum condition**. The "dual" properties are called the **descending chain condition** and the **minimum condition**.

Corollary. *If S satisfies the maximum condition, so does any subset of S.*   (*)

Exercise 6. *Prove that each of the following is equivalent to the ascending chain condition:*

(a) *Let $(a_i)_\mathbf{N}$ be a sequence of elements of S such that $a_k \leq a_{k+1}$ for all $k \in \mathbf{N}$; then the set of terms of $(a_i)_\mathbf{N}$ is finite*

(b) *Let $(a_i)_\mathbf{N}$ be as in (a); then there exists $m \in \mathbf{N}$ such that $a_n = a_m$ for all $n \geq m$.*   (*)

Proposition 4. $\mathbf{N}$, *under* $\leq$, *satisfies the minimum condition.*

Proof: Suppose that $\mathbf{N}$ contained a descending chain; specifically, let G be an order isomorphism of $\mathbf{N}$, under $\geq$, with a subset of $\mathbf{N}$ under $\leq$. Let $G(1) = m$; then since G is order preserving, it must take all of $\mathbf{N} = \{x \mid x \in \mathbf{N}; x \geq 1\}$ into $\mathbf{N}_m = \{x \mid x \in \mathbf{N}; x \leq m\}$. But since G is one-to-one, this would give us a one-to-one correspondence of $\mathbf{N}$ with a subset of the finite set $\mathbf{N}_m$, which is impossible.   //

Corollary. *Any ascending chain satisfies the minimum condition.*   (*)

Theorem 2. *The following statements about the ordered set S are equivalent:*

(1) *No subset of S is an ascending or descending chain—in other words, S satisfies both the maximum and the minimum conditions*

(2) *No infinite subset of S is a chain.*

Proof: (1) is a special case of (2). Conversely, if (1) holds and $A \subseteq S$ is an infinite chain, let a_1 be its greatest element (this exists by Theorem 1 and Exercise 2). Then $A_1 = A - \{a_1\}$ is still an infinite chain; let a_2 be its greatest element, and so on. This procedure defines a function G from $\mathbf{N}$ into A, and readily G is an order isomorphism of $\mathbf{N}$ (under $\geq$) with $G(\mathbf{N})$, so that $G(\mathbf{N})$ is a descending chain, contradicting (1).   //

9. WELL ORDERING AND ZORN'S LEMMA

A chain which satisfies the minimum condition is called **well ordered**.† For example, any finite chain is well ordered, and by the corollary to Proposition 8.4, any ascending chain is well ordered.

Exercise 1. *An ordered set satisfies the minimum condition if and only if all its chains are well ordered.*

Our principal goal in this section is to prove that on any set S there exists an order relation under which S is well ordered. This result will be applied to establish some very useful conditions for the existence of maximal elements in ordered sets.

Lemma 1. *Let A be well ordered, and let $C \subset A$ be a segment (Exercise 7.6); then there exists an $a \in A$ such that $C = \{x \mid x \in A; x < a\}$.* [We shall denote this set by A_a.]

  Proof: Take $a = $ the least element of $A - C$. $\parallel$

Lemma 2. *Let $\mathscr{A}$ be a set of well ordered sets; say $A \in \mathscr{A}$ is well ordered under R_A. Suppose that for all A, B in $\mathscr{A}$, either A is a segment of B under R_B, and the restriction of R_B to A is R_A, or vice versa. Then there exists a unique order relation R^* on $A^* = \bigcup_{\mathscr{A}} A$ such that*

(α) *A^* is well ordered under R^**
(β) *The restriction of R^* to any $A \in \mathscr{A}$ is R_A*
(γ) *Each $A \in \mathscr{A}$ is a segment of A^* (under R^*).*

  Proof; Given a, b in A^*, let $a \in A$, $b \in B$, where A, B are in $\mathscr{A}$, and (say) A is a segment of B. Thus any two elements of A^* are in the same $B \in \mathscr{A}$. Moreover, if a and b are also in $C \in \mathscr{A}$, then R_C is a restriction of R_B or vice versa, so that $a \leq b$ under R_B if and only if $a \leq b$ under R_C. We can thus define R^* as the set of (a, b) such that $(a, b) \in R_B$ for any (or equivalently, every) $B \in \mathscr{A}$ such that a and b are in B. Readily, this R^* is a total order relation on A^*, and the restriction of R^* to any $A \in \mathscr{A}$ is R_A, so that (β) is proved.

  Let $x \in A \in \mathscr{A}$, and let $y \in A^*$ be such that $y \leq x$ under R^*. As above, we have x, y in B for some $B \in \mathscr{A}$ such that A is a segment of B under R_B. (If B is a segment of A, then $y \in A$ and we are done.) But $y \leq x$ under R^*, hence under its restriction R_B, and since A is a segment, this implies that $y \in A$, proving (γ).

  Finally, let $T = G(\mathbf{N})$ be a descending chain in A^* (under R^*), and let $G(1) = a \in A$. Since A is a segment, we have $T \subseteq A$, so that T is a descending chain in A (under R_A), which is impossible since A is well ordered under R_A; this proves (α). $\parallel$

---

† One could also define a "dual" concept using the maximum condition, but we shall not do so.

We can now prove

Theorem 1. *Let S be an ordered set such that every well-ordered subset of S has an upper bound; then S has a maximal element.*

Proof :† It suffices to show that there exists a well-ordered subset A of S which has no strict upper bound. Indeed, such an A must have an upper bound $a \in A$, which is thus its greatest element, and this a must be a maximal element of S, since if we had $a < b$ for some $b \in S$, then b would be a strict upper bound of A.

For any well-ordered $A \subseteq S$, let A' be the set of upper bounds of A, and A'' the set of strict upper bounds of A. Let G be a choice function on S, and let F be the function which takes each A into $G(A'')$ if $A'' \neq \varnothing$, and into $G(A')$ otherwise. By the preceding paragraph, it suffices to find a well-ordered $A \subseteq S$ such that $F(A) \in A$.

Call the well-ordered set $B \subseteq S$ an F-chain if $F(B_x) = x$ for every $x \in B$, where the notation is as in Lemma 1. Let B, C be F-chains; we next show that one of them must be a segment of the other. In fact, let D be the union of all their common segments, that is, the union of all B_x such that $B_x = C_y$, where $x \in B$, $y \in C$. Evidently D is a segment, so that by Lemma 1 we have $D = B_b = C_c$ for some $b \in B$, $c \in C$. But since B and C are F-chains, this implies that $b = F(B_b) = F(C_c) = c$; hence $D \cup \{b\}$ is also a common segment, and since it properly contains D, we have a contradiction to the fact that D is the union of all common segments.

By Lemma 2, it follows that the union A of all the F-chains of S is well ordered. Moreover, any $x \in A$ is in some F-chain B, and readily $A_x = B_x$, so that $F(A_x) = F(B_x) = x$, making A an F-chain. Suppose that $F(A) \notin A$; then $A \cup \{F(A)\}$ would be an F-chain properly containing A, contradiction. We have thus found a well-ordered $A \subseteq S$ such that $F(A) \in A$, as required. //

Note that S must be nonempty, since by hypothesis its well-ordered subset $\varnothing$ must have an upper bound.

Corollary 1 ("Zorn's lemma"). *Let S be an ordered set such that every chain of S has an upper bound; then S has a maximal element.*

An ordered set which satisfies the hypothesis of Zorn's lemma is called **inductive**.

Corollary 2. *If S, ordered by $\leq$, is inductive, then for any $x \in S$ there exists a maximal element z of S such that $x \leq z$.*

Proof: The set $\{y \mid y \in S; x \leq y\}$ is still inductive under the restriction of $\leq$, and a maximal element of this set is evidently maximal in S. //

† This proof is adapted from H. Kneser, "Das Auswahlaxiom und das Lemma von Zorn," *Math. Zeitschr.* **96**, 1967, 62–63.

Exercise 2. *Prove that if an ordered set satisfies the maximum condition, it is empty or inductive. Show by example that the converse is false.*

Zorn's lemma will be used repeatedly in this and the following chapters. As a first application, we use it to prove

Theorem 3 (Hausdorff). *Let S be an ordered set under $\leq$, and let $\mathcal{P}_S$ be ordered under $\subseteq$; then any chain of S is contained in a maximal chain.*

Proof: Let $\mathcal{S}$ be the set of chains (under $\leq$) of S, ordered by $\subseteq$; let $\mathcal{A}$ be any chain (under $\subseteq$) of $\mathcal{S}$; and let $A^* = \bigcup_{\mathcal{A}} A$. For any a, b in A^*, we have $a \in A \in \mathcal{A}$, $b \in B \in \mathcal{A}$, where (say) $A \subseteq B$, since $\mathcal{A}$ is a chain. Thus a and b are both in B, and since B is a chain we have $a \leq b$ or $b \leq a$, proving that A^* is a chain. Since $A \subseteq A^*$ for all $A \in \mathcal{A}$, the chain A^* is an upper bound for $\mathcal{A}$; we have thus proved that $\mathcal{S}$ is inductive. The desired conclusion now follows from Corollary 2 to Theorem 2. $\parallel$

> It can be shown that Zorn's lemma, Hausdorff's theorem, and the axiom of choice are all equivalent; each of them implies all of the others. For proofs of the remaining parts of this assertion, see, for example, A. G. Kurosh, *Lectures on General Algebra*, Chelsea, 1963, pp. 26–29; E. Hewitt and K. Stromberg, *Real and Abstract Analysis*, Springer, 1965, pp. 12–16.

10. DIMENSION

Let a, b be elements of the ordered set S such that $a \leq b$. By a *chain from a to b* is meant a chain of S which has a as its least element and b as its greatest element. [Thus any chain from a to b is contained in the interval $[a, b]$ (Exercise 7.5).] There always exists chains, and even finite chains, from a to b, since $\{a, b\}$ itself (or $\{a\}$, if $a = b$) is such a chain.

A finite chain C which has $n + 1$ elements is said to be of **length** n. (The "length" of C can be thought of as the number of "links," or "steps," in C.) By Proposition 8.2 and Exercise 8.5, there is a unique order isomorphism between C and $\mathbf{N}_n{}^\circ$, so that we can describe C by an expression of the form

$$a = c_0 < c_1 < \cdots < c_n = b.$$

We say that b has **dimension** d over a (notation: dim $(b:a) = d$) if there exists a chain of length d but no chain of length greater than d (and hence no infinite chain) from a to b.

> This concept of "dimension" will play an important role in our study of algebraic structures. We shall see in Chapter XI that this concept, when applied to vector spaces, is equivalent to the familiar definition of dimen-

sion as number of basis elements. Specifically, let V be a vector space, and let $\mathscr{S}$ be the set of its subspaces, ordered by inclusion. Then the subspace S has a d-element basis if and only if S has dimension d (over the subspace $\{0\}$) in the sense just defined—in other words, there exist chains of subspaces

$$\{0\} \subset S_1 \subset \cdots \subset S_d = S$$

of length d, but not longer ones. The advantage of the ordered set definition is that it applies to a much wider variety of cases than the basis definition.

Examples:
  (a) $\dim (b:a) = 0$ if and only if $a = b$
  (b) $\dim (b:a) = 1$ if and only if $a < b$ and there exists no $x \in S$ such that $a < x < b$.

Exercise 1. *Let F be an order isomorphism of S with T, and let a, b in S be such that $\dim (b:a)$ is defined; then $\dim (F(b):F(a))$ is defined and equal to $\dim (b:a)$.*

S is called **finite dimensional** if $\dim (b:a)$ is defined for every a, b in S such that $a \le b$.

Proposition 1. *If $a \le b$, and there exists $m \in \mathbf{N}$ such that there is no chain of length m from a to b, then $\dim (b:a) = d$ for some $d < m$.*

Proof: Since there is no chain of length m, there can be no chain of length greater than m and no infinite chain, since any such would have subsets of length m. Thus the set of $n \in \mathbf{N}$ such that there exists a chain of length n from a to b is nonempty and finite ($\subset \mathbf{N}_m$), and so has a greatest element d. $\parallel$

Corollary. *A finite ordered set is finite dimensional.*

Exercise 2. *An ascending chain is finite dimensional.*   (*)

Proposition 2. *Let $\dim (b:a) = d$, and let $x \in [a, b]$. Then $\dim (x:a) = d'$ and $\dim (b:x) = d''$ are defined, and $d' + d'' \le d$.*

Proof: Let C' be any chain from a to x, and C'' any chain from x to b. By Exercise 6.4, $C' \cup C''$ is a chain from a to b; hence it must be finite and have at most $d + 1$ elements. Thus C' and C'' each have at most $d + 1$ elements, so that by Proposition 1, $\dim (x:a) = d'$ and $\dim (b:x) = d''$ are defined. Let D', D'' be chains of lengths d', d'' from a to x and from x to b, respectively. Since $D' \cap D'' = \{x\}$, the chain $D' \cup D'' = (D' - \{x\}) \cup D''$ from a to b has $d' + (d'' + 1) = (d' + d'') + 1$ elements, that is, length $d' + d''$, and this length cannot exceed d, the dimension of b over a. $\parallel$

Corollary 1. *If S has a least element* 0, *it is finite dimensional if and only if* dim $(x:0)$ *is defined for all* $x \in S$.

Proof: For all a, b in S such that $a \le b$, we have $a \in [0, b]$, so that dim $(b:a)$ is defined and $\le$ dim $(b:0)$.   //

We call dim $(b:0)$ simply the dimension of b ("over 0" understood), and denote it by dim b.

Corollary 2. *If S also has a greatest element* 1, *it is finite dimensional if and only if* dim 1 *is defined.*

Proof: Given $a \le b$ in S, we have $b \in [0, 1]$, so that dim b is defined; now use Corollary 1.   //

Corollary 3. *If S has least and greatest elements and is finite dimensional, it contains no infinite chain.*

Corollary 4. *Let a, b, x be as in the proposition; then*

(1) dim $(b:x) = d$ *if and only if* $x = a$

(2) dim $(x:a) = d$ *if and only if* $x = b$.

Proof: By the proposition, if dim $(b:x) = d$ we must have dim $(x:a) = 0$, that is, $x = a$, and similarly for (2).   //

In general, the $\le$ in Proposition 2 cannot be replaced by $=$; dimension is not "additive." For example, let $\le$ be the order relation on $\{0, 1, x, y, z\}$ represented by the diagram shown here [in other words, $\le$ is the relation

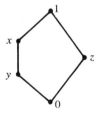

$\{(0, 0),\ (0, x),\ (0, y),\ (0, z),\ (0, 1),\ (x, x),\ (x, 1),\ (y, y),$ $(y, x),\ (y, 1),\ (z, z),\ (z, 1),\ (1, 1)\}]$. Then dim $(1:0) = 3$, since $0 < y < x < 1$ is a chain of length 3, but dim $(1:z)$ $=$ dim $(z:0) = 1$. In the next chapter (Sections 13–14) we shall study an important type of ordered set for which additivity of dimension does hold. A sufficient condition for additivity will be established at the end of this section.

UNREFINABLE CHAINS

If C, D are chains from a to b, and $C \subseteq D$, we say that D is a **refinement** of C; if $C \subset D$, we call D a **proper** refinement of C. A chain from a to b is called **refinable** if it has a proper refinement; otherwise, **unrefinable**. Thus C is unrefinable if and only if it is a maximal element of the set of chains from a to b, ordered by inclusion.

Proposition 3. *Any chain from a to b has an unrefinable refinement.*

Proof: Apply Hausdorff's theorem (9.3) to $[a, b]$.   ∥

Corollary. *If* dim $(b:a) = d$, *any chain from a to b has an unrefinable refinement of length $\leq d$.*

Exercise 3. *If S satisfies the maximum and minimum conditions, any chain in S has a finite unrefinable refinement.* [Hint: Hausdorff's theorem and Theorem 8.2.]

Exercise 4. *Let C be an unrefinable chain from a to x, and D an unrefinable chain from x to b; then $C \cup D$ is an unrefinable chain from a to b.*

Exercise 5. *The chain C from a to b is unrefinable if and only if for all $x \leq y$ in C, the chain $C \cap [x, y]$ is an unrefinable chain from x to y.*

Exercise 6. *The chain $a = c_0 < c_1 < \cdots < c_n = b$ is refinable if and only if for some $k \in \mathbf{N}_n$ there exists an x such that $c_{k-1} < x < c_k$.*

Proposition 4. dim $(b:a) = d$ *if and only if there exists a chain of length d from a to b, and every such chain is unrefinable.*

Proof: If there existed a longer chain, or an infinite chain, from a to b, it would have proper subsets which were refinable chains of length d from a to b. Conversely, if dim $(b:a) = d$, a chain of length d must exist, and no such chain can be refinable since a longer chain cannot exist.   ∥

In general, there can exist unrefinable chains from a to b of more than one length; see, for instance, the example given after Proposition 2. In fact, uniqueness of the length of an unrefinable chain is a sufficient condition for additivity of dimension.

Proposition 5. *Let* dim $(b:a)$ *be defined, and let all unrefinable chains from a to b have length d; then for all $x \in [a, b]$ we have* dim $(b:a) =$ dim $(b:x) +$ dim $(x:a) = d$.

Proof: By Proposition 4, there exists an unrefinable chain of length dim $(b:a)$ from a to b, and since by hypothesis any such chain must have length d, we have dim $(b:a) = d$. Let A, B be chains of lengths dim $(x:a)$ and dim $(b:x)$ from a to x and from x to b, respectively. Then by Proposition 4, A and B are unrefinable, and (Exercise 4 and the proof of Proposition 2)

$A \cup B$ is an unrefinable chain from a to b of length dim $(x:a)$ + dim $(b:x)$; but by hypothesis, any such chain has length d.   //

The converse of Proposition 5 is not true in general; for example, if S is represented by the diagram shown here,

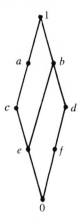

then dim $(1:z)$ + dim $(z:0)$ = dim $(1:0)$ for all $z \in S$, but the unrefinable chains $0 < e < c < a < 1$ and $0 < e < b < 1$ from 0 to 1 have different lengths. However, we can prove

Proposition 6. *The following statements about the finite dimensional ordered set S are equivalent:*

(1) *For all a, b in S such that $a < b$, all unrefinable chains from a to b have the same length*

(2) *For all a, x, b in S such that $a \le x \le b$, we have* dim $(b:a)$ = dim $(b:x)$ + dim $(x:a)$.

Proof: (1) implies (2) by Proposition 5. We prove the converse by induction on the length m of the shortest unrefinable chain from a to b. If $m = 1$, evidently dim $(b:a)$ = 1 and the only chain from a to b is $\{a, b\}$. Suppose that (1) is true for $m \le r$ but not for $m = r + 1$. Let c, d be elements of S such that $c \le d$ and the shortest unrefinable chain from c to d has length $r + 1$, but there exist longer unrefinable chains from c to d, so that dim $(d:c)$ $> r + 1$. Let $c = c_0 < c_1 < \cdots < c_{r+1} = d$ be unrefinable; then dim $(c_1:c_0)$ = 1, and there is an unrefinable chain of length r from c_1 to d. By the induction hypothesis, it follows that any unrefinable chain from c_1 to d has length r, so that dim $(d:c_1)$ = r. Thus by (2) we have dim $(d:c)$ = dim $(d:c_1)$ + dim $(c_1:c)$ = $r + 1$, contradiction.   //

Exercise 7. *Let S be as in Proposition 6, and let $a = a_0 < a_1 < \cdots < a_n = b$ be a chain in S; then* dim $(b:a)$ = $\sum_{i=1}^{n}$ dim $(a_i:a_{i-1})$.

III

LATTICES

As pointed out in Section 7, a subset of an ordered set need not have upper or lower bounds, let alone a sup or an inf. In this chapter we study ordered sets in which sups and infs do always exist, at least for finite subsets.

11. LATTICES

The ordered set S is called a **lattice** if every nonempty finite subset of S has a sup and an inf. S is called a **complete lattice** if every subset of S has a sup and an inf. Note that a complete lattice must have a least element $0 = \sup \varnothing = \inf S$ and a greatest element $1 = \inf \varnothing = \sup S$.

Examples:

(a) Let T be any set; then $\mathscr{P}_T$ is a complete lattice under $\subseteq$ (Section 7, Example (c) preceding Proposition 2).

(b) Any chain is a lattice (Corollary 2 to Proposition 8.1). In particular, **N** is a lattice under $\leq$.

(c) A finite lattice is complete.

Proposition 1. **N** *is a lattice under* $|$.

Proof: By Proposition 3, below, it suffices to show that any x, y in **N** have a **least common multiple** m (such that x and y divide m, and m divides any $m' \in$ **N** which both x and y divide) and a **greatest common divisor** d (such that d divides x and y, and any $d' \in$ **N** which divides both x and y also divides d). To see the first part, note that the set of common multiples of x and y is non-empty (for example, it contains xy); let m be its least element (Proposition 8.4). Let m' be any common multiple of x and y, and let $m' = qm + r$, where $r < m$. Then since x and y divide both m and m', they also divide $r = m' - qm$, so that it too is a common multiple, contradicting the leastness of m.

41

For the second part, let $x = q_0 y + r_1$, where $r_1 < y$, and let $(r_i)_N$ be the sequence of elements of $N°$ defined by $r_{i+1} =$ the remainder left by r_{i-1} upon division by r_i, if $r_i \neq 0$; $r_{i+1} = 0$ if $r_i = 0$ (where r_0 means y). Note that if $r_i \neq 0$ we have $r_{i+1} < r_i$; hence some r_n must be 0, since otherwise $(r_i)_N$ would be a descending chain in $N°$ (Proposition 8.3), which is impossible (Proposition 8.4). Let s be the least element of the set of n such that $r_n = 0$, and let $d = r_{s-1}$; let $r_{i-1} = q_i r_i + r_{i+1}$, $1 \leq i < s$. Then $r_{s-2} = q_{s-1}d$, so that $d \,|\, r_{s-2}$. Moreover, if $d \,|\, r_k$ and $d \,|\, r_{k+1}$, say $r_k = ud$, $r_{k+1} = vd$, we have $r_{k-1} = q_k r_k + r_{k+1} = (q_k u + v)d$, so that $d \,|\, r_{k-1}$. It follows (using induction on s) that d divides all the r's—in particular, that $d \,|\, r_1$ and $d \,|\, y$, so that d also divides $q_0 y + r_1 = x$, making it a common divisor of x and y. On the other hand, let d' be any common divisor of x and y; then d' divides $r_1 = x - q_0 y$, and by an analogous induction argument, it divides all the r's, so that in particular it divides $r_{s-1} = d$.   //

Examples (continued):

(d) A subset of a lattice need not be a lattice under the restriction of the order relation to it. For example, the subset $\{\{x\}, \{y\}\}$ of $\mathscr{P}_{\{x,y\}}$ is not a lattice under $\subseteq$. Even if a subset *is* a lattice under the restricted order relation, the sup and inf in this lattice need not be the same as those in the original lattice. For example, the subset $\{\varnothing, \{x\}, \{y\}, \{x, y, z\}\}$ of $\mathscr{P}_{\{x,y,z\}}$ is a lattice under $\subseteq$, but sup $\{\{x\}, \{y\}\}$ in it is $\{x, y, z\}$, not $\{x, y\}$. If the sup and inf *are* the same in the subset as in the original lattice—in other words, if the subset contains sup A and inf A whenever it contains A—the subset is called a **sublattice**.

(e) If S ordered by R is a lattice or complete lattice, so is S ordered by R^{-1}. Note that the inf in S ordered by R^{-1} is the sup in S ordered by R, and vice versa.

Exercise 1. *Any interval or chain in a lattice is a sublattice.*

Exercise 2. *An order isomorphism takes lattices into lattices.*

Proposition 2. *Let S be an ordered set, A a subset of S, x an element of A, and let $y = \sup (A - \{x\})$. Then $\sup A$ exists if and only if $\sup \{x, y\}$ exists, and if both exist, they are equal.*   (*)

Proof: If z is an upper bound for A, we have $x \leq z$ since $x \in A$, and $y \leq z$ by Exercise 7.7, so that z is an upper bound for $\{x, y\}$. Conversely, if w is an upper bound for $\{x, y\}$, we have $x \leq w$ and $(A - \{x\}) \leq y \leq w$, so that $A \leq w$, that is, w is an upper bound for A. Thus the set of upper bounds for A is the same as the set of upper bounds for $\{x, y\}$, which immediately implies the proposition.   //

Exercise 3. *Let $A = B \cup C$, $b = \sup B$, $c = \sup C$; then $\sup A$ exists if and only if $\sup \{b, c\}$ exists, and if both exist they are equal.*   (*)

Corollary: *If* sup B = sup C = x, *then* sup $(B \cup C)$ = x. (*)

Exercise 4. *Let* A^* = $\bigcup_{\mathscr{A}} A$; *then* sup A^* *exists if and only if*

$$\text{sup}\{\text{sup } A \mid A \in \mathscr{A}\}$$

exists, and if both exist, they are equal. (*)

Corollary: *If* sup A = x *for each* $A \in \mathscr{A}$, *then* sup A^* = x. (*)

Proposition 3. *The ordered set S is a lattice if and only if* sup $\{x, y\}$ *and* inf $\{x, y\}$ *exist for all x, y in S.*

Proof: Necessity is trivial. To prove sufficiency, suppose that any n-element subset of S has a sup and an inf (note that this is trivially true for $n = 1$), and let $A \subseteq S$ have $n + 1$ elements. Let x be any element of A; then by induction hypothesis, the n-element set $A - \{x\}$ has a sup, call it y, and an inf, call it z. By Proposition 2 and its "dual" we then have sup A = sup $\{x, y\}$, inf A = inf $\{x, z\}$. //

From now on we shall abbreviate sup $\{x, y\}$ by $x \vee y$, and inf $\{x, y\}$ by $x \wedge y$; for uniformity, we shall denote sup $\{x\}$ by $x \vee x$ and inf $\{x\}$ by $x \wedge x$.

Proposition 4. *For all x, y, z in the lattice S we have*

(1) $x \vee x = x \wedge x = x$
(2) $x \vee y = y \vee x$ *and* $x \wedge y = y \wedge x$
(3) $x \vee (y \vee z) = (x \vee y) \vee z$ *and* $x \wedge (y \wedge z) = (x \wedge y) \wedge z$
(4) $x \vee (x \wedge y) = x \wedge (x \vee y) = x$.

In words: sup *and* inf *are* **idempotent, commutative, associative,** *and mutually* **absorptive.**

Proof: For (3), apply Proposition 2 to $A = \{x, y, z\}$. For (4), note that $x \wedge y \leq x \leq x \vee y$, and apply Exercise 7.8. //

> It can be shown that the properties of Proposition 4 actually "characterize" the sup and inf in the following sense: Let F, G be functions from $S \times S$ into S such that
>
> (1) $F(x, x) = G(x, x) = x$
> (2) $F(x, y) = F(y, x)$ and $G(x, y) = G(y, x)$
> (3) $F(x, F(y, z)) = F(F(x, y), z)$ and
> $\quad G(x, G(y, z)) = G(G(x, y), z)$
> (4) $F(x, G(x, y)) = G(x, F(x, y)) = x$
> for all x, y, z in S. Then
>
> $$R = \{(x, y) \mid G(x, y) = x\} = \{(x, y) \mid F(x, y) = y\}$$
>
> is an order relation on S, and $F(x, y)$, $G(x, y)$ are respectively the sup and inf of $\{x, y\}$ with respect to R.

Proposition 5. *For all a, b, c, d in the lattice S, if $a \le c$ and $b \le d$, then $a \lor b \le c \lor d$ and $a \land b \le c \land d$.*

Proof: $a \le c \le c \lor d$ and $b \le d \le c \lor d$, so that $c \lor d$ is an upper bound for $\{a, b\}$, and similarly for $\land$. $\|$

Proposition 6. *For all x, y, z in the lattice S we have*

(1) $x \lor (y \land z) \le (x \lor y) \land (x \lor z)$

(2) $(x \land y) \lor (x \land z) \le x \land (y \lor z)$

Proof: Since $x \le x$ and $y \land z \le y$, by Proposition 5 we have $x \lor (y \land z) \le x \lor y$. Similarly, $x \lor (y \land z) \le x \lor z$, so that it is a lower bound for $\{x \lor y, x \lor z\}$, and so is $\le$ their inf, proving (1). The proof of (2) is analogous. $\|$

We conclude this section by establishing a useful equivalent of the maximum condition in a lattice:

Theorem 1. *The lattice S satisfies the maximum condition if and only if the* sup *of any nonempty $A \subseteq S$ exists and is the* sup *of some finite subset of A.* (*)

Proof: Let A^* be the set of sups of the finite subsets of A. Clearly $A^* \ne \varnothing$, since $x = \sup \{x\}$ for any $x \in A$. Let y be a maximal element of A^*, say $y = \sup B$, where B is a finite subset of A. Suppose that $z \le y$ is false for some $z \in A$; let $C = B \cup \{z\}$, so that C is still a finite subset of A, and let $w = \sup C$. Since w is an upper bound for B, we have $y = \sup B \le w$. But since $z \le w = \sup C$, while $z \le y$ is false, we cannot have $y = w$; thus $y < w$, contradicting the maximality of y. Hence $z \le y$ must be true for all $z \in A$, that is, y is an upper bound for A, so that $y = \sup A$ (Exercise 7.7), proving "only if."

To prove "if," let U be an ascending chain in S, say $U = G(\mathbf{N})$, where G is an order isomorphism. By hypothesis, we have $\sup U = \sup V$ for some finite subset V of U. Since V is a finite chain, its sup is its greatest element. Let this element be $v = G(m)$. Now $v = \sup U$, so that v must be the greatest element of U; but $v = G(m) < G(m + 1)$, contradiction, which proves that S cannot contain an ascending chain. $\|$

Corollary. *A lattice which satisfies the maximum and minimum conditions is complete.*

12. INDEPENDENCE AND RANK

Let S be a lattice with least element 0, and let A be a finite, nonempty subset of S which does not contain 0. We call A **independent** if for each $a \in A$ we have

$$a \land \sup (A - \{a\}) = 0.$$

Note that in particular, if A has just one element $a \neq 0$, it is independent, since sup $(A-\{a\}) = \sup \varnothing = 0$; while $A = \{x, y\}$ is independent if and only if

$$x \neq 0; \quad y \neq 0; \quad x \wedge y = 0.$$

This concept of independence is actually a generalization of the familiar notion of independence in vector spaces. To see this, let V be a vector space; then the set of subspaces of V, ordered by inclusion, is a lattice, where the inf of a set of subspaces is their intersection, and the sup is the subspace generated by their union. Let $x_1, \ldots, x_n$ be independent elements of V in the familiar sense, so that $a_1 x_1 + \cdots + a_n x_n = 0$ implies $a_1 = \cdots = a_n = 0$, where the a's are scalars. Now the subspace (x_j) generated by x_j is just the set $\{a_j x_j\}$ of scalar multiples of x_j, while the subspace $(x_1, \ldots, x_{j-1}, x_{j+1}, \ldots, x_n)$ generated by the remaining x's is just the set of all linear combinations $a_1 x_1 + \cdots + a_{j-1} x_{j-1} + a_{j+1} x_{j+1} + \cdots + a_n x_n$. If there were an element common to (x_j) and $(x_1, \ldots, x_{j-1}, x_{j+1}, \ldots, x_n)$, say $b_j x_j = b_1 x_1 + \cdots + b_{j-1} x_{j-1} + b_{j+1} x_{j+1} + \cdots + b_n x_n$, we would have $b_1 x_1 + \cdots + b_{j-1} x_{j-1} + (-b_j) x_j + b_{j+1} x_{j+1} + \cdots + b_n x_n = 0$, so that by the independence of the x's, we have $b_1 = \cdots = b_n = 0$, that is, the only possible common element is 0. In other words, for each j we have $(x_j) \cap (x_1, \ldots, x_{j-1}, x_{j+1}, \ldots, x_n) = \{0\}$. But since $\{0\} = (0)$ is the least element of the lattice of subspaces, we have thus shown that if $x_1, \ldots, x_n$ are independent, then the set of subspaces $(x_1), \ldots, (x_n)$ is an independent subset of the lattice of subspaces.

Conversely, let $(x_1), \ldots, (x_n)$ be independent in the subspace lattice, and suppose that we have $a_1 x_1 + \cdots + a_n x_n = 0$, where some coefficient, say a_k, is $\neq 0$. Now no (x_i) can be (0); hence no x_i can be 0. We would thus have a nonzero element $-a_k x_k = a_1 x_1 + \cdots + a_{k-1} x_{k-1} + a_{k+1} x_{k+1} + \cdots + a_n x_n$ in the intersection of (x_k) and $(x_1, \ldots, x_{k-1}, x_{k+1}, \ldots, x_n)$, contrary to the independence of the (x)'s. Note finally that if $n = 1$, we have x_1 independent provided it is not zero, so that $(x_1) \neq (0)$ is independent, and conversely.

If S is a complete lattice, we can define independence in the same way for nonempty sets which are not necessarily finite. In most of what follows, finiteness is not assumed.

Exercise 1. *If A is independent, there cannot exist x, y in A such that $x < y$.*

Corollary: *A chain cannot be independent if it has more than one element.*

Exercise 2. *An order isomorphism takes independent sets into independent sets.*

Proposition 1. *If A is independent, and x, y are distinct elements of A, then $x \wedge y = 0$.*

Proof: $x \wedge y \leq x \wedge \sup (A - \{x\}) = 0$. //

Corollary: *If A is independent and has more than one element, then $\inf A = 0$.*

Proof: Let x, y be distinct elements of A; then $\inf A \leq x \wedge y = 0$. //

Proposition 2. *Any nonempty subset of an independent set is independent.*

Proof: Let $B \subseteq A$, where A is independent; then for all $x \in B$ we have

$$x \wedge \sup (B - \{x\}) \leq x \wedge \sup (A - \{x\}) = 0. //$$

Proposition 3. *Let A be an independent subset of S, and let F be a function from A into S such that $0 < F(a) \leq a$ for all $a \in A$; then $F(A)$ is independent.*

Proof: $F(a) \wedge \sup (F(A) - \{F(a)\}) \leq a \wedge \sup (A - \{a\}) = 0$. //

Proposition 4. *If A is independent and $B \subset A$, then $\sup B < \sup A$.*

Proof: If not, let $a \in A - B$; then $a \wedge \sup (A - \{a\}) \geq a \wedge \sup B = a \wedge \sup A = a > 0$. //

RANK

In a vector space, the dimension of a subspace is equal to the maximum number of independent elements in it. This suggests the possibility of a relationship, in a lattice, between the dimension of an element x ($=$ the maximum length of a chain from 0 to x) and the maximum size of an independent set each of whose elements is $\leq x$. As we shall see, these two numbers are not in general equal, but they do have somewhat analogous properties.

We say that z has **rank** n if there exists an independent set with n elements each of which $\leq z$, but no such set with more than n elements, and hence (Proposition 2) no infinite one. Note that if $z = 0$ there cannot exist an independent set whose elements $\leq z$; we can thus say that 0 has rank 0. We shall denote the rank of z by $r(z)$. We say that S has finite rank if the rank of every $z \in S$ is defined.

Examples:
(a) If S is a chain, every element of S except 0 has rank 1.
(b) If A is an independent set with n elements, and $r(\sup A)$ is defined, it is at least n.

> Note that Example (b) is the analog of the following statement about dimension: If A is a chain with n elements, and dim $(\sup A)$ is defined, it is at least n.

Proposition 5. *If z has dimension n, its rank is defined and is at most n.*

Proof: Let $A = \{a_1, \ldots, a_k\}$ be an independent set with each $a_i \leq z$. Let $z_i = \sup \{a_1, \ldots, a_i\}$, $1 \leq i \leq k$. Then for each i we have $z_{i-1} < z_i$ (where z_0 means 0). Indeed, clearly $z_{i-1} \leq z_i$; suppose that we had $z_{i-1} = z_i$, that is, $\sup \{z_{i-1}, a_i\} = z_{i-1}$, so that $a_i \leq z_{i-1}$. We would then have $0 = a_i \wedge \sup (A - \{a_i\}) \geq a_i \wedge \sup \{a_1, \ldots, a_{i-1}\} = a_i \wedge z_{i-1} = a_i$, which is impossible. Thus $0 < z_1 < \cdots < z_k \leq z$ is a chain of length at least k from 0 to z, so that dim $z \geq k$. $/\!/$

> It is quite possible to have $r(z) < $ dim z. For example, if S is a chain, dim z can be as large as the number of elements in S (arbitrarily large, if S is infinite), but $r(z) \leq 1$ for all $z \in S$.

Corollary. *A finite dimensional lattice with least element has finite rank.*

The next two propositions are analogs, for rank, of Propositions 10.1 and 10.2 about dimension:

Proposition 6. *If there exists $m \in \mathbf{N}$ such that there is no m-element independent set whose elements $\leq z$, then $r(z) = k$ for some $k < m$.*

Proof: If $z = 0$, this is trivial. Otherwise, the set T of $n \in \mathbf{N}$ such that there exists an n-element independent set whose elements $\leq z$ is nonempty (in fact, $1 \in T$, since $\{z\}$ is such a one-element independent set). But by Proposition 2, if there is no such m-element independent set, there can be none with more than m elements. Thus T is finite ($\subseteq \mathbf{N}_{m-1}$), so that it has a maximal element k, which is then the rank of z by definition. $/\!/$

Proposition 7. *Let $r(z) = k$, and let $y \leq z$; then $r(y)$ is defined and $\leq k$.*

Proof: There cannot be an independent set with more than k elements, all $\leq y$; now use Proposition 6. $/\!/$

Corollary. *If S has a greatest element 1, it has finite rank if and only if $r(1)$ is defined.*

UNREFINABLE INDEPENDENT SETS

Let A, B be independent sets which have the same sup. We say that B is a **refinement** of A if every $a \in A$ is the sup of a subset of B. If in addition $B \neq A$, it is called a **proper** refinement of A; if A has a proper refinement, it is called **refinable**, otherwise **unrefinable**.

> These definitions are not quite as simple as the analogous ones for chains; but it would be useless to call B a refinement of A if $B \supseteq A$, since then A and B could not have the same sup unless they were equal (Proposition 4).

Proposition 8. *"Is a refinement of" is an order relation on the set of independent sets which have a given sup.*

Proof: Evidently any independent set is a refinement of itself, and a refinement of a refinement is a refinement, so that we have reflexivity and transitivity. Let A and B be refinements of each other, and for any $a \in A$, let $a = \sup B'$, where each $b \in B'$ is the sup of a subset of A; hence a is the sup of the union of these subsets, so that by Exercise 1, this union cannot contain an element of A other than a. Thus the only possible case is $b = \sup \{a\} = a$, which implies that $B' = \{a\}$. Since a was any element of A, this proves that $A \subseteq B$, and similarly $B \subseteq A$, proving weak antisymmetry. //

Exercise 3. *An order isomorphism takes unrefinable independent sets into unrefinable independent sets.*

Exercise 4. *Let A be independent, let $a \in A$, and let $a = \sup B$. If $A - \{a\} \cup B$ is independent, it is a refinement of A.*

Exercise 5. *The following statements about $a \neq 0$ are equivalent:*
  (a) *$\{a\}$ is refinable*
  (b) *There exists an independent set B, having more than one element, such that $\sup B = a$*
  (c) *There exist x, y, neither of them 0, such that $x \vee y = a$ and $x \wedge y = 0$.*
[Hint: If $\sup B = a$, where B has more than one element, let $x \in B$ and let $y = \sup (B - \{x\})$.]

Exercise 6. *If A is refinable, there exists $a \in A$ such that $\{a\}$ is refinable.* [Hint: If B is a proper refinement of A, then every $a \in A$ is the sup of a subset of B, and some such subset must have more than one element, since $B \neq A$.]

Corollary: *The following statements about the independent set A are equivalent:*
  (1) *$\{a\}$ is unrefinable for each $a \in A$*
  (2) *Every nonempty subset of A is unrefinable.*

> Exercises 5–6 can be regarded as partial analogs of Exercises 10.5–6. The converse of Exercise 6 is not true in

general; an element of an unrefinable independent set need not be unrefinable. For example, in the lattice

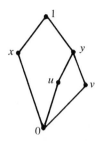

defined by the diagram shown here, we have $\{x, y\}$ independent and $\{y\}$ refinable, but $\{x, y\}$ is unrefinable since $\{x, u, v\}$ is not independent.

If $\mathscr{B}_x$ is the set of subsets of B which have x as their sup, then the union, call it B_x, of the sets in $\mathscr{B}_x$ still has x as its sup. Thus if B is a refinement of A, there is a greatest subset B_a of B which has any given $a \in A$ as its sup—namely, the union of all such subsets of B.

Exercise 7. *Let $\{u, v\}$ be independent, and let $U \le u$, $V \le v$; then $U \cap V \subseteq \{0\}$.* [Hint: Let $w \in U \cap V$; then $w \le u$ and $w \le v$, so that $w \le u \wedge v = 0$.]

Corollary. *Let B be a refinement of A, and let x, y be distinct elements of A; then $B_x \cap B_y = \varnothing$.*

Proposition 9. *If A is a finite independent set, and B is a proper refinement of A, then B is infinite or has more elements than A.*

Proof: Let A have n elements; if B is finite, so is every B_x, say B_x has n_x elements. By Exercises 5–6, some n_x is greater than 1, so that the sum of the n_x's is greater than n; and by Exercise 7, the number of elements of B is at least equal to the sum of the n_x's. $/\!/$

Corollary. *If* dim (sup A) *is defined, A has a finite unrefinable refinement.*

Proof: By Proposition 5, no refinement can have more elements than dim (sup A); and a refinement with the largest possible number of elements must be unrefinable. $/\!/$

As a partial analog of Proposition 10.4, we finally have

Proposition 10. *If $r(z) = k$, there exists a k-element independent set whose elements $\le z$, and every such set is unrefinable.*

Proof: Since $r(z) = k$, such a set must exist; and if any such set were refinable, its proper refinement would be an independent set with the same sup—hence with all its elements still $\leq z$—and with more than k elements (Proposition 8), contradicting $r(z) = k$. $/\!/$

13. DISTRIBUTIVITY AND MODULARITY

A lattice in which sup and inf distribute over each other—in other words, such that for all x, y, z we have

$$x \vee (y \wedge z) = (x \vee y) \wedge (x \vee z); \qquad x \wedge (y \vee z) = (x \wedge y) \vee (x \wedge z)$$

—is called **distributive**.

Examples:
 (a) For any set T, the lattice $\mathscr{P}_T$ under $\subseteq$ is distributive
 (b) Any chain is distributive; in particular, $\mathbf{N}$ under $\leq$ is distributive
 (c) $\mathbf{N}$ under $\mid$ is distributive
 (d) A sublattice of a distributive lattice is distributive
 (e) If S ordered by R is distributive, so is S ordered by R^{-1}.

Exercise 1. *Prove* (b–c). [Hint: For (c), use the results of Section 35.]

By Proposition 11.6, a kind of "subdistributivity" holds in any lattice. However, not every lattice is distributive;

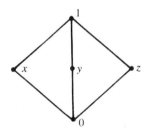

for example, the diagram shown here defines a non-distributive lattice.

Exercise 2. *Prove that if either of the $\leq$'s in Proposition* 11.6 *can be replaced by* =, *so can the other—in other words, if* sup *distributes over* inf, *then* inf *distributes over* sup, *and conversely.*

The lattices which play important roles in algebra are usually not distributive. However, many of them have a very useful property, called modularity, which is a weakened version of distributivity.

The lattice S is called **modular** if for all x, y, z in S such that $x \leq z$ we have

$$x \vee (y \wedge z) = (x \vee y) \wedge z.$$

[To see that distributivity implies modularity, note that if $x \vee (y \wedge z) =$ $(x \vee y) \wedge (x \vee z)$ and $x \leq z$, then $x \vee z = z$, so that the right member becomes $(x \vee y) \wedge z$.]

Theorem 1. *Let S be a modular lattice; then for any a, b in S, the intervals* $[a \wedge b, a]$ *and* $[b, a \vee b]$ *are order isomorphic.*

Proof: Define functions F and G from S into S by $F(x) = x \vee b$, $G(x) = x \wedge a$ for all $x \in S$. If $x \leq a$, we have $b \leq x \vee b \leq a \vee b$, so that F takes $[a \wedge b, a]$ into $[b, a \vee b]$; and similarly, G takes $[b, a \vee b]$ into $[a \wedge b, a]$. But if $a \wedge b \leq x \leq a$, we have (using modularity) $G(F(x)) = (x \vee b) \wedge a = x \vee (a \wedge b) = x$; similarly, if $b \leq x \leq a \vee b$, we have $F(G(x)) = (x \wedge a) \vee b = x \wedge (a \vee b) = x$. By the corollary to Proposition 3.6, it follows that F is a one-to-one correspondence of $[a \wedge b, a]$ with $[b, a \vee b]$, and G is its inverse. Since by Proposition 11.5 F and G are order preserving, the theorem is proved. //

We shall see in Section 14 that in a finite dimensional lattice, the property of Theorem 1 is actually equivalent to modularity.

Theorem 2. *S is modular if and only if* $a \leq b$, $a \vee c = b \vee c$, $a \wedge c = b \wedge c$ *imply* $a = b$ *for all a, b, c in S.*

Proof: If S is modular and $a \leq b$, then $a \vee (b \wedge c) = b \wedge (a \vee c)$, so that if $b \wedge c = a \wedge c$ and $a \vee c = b \vee c$, we have $a = a \vee (a \wedge c) = b \wedge (b \wedge c) = b$. Conversely, if $a \leq b$ we have in any lattice $a \vee (b \wedge c) \leq b \wedge (a \vee c)$ (Proposition 11.6). Let $a' = a \vee (b \wedge c)$, $b' = b \wedge (a \vee c)$. Now $b' \wedge c = b \wedge c \leq a'$, so that $b' \wedge c \leq a' \wedge c$; but since $a' \leq b'$ we have $a' \wedge c \leq b' \wedge c$, so that the two are equal. Similarly, $b' \leq a \vee c \leq a' \vee c$, so that $b' \vee c \leq a' \vee c$; but $a' \vee c \leq b' \vee c$, so that these must also be equal. By hypothesis we thus have $a' = b'$, proving S modular. //

It follows from Theorem 2 that a lattice is modular if and only if it has no sublattice with the diagram shown here.

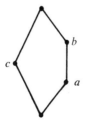

Corollary. *S is modular if and only if* $a \leq b \leq c \vee d$, $d \wedge (a \vee c) =$ $d \wedge (b \vee c)$, $a \wedge c = b \wedge c$ *imply* $a = b$ *for all a, b, c, d in S.*

Proof: For "if" set $d = a \vee b \vee c$ and apply the theorem. For "only if" put $a \vee c$ for a, $b \vee c$ for b, and d for c in the theorem to prove $a \vee c = b \vee c$; then apply the theorem to a, b, and c to prove $a = b$.   ‖

Exercise 3. *S is modular if and only if $c \wedge d \leq a \leq b$, $d \vee (a \wedge c) = d \vee (b \wedge c)$, $a \vee c = b \vee c$ imply $a = b$ for all a, b, c, d in S.*

We conclude this section by applying Theorem 2 and its corollary to establish two useful criteria for a modular lattice to satisfy the maximum condition (or minimum condition). In the following two propositions, S is a modular lattice; x is an element of S; $S_x = \{a \mid a \in S, a \leq x\}$, and $S^x = \{a \mid a \in S, x \leq a\}$.

Proposition 1. *If S_x and S^x both satisfy the maximum condition, so does S.* (*)

Proof: Let $(a_i)_N$ be a sequence of elements of S such that $a_k < a_{k+1}$ for all $k \in N$. Then $(a_i \wedge x)_N$ and $(a_i \vee x)_N$ are sequences of elements of S_x and S^x, respectively, and for all $k \in N$ we have $a_k \wedge x \leq a_{k+1} \wedge x$ and $a_k \vee x \leq a_{k+1} \vee x$. It follows (using Exercise 8.6) that there exists $m \in N$ such that $a_n \wedge x = a_m \wedge x$ and $a_n \vee x = a_m \vee x$ for all $n \geq m$. But since $a_m \leq a_n$, this implies by Theorem 2 that $a_m = a_n$, contradicting the definition of $(a_i)_N$ (see Proposition 8.3).   ‖

Proposition 2. *If S_x and S_y both satisfy the maximum condition, so does $S_{x \vee y}$.* (*)

Proof: Let $(a_i)_N$ be a sequence of elements of $S_{x \vee y}$ such that $a_k < a_{k+1}$ for all $k \in N$, and consider the sequences $(a_i \wedge x)_N$ and $(y \wedge (a_i \vee x))_N$, whose terms are in S_x and S_y, respectively. By the argument used to prove Proposition 1, there exists $m \in N$ such that $a_n \wedge x = a_m \wedge x$ and $y \wedge (a_n \vee x) = y \wedge (a_m \vee x)$ for all $n \geq m$. Since $a_m \leq a_n \leq x \vee y$, by the corollary to Theorem 2 this implies that $a_m = a_n$, contradiction.   ‖

Exercise 4. *If S^x and S^y both satisfy the maximum condition, so does $S^{x \wedge y}$.* (*) [Hint: Use Exercise 3 in place of the corollary to Theorem 2.]

14. DIMENSION IN MODULAR LATTICES

We prove in this section that in a modular lattice, dimension has two important additivity properties:
  (1) For all a, x, b such that $a \leq x \leq b$ and $\dim (b:a)$ is defined, we have

$$\dim (b:a) = \dim (b:x) + \dim (x:a)$$

(2) For all x, y such that $\dim (x \vee y : x \wedge y)$ is defined, we have

$$\dim (x \vee y : x \wedge y)$$
$$= \dim (x : x \wedge y) + \dim (y : x \wedge y).$$

As shown at the end of Section 10, we can prove the first of these properties if we can show that all unrefinable chains between two given elements have the same length. We now prove this assertion, which is a kind of lattice-theoretic Jordan–Hölder theorem, by first establishing a lattice analog of the Schreier refinement theorem.

Theorem 1. *Let* A, B *be finite chains from* a *to* b *in a modular lattice. Then there exist refinements* A^* *of* A *and* B^* *of* B *which have the same length, say* $A^* = \{a_0^*, \ldots, a_r^*\}$ *and* $B^* = \{b_0^*, \ldots, b_r^*\}$, *where* $a = a_0^* < \cdots < a_r^* = b$ *and* $a = b_0^* < \cdots < b_r^* = b$; *and there exists a permutation* G *of* $\mathbf{N}_r^\circ$ *such that* $[a_{k-1}^*, a_k^*]$ *is order isomorphic to* $[b_{G(k)-1}^*, b_{G(k)}^*]$, $1 \le k \le r$.

Proof: Let $A = \{a_0, \ldots, a_m\}$, $B = \{b_0, \ldots, b_n\}$, where $a = a_0 < \cdots < a_m = b$ and $a = b_0 < \cdots < b_n = b$. Let

$$a_{i,j} = a_{i-1} \vee (a_i \wedge b_j) \quad 1 \le i \le m, \ 0 \le j \le n$$
$$b_{j,i} = b_{j-1} \vee (a_i \wedge b_j) \quad 0 \le i \le m, \ 1 \le j \le n.$$

Readily, we have

and
$$a_{i-1} = a_{i,0} \le \cdots \le a_{i,n} = a_i$$

$$b_{j-1} = b_{j,0} \le \cdots \le b_{j,m} = b_j.$$

Moreover,

$$a_{i,j-1} \vee (a_i \wedge b_j) = [a_{i-1} \vee (a_i \wedge b_{j-1})] \vee (a_i \wedge b_j)$$
$$= a_{i-1} \vee (a_i \wedge b_j) = a_{i,j}$$

and

$$a_{i,j-1} \wedge (a_i \wedge b_j) = [a_{i-1} \vee (a_i \wedge b_{j-1})] \wedge (a_i \wedge b_j)$$
$$= (a_i \wedge b_{j-1}) \vee [a_{i-1} \wedge (a_i \wedge b_j)] \quad \text{(modularity)}$$
$$= (a_i \wedge b_{j-1}) \vee (a_{i-1} \wedge b_j).$$

Hence by Theorem 13.1, $[a_{i,j-1}, a_{i,j}]$ is order isomorphic to $[(a_i \wedge b_{j-1}) \vee (a_{i-1} \wedge b_j), a_i \wedge b_j]$. Similarly, $[b_{j,i-1}, b_{j,i}]$ is order isomorphic to this same interval (just interchange a's and b's, i's and j's in the proof), so that $[a_{i,j-1}, a_{i,j}]$ and $[b_{j,i-1}, b_{j,i}]$ are order isomorphic to each other. In particular, we have $a_{i,j-1} < a_{i,j}$ if and only if $b_{j,i-1} < b_{j,i}$, so that $A^* = \{a_{i,j} \mid i \le i \le m,$

$0 \le j \le n\}$ and $B^* = \{b_{j,i} \mid 0 \le i \le m, 1 \le j \le n\}$ must have the same number (say r) of distinct elements (prove this!), and

$$H = \{(a_{i,j}, b_{j,i}) \mid a_{i,j} \in A^*\}$$

defines the desired permutation. $\parallel$

Corollary. *All finite unrefinable chains from a to b in a modular lattice have the same length.*

For unrefinable chains, the "steps" are automatically *all* order isomorphic to each other by Exercise 10.6.

As an immediate consequence of Theorem 1 we have

Theorem 2. *If there exists an unrefinable chain of length d from a to b in a modular lattice, then* dim $(b:a) = d$, *and all unrefinable chains from a to b have length d.*

Proof: Let A be an unrefinable chain from a to b of length d, and let C be any other chain from a to b. If C is infinite or has length $> d$, it has a finite subchain B of length $> d$. But by Theorem 1, A and B have refinements of the same length, and since A is unrefinable, this length must be d, which is impossible since B already has length $> d$. Thus any chain C from a to b has length $\le d$, so that dim $(b:a) = d$. The last part is the corollary to Theorem 1. $\parallel$

Corollary 1. *In a modular lattice, if* dim $(b:a) = d$, *then all unrefinable chains from a to b have length d.*

Corollary 2. *In a modular lattice, if* dim $(b:a)$ *is defined and $a \le x \le b$, then* dim $(b:a) =$ dim $(b:x) +$ dim $(x:a)$.

Corollary 3. *In a modular lattice, if* dim $(b:a)$ *is defined, and $a = a_0 < \cdots < a_m = b$, then* dim $(b:a) = \sum_{i=1}^{m}$ dim $(a_i : a_{i-1})$.

Corollary 4. *A modular lattice which satisfies the maximum and minimum conditions is finite dimensional.*

Proof: For any a, b such that $a \le b$, there exists a finite unrefinable chain from a to b (Exercise 10.3); now use Theorem 2. $\parallel$

Exercise 1. *Let S be a modular lattice with least element 0 and greatest element 1. If there exists a finite unrefinable chain from 0 to 1, S is finite dimensional.*

We now consider the other type of additivity of dimension in a modular lattice:

Proposition 1. *For all a, b in a modular lattice, if* dim $(a : a \wedge b)$ *is defined, so is* dim $(a \vee b : b)$ *(and vice versa), and the two are equal.*

Proof: Theorem 13.1 and Exercise 10.1.   //

Corollary 1. *For all x, y in a modular lattice such that* dim $(x \vee y : x \wedge y)$ *is defined, we have* dim $(x \vee y : x \wedge y) = $ dim $(x : x \wedge y) + $ dim $(y : x \wedge y)$.

Proof: By Corollary 2 to Theorem 2,

$$\dim (x \vee y : x \wedge y) = \dim (x \vee y : y) + \dim (y : x \wedge y);$$

by the proposition, dim $(x \vee y : y) = $ dim $(x : x \wedge y)$.   //

Corollary 2. *For all w, x, y in a modular lattice such that* $w \leq x \wedge y$ *and* dim $(x \vee y : w)$ *is defined, we have*

$$\dim (x \vee y : w) + \dim (x \wedge y : w) = \dim (x:w) + \dim (y:w).$$

Proof: For any z such that $x \wedge y \leq z$ we have

$$\dim (z:w) = \dim (z : x \wedge y) + \dim (x \wedge y : w);$$

apply this to each of the three dimensions in Corollary 1.   //

Corollary 3. *Let* $T = \{x_1, \ldots, x_n\}$ *be a finite subset of a modular lattice, and let* $w \leq$ inf T *be such that* dim $(\sup T:w)$ *is defined; then* dim $(\sup T:w) \leq \sum_{i=1}^{n}$ dim $(x_i:w)$.

Corollary 4. *Let w, a, b, c be elements of a modular lattice such that* $w \leq a \wedge b \wedge c$; $a \leq b \vee c$; dim $(b \vee c : w)$ *is defined;* dim $(b:w) = $ dim $(a:w)$; *and* dim $(b \wedge c : w) = $ dim $(a \wedge c : w)$. *Then* $b \vee c = a \vee c$.

Proof: Since $w \leq a \vee c \leq b \vee c$, dim $(a \vee c : w)$ is defined, and we have dim $(a \vee c : w) + $ dim $(a \wedge c : w) = $ dim $(a:w) + $ dim $(c:w) = $ dim $(b:w) + $ dim $(c:w) = $ dim $(b \vee c : w) + $ dim $(b \wedge c : w)$.   Thus   dim $(a \vee c : w) = $ dim $(b \vee c : w)$; now use Corollary 4 to Proposition 10.2.   //

Exercise 2. *State and prove analogs of Corollary* 4 *in which other pairs of dimensions are assumed to be equal.*

In a finite dimensional lattice, each of the dimension properties of Proposition 1 and its Corollaries 1–2 is actually equivalent to modularity. In fact, we have

Theorem 3. *The following statements about the finite dimensional lattice S are equivalent:*

(1) *S is modular*
(2) *For all a, b in S, the intervals* $[a \wedge b, a]$ *and* $[b, a \vee b]$ *are order isomorphic*
(3) *For all a, b in S,* dim $(a : a \wedge b) = $ dim $(a \vee b : b)$.

Proof: (1) implies (2) is Theorem 13.1, and (2) implies (3) as in the proof of Proposition 1. To prove that (3) implies (1), note first that for all x, y, z in S such that $x \le y$, we have by (3)

$$\dim (x \vee (y \wedge z) : y \wedge z) = \dim (x : x \wedge (y \wedge z)),$$

where the right member reduces to $\dim (x : x \wedge z)$ since $x \le y$. Using (3) again, we have

$$\dim (x : x \wedge z) = \dim (x \vee z : z) \ge \dim ((y \wedge (x \vee z)) \vee z : z),$$

since $z \le (y \wedge (x \vee z)) \vee z \le x \vee z$. Using (3) once more, we have

$$\dim ((y \wedge (x \vee z)) \vee z : z) = \dim (y \wedge (x \vee z) : (y \wedge (x \vee z)) \wedge z).$$

Since $(y \wedge (x \vee z)) \wedge z = y \wedge z$, we have thus shown that

$$\dim (x \vee (y \wedge z) : y \wedge z) \ge \dim (y \wedge (x \vee z) : y \wedge z).$$

But in any lattice, if $x \le y$ we have $y \wedge z \le x \vee (y \wedge z) \le y \wedge (x \vee z)$ (Proposition 11.6); hence

$$\dim (x \vee (y \wedge z) : y \wedge z) \le \dim (y \wedge (x \vee z) : y \wedge z),$$

so that the two dimensions are equal. By Corollary 4 to Proposition 10.2, we thus have $x \vee (y \wedge z) = y \wedge (x \vee z)$, proving modularity. $/\!/$

Theorem 4. *The following statements about the finite dimensional lattice S are equivalent:*

(1) *S is modular*

(2) *For all w, x, y in S such that $w \le x \wedge y$ we have $\dim (x \vee y : w) + \dim (x \wedge y : w) = \dim (x : w) + \dim (y : w)$*

(3) *For all x, y in S we have $\dim (x \vee y : x \wedge y) = \dim (x : x \wedge y) + \dim (y : x \wedge y)$.*

Proof: (1) implies (2) is Corollary 2 to Proposition 1, and (3) is a special case of (2). To prove that (3) implies (1), let a, b, c in S be such that $a \le b$, $a \vee c = b \vee c$, and $a \wedge c = b \wedge c$. Then

$$
\begin{aligned}
\dim (a : a \wedge c) + \dim (c : a \wedge c) &= \dim (a \vee c : a \wedge c) \\
&= \dim (b \vee c : b \wedge c) \\
&= \dim (b : b \wedge c) + \dim (c : b \wedge c) \\
&= \dim (b : a \wedge c) + \dim (c : a \wedge c),
\end{aligned}
$$

whence $\dim (a : a \wedge c) = \dim (b : a \wedge c)$. But $a \wedge c \le a \le b$, so that this implies $a = b$, proving modularity by Theorem 13.2. $/\!/$

Exercise 3. *Show that the property of Corollary 4 to Proposition 1 is not equivalent to modularity.*

Exercise 4. *Show that the properties of Corollaries 1–2 to Theorem 2 are not equivalent to modularity.*

15. INDEPENDENCE IN MODULAR LATTICES

In a modular lattice we can say much more about independence and rank; in particular, we can establish a more complete analogy between chains and independent sets, dimension and rank. We begin by proving an additivity property for dimension, analogous to Corollaries 2–3, Theorem 14.2. *In this section S is a modular lattice with least element 0; we recall that* dim x *means* dim $(x:0)$.

Proposition 1. *Let A be a nonempty subset of S not containing 0, and let* dim (sup A) *be defined. Then A is independent if and only if*

$$\dim (\sup A) = \dim x + \dim (\sup (A - \{x\})) \qquad (\alpha)$$

for each $x \in A$.

Proof: Since $x \vee \sup (A - \{x\}) = \sup A$ (Proposition 11.2), by Corollary 2 to Proposition 14.1 we have

$$\dim (\sup A) + \dim (x \wedge \sup (A - \{x\})) = \dim x + \dim (\sup (A - \{x\})). \qquad (\beta)$$

Hence (α) holds if and only if dim $(x \wedge \sup (A - \{x\})) = 0$, that is, if and only if $x \wedge \sup (A - \{x\}) = 0$, which is the definition of independence. ∥

Note that by Proposition 12.5, since dim (sup A) is defined, A must be finite.

Proposition 2. *Let A be as in Proposition 1; then A is independent if and only if*

$$\dim (\sup A) = \sum_{a \in A} \dim a. \qquad (\gamma)$$

Proof: "Only if" follows from Proposition 1 by induction, since $A - \{x\}$ is still independent. Conversely, using (β), (γ), and Corollary 3 to Proposition 14.1, we have for any $x \in A$

$$\sum_{a \in A} \dim a + \dim (x \wedge \sup (A - \{x\})) \le \dim x + \sum_{a \in A - \{x\}} \dim a$$

so that dim $(x \wedge \sup (A - \{x\})) \le 0$, proving "if." ∥

Corollary. *Let A, B be independent, and let u, v be upper bounds for A, B, respectively, such that $\{u, v\}$ is independent and* dim $(u \vee v)$ *is defined; then $A \cup B$ is independent.*

Proof: Since $0 < \sup A \le u$ and $0 < \sup B \le v$, by Proposition 12.3 $\sup A$ and $\sup B$ are independent. Thus

$$\dim (\sup (A \cup B)) = \dim (\sup \{\sup A, \sup B\}) = \dim (\sup A) + \dim (\sup B)$$
$$= \sum_{x \in A} \dim x + \sum_{x \in B} \dim x = \sum_{x \in A \cup B} \dim x,$$

since A and B are disjoint by Exercise 12.7.   //

Proposition 3. *Let A be an independent subset of S such that $\dim (\sup A)$ is defined; then the following statements are equivalent:*

(1) $\{a\}$ *is unrefinable for each $a \in A$*

(2) *A is unrefinable*

(3) *For each $a \in A$ there exists no $B \subseteq S$ having more than one element such that $a = \sup B$ and $A - \{a\} \cup B$ is independent.*

Proof: Without using the assumptions of modularity and finite dimensionality, we have (1) implies (2) by Exercise 12.6, and (2) implies (3) by Exercise 12.4. Conversely, let (1) be false for some $x \in A$, so that (Exercise 12.5) there exists an independent set B, having more than one element, such that $x = \sup B$. Then using Propositions 1–2 we have

$$\dim (\sup A) = \dim x + \dim (\sup (A - \{x\})) = \sum_{b \in B} \dim b + \sum_{a \in A - \{x\}} \dim a.$$

But

$$\sup A = \sup \{x, \sup (A - \{x\})\} = \sup \{\sup B, \sup (A - \{x\})\}$$
$$= \sup (B \cup A - \{x\}).$$

Hence

$$\sum_{b \in B} \dim b + \sum_{a \in A - \{x\}} \dim a = \dim (\sup A) = \dim (\sup (B \cup A - \{x\})),$$

making $B \cup A - \{x\}$ independent by Proposition 2, so that (3) is violated.   //

Our principal goal in the remainder of this section is to prove, in analogy with Corollary 1 to Theorem 14.2, that all unrefinable independent sets with the same finite-dimensional sup must have the same number of elements.

Lemma 1. *Let A, B be independent sets such that $\dim (\sup A)$ and $\dim (\sup B)$ are defined. Let $a \in A$, $b \in B$, and let $\bar{a} = \sup (A - \{a\})$, $\bar{b} = \sup (B - \{b\})$. Then the following statements are equivalent:*

(1) $\bar{a} \vee b = \sup A$ *and $a \vee \bar{b} = \sup B$*

(2) $a \le \sup B$, $b \le \sup A$; $\bar{a} \wedge b = a \wedge \bar{b} = 0$; *and $[0, a]$ and $[0, b]$ are order isomorphic.*

Proof: To see that (2) implies (1), take $c = \bar{b}$ (or $\bar{a}$, with a and b interchanged) in Corollary 4 to Proposition 14.1. To prove the converse, note first that $\dim b + \dim \bar{b} = \dim (b \vee \bar{b}) = \dim (\sup B) = \dim (a \vee \bar{b}) \leq \dim a + \dim \bar{b}$, so that $\dim b \leq \dim a$, and similarly $\dim a \leq \dim b$, so that they must be equal. Hence

$$\dim (a \wedge \bar{b}) = \dim a + \dim \bar{b} - \dim (a \vee \bar{b}) = 0,$$

so that $a \wedge \bar{b} = 0$, and similarly $\bar{a} \wedge b = 0$. It follows that $[0, a] = [a \wedge \bar{b}, a]$ is order isomorphic to $[\bar{b}, a \vee \bar{b}] = [\bar{b}, \sup B] = [\bar{b}, b \vee \bar{b}]$, which in turn is order isomorphic to $[b \wedge \bar{b}, b] = [0, b]$. //

If the conditions of Lemma 1 hold, we say that a and b are *interchangeable* in (A, B).

Lemma 2. *If a and b are interchangeable in (A, B), then $A^* = A - \{a\} \cup \{b\}$ and $B^* = B - \{b\} \cup \{a\}$ are independent.*

Proof: $\dim (\sup A^*) = \dim (\bar{a} \vee b) = \dim (\sup A) = \sum_{x \in A} \dim x = \sum_{x \in A - \{a\}} \dim x + \dim b$, proving A^* independent by Proposition 2, and similarly for B^*. //

Lemma 3. *Let A, B be independent sets such that $\dim (\sup A)$ is defined. Suppose that for every $a \in A$, and every independent set A^* such that $a \in A^*$ and $\sup A = \sup A^*$, there exists $b \in B$ such that a and b are interchangeable in (A^*, B). Then there exists a one-to-one function F from A into B such that $\sup A = \sup F(A)$, and $[0, a]$ and $[0, F(a)]$ are order isomorphic for each $a \in A$.*

Proof: Let $A = \{a_1, \ldots, a_n\}$. By hypothesis, a_1 is interchangeable in (A, B) with some $b_1 \in B$. Let $A_1 = A - \{a_1\} \cup \{b_1\}$; by Lemmas 1–2, A_1 is independent and $\sup A_1 = \sup A$, so that by hypothesis, $a_2 \in A_1$ is interchangeable in (A_1, B) with some $b_2 \in B$. Let $A_2 = A_1 - \{a_2\} \cup \{b_2\}$; since $\sup A_2 = \sup A_1$, by Proposition 12.4 we have $b_2 \notin A_1 - \{a_2\}$, and in particular $b_2 \neq b_1$. Repeating this process (induction!) defines a one-to-one function $\{(a_i, b_i) \mid 1 \leq i \leq n\}$, where $[0, a_i]$ and $[0, b_i]$ are order isomorphic by Lemma 1. //

We are now ready to prove that all unrefinable independent sets with a given finite-dimensional sup have the same number of elements. In fact, we have

Theorem 1. *Let A, B be unrefinable independent sets such that $\sup A = \sup B$ and $\dim (\sup A)$ is defined. Then there exists a one-to-one correspondence F of A with B such that, for each $a \in A$, $[0, a]$ and $[0, F(a)]$ are order isomorphic.*

Proof: We shall show, for any A, B satisfying the hypothesis, that any $a \in A$ is interchangeable with some $b \in B$. It we can do this, then by Proposition 3 and Lemmas 1–2, $A^* = A - \{a\} \cup \{b\}$ and B still satisfy the hypothesis. Hence the proof of Lemma 3 applies to yield a one-to-one correspondence

F of A with a subset of B. The same argument with A and B interchanged shows that B is in one-to-one correspondence with a subset of A, so that A and B have the same number of elements; hence F is onto, and the theorem is proved.

We shall prove the required interchangeability by induction on dim (sup A). If this is 1, we must have $A = \{\sup A\} = \{\sup B\} = B$, and the theorem is trivially true. Suppose it is true whenever dim (sup A) < d, and let dim (sup A) = d > 1. Given $a \in A$, one of the following three statements must be true:

(a) $a \lor \bar{b} = b \lor \bar{a} = \sup A$ for some $b \in B$

(b) $a \lor \bar{b} \neq \sup A$ for some $b \in B$

(c) $a \lor \bar{y} = \sup A$ and $\bar{a} \lor y \neq \sup A$ for all $y \in B$,

where the notation is as in Lemma 1. If (a) holds, a and b are interchangeable in (A, B), which is what we need. If (b) holds, we shall show that there exists some $b^* \in B$ such that a and b^* are interchangeable in (A, B), which is again what we need. Finally, we shall show that (c) is impossible.

Let (b) hold; since $a \leq \sup A$ and $\bar{b} \leq \sup B = \sup A$, we have $a \lor \bar{b} <$ sup A. Let b' be any element of $B - \{b\}$; thus $b' \leq \bar{b}$, so that $a \lor b' \leq a \lor \bar{b} < \sup A$. Let $a \lor b' = c$; since $c < \sup A$, its dimension is $< d$. Now $a \land (c \land \bar{a}) \leq a \land \bar{a} = 0$, while $a \lor (c \land \bar{a}) = c \land (a \lor \bar{a}) = c \land$ sup $A = c$, so that $\{a, c \land \bar{a}\}$ is a refinement of $\{c\}$, provided $c \land \bar{a} \neq 0$. Similarly, $\{b', c \land \bar{b}'\}$ is a refinement of $\{c\}$, where $\bar{b}' = \sup (B - \{b'\})$, provided that $c \land \bar{b}' \neq 0$.

If $c \land \bar{a} = 0$, then by Theorem 13.2 we have $a = c$, so that $\{b', c \land \bar{b}'\}$ is a refinement of $\{a\}$. But by Proposition 3, $\{a\}$ is unrefinable, so that we must have $c \land \bar{b}' = 0$, whence $c = b'$. Similarly, if $c \land \bar{b}' = 0$, then $c \land \bar{a} = 0$ and $b' = c = a$. Thus in this case a and b' are trivially interchangeable.

Otherwise, $\{a, c \land \bar{a}\}$ and $\{b', c \land \bar{b}'\}$ are refinements of $\{c\}$. Let A' and B' be unrefinable refinements of $\{a, c \land \bar{a}\}$ and $\{b', c \land \bar{b}'\}$, respectively (corollary to Proposition 12.8). Since $\{a\}$ and $\{b'\}$ are unrefinable, we must have $a \in A'$ and $b' \in B'$. Moreover, since sup $A' = \sup B' = c$, and dim $c < d$, by induction hypothesis there exists $b'' \in B'$ such that a and b'' are interchangeable in (A', B'). If $b'' = b'$, then by interchangeability we have

$$0 = a \land \sup (B' - \{b'\}) = a \land (c \land \bar{b}') = a \land \bar{b}',$$

and

$$0 = b' \land \sup (A' - \{a\}) = b' \land (c \land \bar{a}) = b' \land \bar{a}.$$

Thus in this case a and b' are interchangeable in (A, B).

If $b'' \neq b'$, then $b'' \leq \sup (B' - \{b'\}) = c \land \bar{b}'$. Hence by interchangeability we have $0 = b'' \land \sup (A' - \{a\}) = b'' \land (c \land \bar{a}) = b'' \land \bar{a}$, and dim $b'' = $ dim a. By Corollary 4 to Proposition 14.1 we thus have $b'' \lor \bar{a} = $ sup A. It follows that $b'' \lor (\bar{a} \land \bar{b}') = \bar{b}' \land (b'' \lor \bar{a}) = \bar{b}' \land \sup A = \bar{b}'$, while $b'' \land (\bar{a} \land \bar{b}') = b'' \land \bar{a} = 0$. Thus $\{b'', \bar{a} \land \bar{b}'\}$ is a refinement of $\{\bar{b}'\}$, provided $\bar{a} \wedge \bar{b}' \neq 0$. But in fact, if $\bar{a} \wedge \bar{b}' = 0$, then $b'' = \bar{b}'$, so that $c = b' \vee (c \wedge \bar{b}') = b' \vee (c \wedge b'') = b' \vee b'' = b' \vee b' = \sup A$, contradiction. Let C be an unrefinable refinement of $\{b'', \bar{a} \wedge \bar{b}'\}$. Since $b'' \in B'$, $\{b''\}$ is unrefinable, so we must have $b'' \in C$. Now $B - \{b'\}$ is also an unrefinable refinement of $\{\bar{b}'\}$. Since dim $\bar{b}' < d$, by induction hypothesis there exists $b^* \in B - \{b'\}$ such that b'' and b^* are interchangeable in $(C, B - \{b'\})$.

We show that a and b^* are interchangeable in (A, B). Note first that by interchangeability we have dim $b^* = $ dim $b'' = $ dim a, while $0 = b^* \wedge \sup (C - \{b''\}) = b^* \wedge (\bar{a} \wedge \bar{b}') = b^* \wedge \bar{a}$; hence by Corollary 4 to Proposition 14.1, $b^* \vee \bar{a} = \sup A$. Next, note that by interchangeability we also have $b'' \vee \sup (B - \{b', b^*\}) = \bar{b}'$; hence $b'' \vee \sup (B - \{b^*\}) = [b'' \vee \sup (B - \{b', b^*\})] \vee b' = \bar{b}' \vee b' = \sup A$. Now $b^* \in B - \{b'\}$, so that $b' \in B - \{b^*\}$, and we have

$$b'' \leq \sup B' = c = a \vee b' \leq a \vee \sup (B - \{b^*\}).$$

Hence $\sup A = b'' \vee \sup (B - \{b^*\}) \leq a \vee \sup (B - \{b^*\}) \leq \sup A$, so that $a \vee \sup (B - \{b^*\}) = \sup A$. By Lemma 1, this together with $b^* \vee \bar{a} = \sup A$ proves that a and b^* are interchangeable in (A, B), completing the proof if (b) holds.

It remains only to show that (c) is impossible. If (c) holds, then by case (b) with A and B interchanged, for any $y \in B$ there exists an $x \in A$ such that x and y are interchangeable in (A, B). Since a and y cannot be interchangeable, we must have $x \in A - \{a\}$. By the proof of Theorem 13.1, the function F which takes z into $z \vee x$ is an order isomorphism of $[0, \bar{y}] = [x \wedge \bar{y}, \bar{y}]$ with $[x, x \vee \bar{y}] = [x, \sup A] = [x, x \vee \bar{x}]$; and the function G which takes z into $z \wedge \bar{x}$ is an order isomorphism of $[x, x \vee \bar{x}]$ with $[x \wedge \bar{x}, \bar{x}] = [0, \bar{x}]$. Thus the function $H = F \circ G$ is an order isomorphism of $[0, \bar{y}]$ with $[0, \bar{x}]$. Hence $(B - \{y\})$ is independent and unrefinable, and its sup is $H(\sup (B - \{y\})) = H(\bar{y}) = \bar{x} = \sup (A - \{x\})$. Since dim $\bar{x} < d$, by induction hypothesis a and some $H(b) \neq H(y)$ are interchangeable in $(A - \{x\}, H(B - \{y\}))$. We then have

$$\sup A = \bar{x} \vee x = [a \vee \sup (A - \{x, a\})] \vee x$$
$$= [H(b) \vee \sup (A - \{x, a\})] \vee x = H(b) \vee \bar{a}.$$

But $H(b) \leq H(b) \vee x = [(b \vee x) \wedge \bar{x}] \vee x = (b \vee x) \wedge [x \vee \bar{x}] = b \vee x \leq b \vee \bar{a}$. Hence $\sup A = H(b) \vee \bar{a} \leq b \vee \bar{a} \leq \sup A$, so that $b \vee \bar{a} = \sup A$, contradiction. //

Just as Corollary 1 to Theorem 14.2 is a lattice analog of the Jordan–Hölder theorem, so Theorem 1 can be thought of as a lattice version of the Krull–Schmidt theorem. As an analog of Theorem 14.1 we have

Corollary. *Let* A, B *be independent sets such that* sup A = sup B *and* dim (sup A) *is defined. Then there exist refinements* $\overline{A}$ *of* A *and* $\overline{B}$ *of* B, *and a one-to-one correspondence* F *of* $\overline{A}$ *with* $\overline{B}$, *such that* $[0, x]$ *and* $[0, F(x)]$ *are order isomorphic for all* $x \in \overline{A}$.

Proof; The theorem and the corollary to Proposition 12.8.   //

Unfortunately, we have no good analog here of Theorem 14.2 itself. If there is an unrefinable independent set with n elements whose sup is z, where dim z is defined, then by the theorem and its corollary, any independent set whose sup is z has at most n elements, and any unrefinable one has exactly n elements. However, an independent set whose sup is $< z$ can still have more than n elements, so that z can have rank $> n$. For example, in the lattice

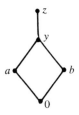

defined by the diagram shown here, $\{z\}$ is the only independent set whose sup is z, but z has rank 2.

16. INCLUSION-ORDERED LATTICES

In this section we briefly consider a very useful class of examples of lattices.

Proposition 1. *Let* A *be any set, and* $\mathscr{A}$ *any set of subsets of* A *which contains* A *itself and is "closed under intersection"—that is, for all nonempty* $\mathscr{B} \subseteq \mathscr{A}$ *we have* $\bigcap_{\mathscr{B}} B \in \mathscr{A}$. *Then* $\mathscr{A}$, *ordered by* $\subseteq$, *is a complete lattice.*

Proof: For any nonempty $\mathscr{B} \subseteq \mathscr{A}$ we evidently have inf $\mathscr{B} = \bigcap_{\mathscr{B}} B$. On the other hand, let $\mathscr{B}^*$ be the set of upper bounds of $\mathscr{B}$ in $\mathscr{A}$—that is, the set of $B^* \in \mathscr{A}$ such that $B \subseteq B^*$ for all $B \in \mathscr{B}$. Then $\mathscr{B}^* \neq \varnothing$, since $A \in \mathscr{B}^*$, and evidently $\bigcap_{\mathscr{B}^*} B^* = \sup \mathscr{B}$.   //

We shall call such an $\mathscr{A}$ an *I-lattice* on A. Example: Let A' be any subset of A, and let $\mathscr{A}$ be the set of subsets of A which contain A'. (Note that in this example, the sup is just the union.)

In later chapters we shall encounter many nontrivial examples of I-lattices. In fact, the subgroups of a group, the subrings of a ring, the subspaces of a vector space, the normal subgroups of a group, the ideals of a ring, etc. etc. are all "closed under intersection" and so are *I*-lattices.

Exercise 1. *Let $\mathscr{A}$ be a set of subsets of A such that $\varnothing \in \mathscr{A}$ and $\mathscr{A}$ is "closed under union"; then $\mathscr{A}$, ordered by $\subseteq$, is a complete lattice.*

Exercise 2. *Let $\mathscr{S}, \mathscr{T}$ be I-lattices on S, T, respectively, and let F be a function from S into T which takes elements of $\mathscr{S}$ into elements of $\mathscr{T}$. Then $\tilde{F}$ restricted to $\mathscr{S}$ is an order-preserving function from $\mathscr{S}$ into $\mathscr{T}$. State and prove the analogous assertion about F^{-1}.*

For *I*-lattices we can develop a generalization of the notion "sub . . . generated by a set":

Let $\mathscr{A}$ be an *I*-lattice on *A*, and let *S* be any subset of *A*. Evidently the intersection of all the elements of $\mathscr{A}$ which contain *S* is the smallest element of $\mathscr{A}$ which contains *S*; it is called the element of $\mathscr{A}$ **generated** by *S*, and is denoted by $(S)_{\mathscr{A}}$. [We shall omit the subscript from now on unless there is danger of confusion as to which *I*-lattice is meant.] Clearly $T \subseteq S$ implies $(T) \subseteq (S)$; also $((S)) = (S)$, so that every element of $\mathscr{A}$ is generated by some subset of *A* (namely, itself). If *S* is finite, we say that (S) is **finitely generated**; if $S = \{x\}$ has only one element, $(\{x\})$ is called **monogenic**. It is customary to abbreviate $(\{x\})$ by (x), and $(\{x_1, \ldots, x_n\})$ by $(x_1, \ldots, x_n)$, relying on the context to avoid confusion with the notation for *n*-tuples.

Exercise 3. *Let $\mathscr{S}$ be a set of subsets of A; then $\sup \{(S) \mid S \in \mathscr{S}\} = (\bigcup_{\mathscr{S}} S)$.*

Corollary: *The* sup *of a finite set of finitely generated (S)'s is finitely generated.*

Proposition 2. *Let $\mathscr{A}$ be an I-lattice which satisfies the maximum condition; then every element of $\mathscr{A}$ is finitely generated.*

Proof: Let $(S) \in \mathscr{A}$, and let $\mathscr{B} = \{(T) \mid T \subseteq S, T \text{ finite}\}$; then $\mathscr{B}$ has a maximal element (T^*). If $(T^*) = S$, we are done. But if $(T^*) \subset (S)$, let y be any element of $(S) - (T^*)$; then $T^* \cup \{y\}$ is still finite, and $(T^*) \subset (T^* \cup \{y\})$ (since the latter contains y), contradicting the maximality of (T^*). $\parallel$

The converse of Proposition 2 is not true in general; however, we have

Proposition 3. *Let $\mathscr{A}$ be an I-lattice which is "closed under union of chains"— that is, in which the sup of any chain is its union. Then if every element of $\mathscr{A}$ is finitely generated, $\mathscr{A}$ satisfies the maximum condition.*

Proof: Let $\mathscr{B} = G(\mathbf{N})$ be an ascending chain in $\mathscr{A}$; then $B^* = \bigcup_{\mathscr{B}} B = \sup \mathscr{B}$ is in $\mathscr{A}$, and so must be finitely generated, say $B^* = (b_1, \ldots, b_n)$.

Let $b_i \in G(m_i)$, $1 \le i \le n$, and let $m = \sup \{m_1, \ldots, m_n\}$. Then $b_i \in G(m_i) \subseteq G(m)$ for each i, so that $B^* \subseteq G(m)$; but then $B^* \subset G(m + 1)$, contradiction. $\parallel$

> As we shall see, the *I*-lattices which arise in algebra are usually of this special type. Note that a nonempty set of sets, ordered by $\subseteq$, which is closed under union of chains is inductive.

Exercise 4. *In an I-lattice which satisfies the maximum condition, the sup of any chain is its union.*

Corollary: *An I-lattice satisfies the maximum condition if and only if every element of it is finitely generated and the sup of any chain in it is its union.*

Given an *I*-lattice $\mathscr{A}$ on A, we can define a notion of independence for subsets of A. Specifically, we call the set $B \subseteq A$ **independent** if $\{(b) \mid b \in B\}$ is an independent subset of $\mathscr{A}$.

> As pointed out at the beginning of Section 12, this generalizes the familiar concept of independence in a vector space; the vectors $b_1, \ldots, b_n$ are linearly independent if and only if the subspaces $(b_1), \ldots, (b_n)$ which they generate are independent in the lattice of subspaces.

Proposition 4. *If B is independent, no proper subset of B generates* (B)*; in other words, an independent set is a minimal set of generators.*

Proof: If $(B') = (B)$ for some $B' \subset B$, let $b \in B - B'$. Then $(B) = (B') \subseteq (B - \{b\}) \subseteq (B)$, so that $(b) \cap (B - \{b\}) = (b) \cap (B) = (b) \supset 0$, contradicting the independence of B. $\parallel$

IV

QUOTIENT SETS, PRODUCT SETS, AND CARDINAL NUMBERS

In this chapter we develop the remaining prerequisites which will be needed in our study of algebraic structures. The first two sections deal with equivalence relations, with emphasis on their relationship to functions. The third section introduces products of arbitrary sets of sets, and the fourth and fifth sections derive certain properties of cardinal numbers which will be used in later chapters.

17. EQUIVALENCES AND QUOTIENT SETS

The relation E on the set S is called an **equivalence** if it is **reflexive, symmetric,** and **transitive**—in other words, if for all x, y, z in S we have

(1) $(x, x) \in E$
(2) $(x, y) \in E$ implies $(y, x) \in E$
(3) $(x, y) \in E$ and $(y, z) \in E$ imply $(x, z) \in E$

or, more concisely,

$$(1) \ I_S \subseteq E; \quad (2) \ E^{-1} \subseteq E; \quad (3) \ E \circ E \subseteq E.$$

Just as "order relation" generalizes $\subseteq$ and $\leq$, so "equivalence" generalizes $=$.

Examples:

(a) The equality relation I_S and the trivial relation $S \times S$ are equivalences on any set S.
(b) "Is in one-to-one correspondence with" is an equivalence on any set of sets (Proposition 3.4 and Exercise 3.15).
(c) "Is order isomorphic to" is an equivalence on any set of ordered sets (Examples (e, h, i) preceding Exercise 6.5).

(d) The relation $\{(m, n) \mid m$ and n have the same remainder on division by $d\}$ is an equivalence on $\mathbf{N}^\circ$. [This relation is called "congruence modulo d."]

(e) Any intersection of equivalences on S is an equivalence on S.

(f) The restriction of an equivalence to a subset is an equivalence on the subset.

(g) If A is any subset of S, and E is any equivalence on A, then $E \cup I_S$ is an equivalence on S, and its restriction to A is E.

(h) If F is any function defined on S, the relation $\{(x, y) \mid F(x) = F(y)\}$ is an equivalence on S. [This generalizes Example (d).]

Exercise 1. *I_S is the only function from S into S which is an equivalence on S.*

Exercise 2. *Give an example of a relation which is (a) an equivalence but not an order relation; (b) vice versa; (c) neither; (d) both.*

Exercise 3. *A relation on S is an equivalence on a subset of S if and only if it is symmetric and transitive.*

Exercise 4. *Let P, Q, R be relations on the set S.*
 (a) *If R is reflexive, then $Q \subseteq Q \circ R$ and $Q \subseteq R \circ Q$ for all Q.*
 (b) *If R is symmetric and $Q \subseteq R$, then $Q^{-1} \subseteq R$.*
 (c) *If R is transitive and P, Q each $\subseteq R$, then $P \circ Q \subseteq R$.*

Corollary 1. *If $Q \subseteq R$, where Q is reflexive and R is transitive, then $Q \circ R = R \circ Q = R$. In particular, if R is reflexive and transitive, then $R \circ R = R$.*

Corollary 2. *R is symmetric if and only if $R^{-1} = R$.*

Exercise 5. *Let Q, R be relations on S.*
 (a) *If Q and R are reflexive, so is $Q \circ R$.*
 (b) *If Q and R are symmetric, then $Q \circ R$ is symmetric if and only if $Q \circ R = R \circ Q$.*
 (c) *If Q and R are transitive, then $Q \circ R$ is transitive provided that $Q \circ R = R \circ Q$.*
[Hint: Use Exercises 2.2–4.]

Exercise 6. *If E is an equivalence, then $E^{-1} = E \circ E = E$.*

Corollary: *The inverse of an equivalence is an equivalence. Is a composite of equivalences necessarily an equivalence?*

QUOTIENT SETS AND EQUIVALENCE CLASSES

Let S be a set, and let $\mathscr{A}$ be a set of subsets of S such that

(1) $\varnothing \notin \mathscr{A}$
(2) For all A, B in $\mathscr{A}$, either $A = B$ or $A \cap B = \varnothing$.
(3) $\bigcup_{\mathscr{A}} A = S$.

(In words: the sets in $\mathscr{A}$ are *nonempty*, *disjoint*, and *cover S*.) Such an $\mathscr{A}$ is called a **quotient set** of S.

> The term "quotient set" suggests the fact that S is *divided* into nonempty, nonoverlapping *parts*. A quotient set is sometimes called a **partition**.

Examples:

(a) The only quotient set of $\varnothing$ is $\varnothing$; the only quotient set of $\{x\}$ is $\{\{x\}\}$; the only quotient sets of $\{x, y\}$ are $\{\{x, y\}\}$ and $\{\{x\}, \{y\}\}$.

(b) Any nonempty set S has the **trivial** quotient set $\{S\}$; any set S has the **discrete** quotient set $\{\{x\} \mid x \in S\}$.

Exercise 7. *Any quotient set of a finite set is finite.*

Let E be an equivalence on S, and for any $x \in S$, let $E_x = \{y \mid (x, y) \in E\}$. This set is called the **equivalence class** of x ("with respect to E" understood; we shall sometimes say "E-class" for short).

> Note that in terms of E-classes, the properties of reflexivity, symmetry, and transitivity can be restated as (1) $x \in E_x$; (2) $y \in E_x$ implies $x \in E_y$; (3) $y \in E_x$ and $z \in E_y$ imply $z \in E_x$.

Examples:

(a) $(I_S)_x = \{x\}$ and $(S \times S)_x = S$ for all $x \in S$.

(b) If $\mathscr{E}$ is a set of equivalences on S, then $(\bigcap_{\mathscr{E}} E)_x = \bigcap_{\mathscr{E}} E_x$ for all $x \in S$.

(c) $(E \cap (A \times A))_x = E_x \cap (A \times A)$ for all $x \in A$.

(d) If E is an equivalence on $A \subseteq S$, then $(E \cup I_S)_x = E_x$, if $x \in A$; $= \{x\}$, otherwise.

Exercise 8. *The following statements are equivalent:*
(1) $(x, y) \in E$ (2) $y \in E_x$ (3) $E_y = E_x$.

Exercise 9. *The following statements are equivalent:*
(1) $A \times A \subseteq E$
(2) A *is contained in an E-class.*

Exercise 10. *For any nonempty $A \subseteq S$ there exists an equivalence E on S such that A is an E-class.* [Hint: $E = (A \times A) \cup I_S$.]

Proposition 1. *If E is an equivalence on S, then $\{E_x \mid x \in S\}$ is a quotient set of S.*

Proof: Since $x \in E_x$, no E_x is empty, and they cover S. Moreover, if $z \in E_x \cap E_y$, we have $E_x = E_z = E_y$ by Exercise 8, so that distinct E_x's must be disjoint. $\parallel$

This quotient set is denoted by S/E.

Conversely, let $\mathscr{A}$ be a quotient set of S. Since the elements of $\mathscr{A}$ are disjoint and cover S, any $x \in S$ is in exactly one of them, call it A_x. It is then easy to verify

Proposition 2. *Let $\mathscr{A}$ be a quotient set of S; then the relation*

$$E_{\mathscr{A}} = \{(x, y) \mid A_x = A_y\}$$

is an equivalence on S.

By Propositions 1–2, any equivalence defines a quotient set, and vice versa. In fact, there is a natural one-to-one correspondence between the set $\mathscr{E}_S$ of all equivalences on S and the set $\mathscr{Q}_S$ of all quotient sets of S. To see this, let F be the function $\{(E, S/E) \mid E \in \mathscr{E}_S\}$ from $\mathscr{E}_S$ into $\mathscr{Q}_S$, and G the function $\{(\mathscr{A}, E_{\mathscr{A}}) \mid \mathscr{A} \in \mathscr{Q}_S\}$ from $\mathscr{Q}_S$ into $\mathscr{E}_S$.

Proposition 3. $F \circ G = I_{\mathscr{E}_S}$—*in other words, $E_{(S/E)} = E$ for all $E \in \mathscr{E}_S$.*

Proof: $(x, y) \in E_{(S/E)}$ means that x and y belong to the same element of S/E, so that $E_x = E_y$; hence $(x, y) \in E$, and conversely. $\parallel$

Proposition 4. $G \circ F = I_{\mathscr{Q}_S}$—*in other words, $S/E_{\mathscr{A}} = \mathscr{A}$ for all $\mathscr{A} \in \mathscr{Q}_S$.*

Proof: $A \in S/E_{\mathscr{A}}$ means that $A = (E_{\mathscr{A}})_x$ for some $x \in S$; but evidently $(E_{\mathscr{A}})_x = A_x \in \mathscr{A}$. $\parallel$

Propositions 3–4 and the corollary to Proposition 3.6 combine to give us

Theorem 1. $\{(E, S/E) \mid E \in \mathscr{E}_S\}$ *is a one-to-one correspondence of $\mathscr{E}_S$ with $\mathscr{Q}_S$.*

THE LATTICE OF EQUIVALENCES

Since any intersection of equivalences is an equivalence, Proposition 16.1 tells us that $\mathscr{E}_S$, ordered by $\subseteq$, is a complete lattice. The following proposition gives us a simple description of the sup in this lattice in certain cases:

Proposition 5. *Let D, E be equivalences on S; then the following statements are equivalent:*

(1) $D \circ E$ *is the* sup *of D and E in $\mathscr{E}_S$*
(2) $D \circ E$ *is an equivalence*
(3) $D \circ E$ *is symmetric*
(4) $D \circ E = E \circ D$ *(" D and E commute")*

Proof: Clearly (1) implies (2) implies (3), while (3) and (4) are equivalent by Exercise 5(b); the same exercise also shows that (4) implies (2). Finally, by Exercise 4(c) any transitive relation containing D and E must contain $D \circ E$, so that if $D \circ E$ is an equivalence, it must be the sup of D and E in $\mathscr{E}_S$, proving that (2) implies (1). $\parallel$

Corollary 1. *If $D \circ E = S \times S$, then D and E commute.*

Corollary 2. *If $D \subseteq E$, then D and E commute.*

Proof: See Corollary 1 to Exercise 4. $/\!/$

In later chapters we will study special sublattices of equivalences all of which commute, so that in these sublattices the sup is always the composite.

Exercise 11. *Let D and E be equivalences on S; then $\sup \{D, E\}$ in $\mathscr{E}_S$ is the set of $(x, y) \in S \times S$ such that there exist $n \in \mathbf{N}°$ and $x_0, \ldots, x_n$ in S with $x_0 = x$, $x_n = y$, and $(x_{i-1}, x_i) \in D \cup E$, $1 \le i \le n$.*

Exercise 12. *D and E commute if and only if $D_x \cap E_y = \varnothing$ implies $D_y \cap E_x = \varnothing$ for all x, y in S.*

Exercise 13. *Let S be a set such that all equivalences on S commute; then S has at most two elements.* [Hint: If S has three distinct elements a, b, c, let D, E be the equivalences $I_S \cup \{(a, b), (b, a)\}$ and $I_S \cup \{(b, c), (c, b)\}$; verify that (a, c) is in $D \circ E$ but not in $E \circ D$.]

Exercise 14.

(a) *Any relation which contains a reflexive relation is reflexive*

(b) *Any union of symmetric relations is symmetric*

(c) *The union of a chain (under $\subseteq$) of transitive relations is transitive.*

Corollary: *In $\mathscr{E}_S$, the sup of any chain is its union.*

18. EQUIVALENCES AND CANONICAL FUNCTIONS

Let E be an equivalence on S, and let $F_E = \{(x, E_x) \mid x \in S\}$. Readily, F_E is a function from S onto S/E; it is called the **canonical function** of E.

Proposition 1. $F_E \circ F_E^{-1} = E$.

Proof: $(x, y) \in F_E \circ F_E^{-1}$ means that $E_x = E_y$, which is equivalent to $(x, y) \in E$. $/\!/$

Conversely (Section 17, Example (h)), if F is any function defined on S, then $\{(x, y) \mid F(x) = F(y)\}$ is an equivalence on S (prove this!). Note that this equivalence is just $F \circ F^{-1}$; we shall denote it by E_F.

Exercise 1. *F is one-to-one if and only if $E_F = I_S$; F is constant if and only if $E_F = S \times S$.*

Exercise 2. $F^{-1}(F(x)) = (E_F)_x$ *for all $x \in S$.*

Proposition 2. $E_{(F_E)} = E$.

Proof: $E_{(F_E)} = F_E \circ F_E^{-1} = E$ by Proposition 1. $/\!/$

Corollary. $\{(E, F_E) \mid E \in \mathcal{E}_S\}$ *is a one-to-one function from* $\mathcal{E}_S$ *into* $\mathcal{F}_S$ *(where* $\mathcal{F}_S$ *is the set of functions defined on* S*), and* $\{(F, E_F) \mid F \in \mathcal{F}_S\}$ *is a function from* $\mathcal{F}_S$ *onto* $\mathcal{E}_S$. *In other words: Every equivalence is defined by some function (in fact, by its canonical function), and no two equivalences have the same canonical function.*

Proof: Proposition 3.6.   ∥

Proposition 3. *If* $I_S \subseteq R \subseteq E_F$, *then* $R \circ F = F$.

Proof: If $(x, F(y)) \in R \circ F$, we must have $(x, z) \in R$ for some z such that $F(z) = F(y)$; but then $(x, z) \in E_F$, so that $F(x) = F(z) = F(y)$, proving $(x, F(y)) \in F$. Thus $R \circ F \subseteq F$; for the reverse inclusion, use Exercise 17.4(a).   ∥

Corollary. *If* $I_S \subseteq R \subseteq E$, *then* $R \circ F_E = F_E$.

Proposition 4. *Let* F, G *be functions defined on* S *such that* $E_F \subseteq E_G$; *then* $F^{-1} \circ G$ *is a function from* $F(S)$ *onto* $G(S)$.

Proof: For all $F(x) \in F(S)$ we have $(F(x), G(x)) \in F^{-1} \circ G$, and the same for any $G(x) \in G(S)$; thus it remains only to show that if $(F(x), G(y))$ is also in $F^{-1} \circ G$, then $G(y) = G(x)$. But indeed $(F(x), G(y)) \in F^{-1} \circ G$ means that for some $z \in S$ we have $F(x) = F(z)$ and $G(z) = G(y)$, that is, $(x, z) \in E_F \subseteq E_G$ and $(z, y) \in E_G$, so that $(x, y) \in E_G$.   ∥

Corollary. *If* $E \subseteq E_G$, *then* $F_E^{-1} \circ G$ *is a function from* S/E *onto* $G(S)$.

Theorem 1. *If* F *is any function defined on* S, *then* $F_{(E_F)}^{-1} \circ F$ *is a one-to-one correspondence of* S/E_F *with* $F(S)$.

Proof: Take $E = E_F$ in the corollary to Proposition 4 to see that $F_{(E_F)}^{-1} \circ F$ is a function and onto. Moreover, we have

$$
\begin{aligned}
(F_{(E_F)}^{-1} \circ F) \circ (F_{(E_F)}^{-1} \circ F)^{-1} &= (F_{(E_F)}^{-1} \circ F) \circ (F^{-1} \circ F_{(E_F)}) \\
&= F_{(E_F)}^{-1} \circ (F \circ F^{-1}) \circ F_{(E_F)} \\
&= F_{(E_F)}^{-1} \circ E_F \circ F_{(E_F)} \\
&= F_{(E_F)}^{-1} \circ F_{(E_F)} \quad \text{[Corollary to Proposition 3,} \\
&\qquad\qquad\qquad\qquad \text{with } R = E = E_F] \\
&= I_{S/E_F} \quad \text{[Proposition 3.2].}
\end{aligned}
$$

Hence $F_{(E_F)}^{-1} \circ F$ is one-to-one (Exercise 1).   ∥

The canonical function makes any quotient set an image set; Theorem 1 shows, "conversely," that any image set is in one-to-one correspondence with a quotient set.

Corollary 1. *Any function is the composite of an onto function and a one-to-one correspondence.*

Proof: For any F we have $F = E_F \circ F$ (Proposition 3) $= (F_{(E_F)} \circ F_{(E_F)}^{-1}) \circ F$
$= F_{(E_F)} \circ (F_{(E_F)}^{-1} \circ F)$. $\parallel$

As an immediate generalization of Theorem 1 we have

Corollary 2. *Let F be a function defined on S, and A a subset of S. Let F' be the restriction of F to A, and $E_F' = E_F \cap (A \times A)$ the restriction of E_F to A. Then $F_{E_F'}^{-1} \circ F'$ is a one-to-one correspondence of A/E_F' with $F(A)$.*

Proof: Apply Theorem 1 to F'. $\parallel$

Corollary 3. *Let E be an equivalence on S, and A a subset of S. Let $E' = E \cap (A \times A)$ be the restriction of E to A, and F_E' the restriction of F_E to A. Then $F_{E'}^{-1} \circ F_E'$ is a one-to-one correspondence of A/E' with $F_E(A)$.*

Proof: Take $F = F_E$ in Corollary 2. $\parallel$

Note that if $A = S$, the one-to-one correspondence of Corollary 3 reduces to the identity function.

EQUIVALENCES ON IMAGE SETS

Proposition 5. *Let F be a function defined on S, and E an equivalence on S such that E and E_F commute; then $F^{-1} \circ E \circ F$ is an equivalence on $F(S)$.*

Proof: For any $F(x) \in F(S)$ we have $(F(x), x) \in F^{-1}$, $(x, x) \in E$, and $(x, F(x)) \in F$, so that $(F(x), F(x)) \in F^{-1} \circ E \circ F$, proving $F^{-1} \circ E \circ F$ reflexive. We also have $(F^{-1} \circ E \circ F)^{-1} = F^{-1} \circ E^{-1} \circ F = F^{-1} \circ E \circ F$, so that $F^{-1} \circ E \circ F$ is symmetric. Finally, we have

$$\begin{aligned}
(F^{-1} \circ E \circ F) \circ (F^{-1} \circ E \circ F) &= F^{-1} \circ E \circ (F \circ F^{-1}) \circ E \circ F \\
&= F^{-1} \circ E \circ E_F \circ E \circ F \\
&= F^{-1} \circ (E \circ E) \circ (E_F \circ F) \\
&= F^{-1} \circ E \circ F \quad \text{(Proposition 3),}
\end{aligned}$$

so that $F^{-1} \circ E \circ F$ is transitive. $\parallel$

Examples:
   (a) If $E \subseteq E_F$, then $F^{-1} \circ E \circ F = I_{F(S)}$
      (Proposition 3 and Proposition 3.2).
   (b) If $E = S \times S$, then $F^{-1} \circ E \circ F = F(S) \times F(S)$.

Corollary 1. *If $E \supseteq E_F$, then $F^{-1} \circ E \circ F$ is an equivalence.*

Proof: Corollary 2 to Proposition 17.5. $\parallel$

Corollary 2. *If F is a one-to-one function defined on S, and E is any equivalence on S, then $F^{-1} \circ E \circ F$ is an equivalence.*

Proof: Exercise 1. $\parallel$

Exercise 3. *Let E, F be as in Proposition 5; then $(x, y) \in E$ if and only if $(F(x), F(y)) \in F^{-1} \circ E \circ F$.*

Proposition 6. *Let F be a function defined on S, and E any equivalence on F(S); then $F \circ E \circ F^{-1}$ is an equivalence on S and contains E_F.*

Proof: For any $x \in S$ we have $(x, F(x)) \in F$, $(F(x), F(x)) \in E$, and $(F(x), x) \in F^{-1}$, so that $(x, x) \in F \circ E \circ F^{-1}$, proving it reflexive. It is symmetric, as in the proof of Proposition 5; and $(F \circ E \circ F^{-1}) \circ (F \circ E \circ F^{-1}) = F \circ E \circ (F^{-1} \circ F) \circ E \circ F^{-1} = F \circ E \circ I_{F(S)} \circ E \circ F^{-1}$, where $E \circ (I_{F(S)} \circ E) = E \circ E = E$, which proves it transitive. Finally, $E_F = F \circ F^{-1} = F \circ I_{F(S)} \circ F^{-1} \subseteq F \circ E \circ F^{-1}$.   ∥

Examples:

    (a) If $E = I_{F(S)}$, then $F \circ E \circ F^{-1} = E_F$.
    (b) If $E = F(S) \times F(S)$, then $F \circ E \circ F^{-1} = S \times S$.

Let $\mathscr{E}_{S, E_F}$ be the set of equivalences on S which contain E_F. Evidently $\mathscr{E}_{S, E_F}$ is closed under intersection, so that it too is an *I*-lattice.

Theorem 2. *Let F be any function defined on S; then*

$$\{(E, F^{-1} \circ E \circ F) \mid E \in \mathscr{E}_{S, E_F}\}$$

is an order isomorphism of $\mathscr{E}_{S, E_F}$ with $\mathscr{E}_{F(S)}$.

Proof: By Corollary 1 to Proposition 5, Proposition 6, and the corollary to Proposition 3.6, this function is a one-to-one correspondence, and its inverse is $\{(E, F \circ E \circ F^{-1}) \mid E \in \mathscr{E}_{F(S)}\}$, so that clearly both it and its inverse are inclusion-preserving.   ∥

Corollary. *Let D be any equivalence on S; then $\{(E, F_D{}^{-1} \circ E \circ F_D) \mid E \in \mathscr{E}_{S, D}\}$ is an order isomorphism of $\mathscr{E}_{S, D}$ with $\mathscr{E}_{S/D}$.*

By Theorem 2, the lattice of equivalences on any image set $F(S)$ is order isomorphic to the lattice of equivalences on S which contain E_F. We next show that equivalences which correspond under this order isomorphism have quotient sets which are in one-to-one correspondence.

Proposition 7. *Let E, F be as in Proposition 5; then for all $x \in S$ we have $F(E_x) = (F^{-1} \circ E \circ F)_{F(x)}$—in other words, F takes E-classes into $(F^{-1} \circ E \circ F)$-classes.*

Proof: Let $F(a), F(b)$ be in $F(E_x)$, where a, b are in E_x; then $(F(a), a) \in F^{-1}$, $(a, b) \in E$, and $(b, F(b)) \in F$, so that $(F(a), F(b)) \in F^{-1} \circ E \circ F$, proving that $F(E_x)$ is contained in a $(F^{-1} \circ E \circ F)$-class. Conversely, let $F(y) \in F(S)$ be such that $(F(y), F(x)) \in F^{-1} \circ E \circ F$; then $(y, x) \in E$, so that $y \in E_x$ and $F(y) \in F(E_x)$, which proves that $F(E_x)$ contains $(F^{-1} \circ E \circ F)_{F(x)}$.   ∥

Corollary. $\tilde{F}$ *restricted to* S/E *is a function from* S/E *onto* $F(S)/F^{-1} \circ E \circ F$.

Theorem 3. *Let* F *be a function defined on* S, *and* E *an equivalence on* S *such that* E *and* E_F *commute; then* $\tilde{F}$ *restricted to* S/E *is a one-to-one correspondence.*

Proof: By Exercise 3, $(F^{-1} \circ E \circ F)_{F(x)} = (F^{-1} \circ E \circ F)_{F(y)}$ implies $E_x = E_y$. ‖

Corollary. *Let* D, E *be equivalences on* S *which commute; then* $\tilde{F}_D$ *restricted to* S/E *is a one-to-one correspondence of* S/E *with* $(S/D)/F_D^{-1} \circ E \circ F_D$.

This last result suggests the notation "E/D" for $F_D^{-1} \circ E \circ F_D$, which allows us to rewrite the corollary concisely as $S/E \sim (S/D)/(E/D)$. Note that if we take $E = E_F$ in Theorem 3, we have $F^{-1} \circ E_F \circ F = F^{-1} \circ F = I_{F(S)}$, so that $F(S)/F^{-1} \circ E_F \circ F = F(S)/I_{F(S)} = \{\{y\} \mid y \in F(S)\}$ is trivially in one-to-one correspondence with $F(S)$; thus Theorem 1 is a special case of Theorem 3.

INVARIANT SUBSETS AND SUBSETS OF IMAGE SETS

Let E be an equivalence on S and A a subset of S. Let

$$EA = \{x \mid x \in S; \ (x, a) \in E \ \text{for some} \ a \in A\}.$$

Thus EA is the union of the E-classes which have elements in A.

Examples:
  (a) $E\varnothing = \varnothing$; $E\{x\} = EE_x = E_x$; $ES = S$.
  (b) $I_S A = A$; $(S \times S)A = S$ provided $A \neq \varnothing$.

Exercise 4. $A \subseteq EA = E(EA)$; $D(EA) = (D \circ E)A$.

Proposition 8. *Let* F *be any function defined on* S; *then* $F^{-1}(F(A)) = E_F A$ *for all* $A \subseteq S$.

Proof: If $x \in F^{-1}(F(A))$ we have $F(x) \in F(A)$, say $F(x) = F(a)$ where $a \in A$, so that $(x, a) \in E_F$ and $x \in E_F A$. Conversely, if $x \in E_F A$ we have $(x, a) \in E_F$ for some $a \in A$; thus $F(x) = F(a)$, so that $x \in F^{-1}(F(a)) \subseteq F^{-1}(F(A))$. ‖

Corollary 1. $F(E_F A) = F(A)$.

Corollary 2. *Let* E *be any equivalence on* S; *then* $EA = F_E^{-1}(F_E(A))$ *for all* $A \subseteq S$.

Corollary 3. $F_E(EA) = F_E(A)$.

Corollary 4. *For any equivalence* E *on* S, *and any* $A \subseteq S$, *we have*

$$A/E \cap (A \times A) \sim EA/E \cap (EA \times EA).$$

Proof: Corollary 3 to Theorem 1 and the preceding corollary.   ∥

If $EA = A$, we call A *E*-**invariant**. [Thus by Examples (a–b) and Exercise 4, $\varnothing$, S, any *E*-class, and any EA are *E*-invariant for any E, and any set is I_S-invariant.] Note that if A is *E*-invariant and $a \in A$, we have $x \in A$ for any $x \in S$ such that $(x, a) \in E$, so that $E_a \subseteq A$.

Exercise 5. *Any intersection of E-invariant sets is E-invariant.*

Proposition 9. *A nonempty subset is E-invariant if and only if it is a union of E-classes.*

Proof: If A is a union of *E*-classes, and $(x, a) \in E$ for some $a \in A$, let $a \in E_z \subseteq A$; then $E_a = E_z$ and $x \in E_a \subseteq A$. Conversely, if A is *E*-invariant, it is the union of the E_a such that $a \in A$.   ∥

Proposition 10. *Let F be a function defined on S, and let B be any subset of F(S); then $F^{-1}(B)$ is E_F-invariant.*

Proof: $F^{-1}(B)$ is the union of the E_F-classes $F^{-1}(F(b))$, where $F(b) \in B$ (see Exercise 2).   ∥

Let $\mathscr{P}_S^{(E)}$ denote the set of *E*-invariant subsets of S. By Exercise 5, $\mathscr{P}_S^{(E)}$ is an *I*-lattice.

Theorem 4. *Let F be a function defined on S; then the restriction of $\tilde{F}$ to $\mathscr{P}_S^{(E_F)}$ is an order isomorphism of $\mathscr{P}_S^{(E_F)}$ with $\mathscr{P}_{F(S)}$.*

Proof: $\tilde{F}$ restricted to $\mathscr{P}_S^{(E_F)}$ is certainly a function from $\mathscr{P}_S^{(E_F)}$ into $\mathscr{P}_{F(S)}$, while by Proposition 10, F^{-1} is a function from $\mathscr{P}_{F(S)}$ into $\mathscr{P}_S^{(E_F)}$. Now for any $B \subseteq F(S)$ we have $F(F^{-1}(B)) = B$, while by Proposition 8, if $A \subseteq S$ is E_F-invariant we have $F^{-1}(F(A)) = A$. Hence by the corollary to Proposition 3.6, $\tilde{F}$ restricted to $\mathscr{P}_S^{(E_F)}$ is a one-to-one correspondence, while both it and F^{-1} are certainly inclusion-preserving.   ∥

In words: The lattice of subsets of any image set $F(S)$ is order isomorphic to the lattice of E_F-invariant subsets of S.

Corollary. *Let E be an equivalence on S; then the restriction of $\tilde{F}_E$ to $\mathscr{P}_S^{(E)}$ is an order isomorphism of $\mathscr{P}_S^{(E)}$ with $\mathscr{P}_{S/E}$.*

19. PRODUCT SETS

Let I, A be sets, and F a function from I into A. In analogy with the definition of "*n*-tuple," we can call F an *I*-**tuple** of elements of A, and denote it by $(a_i)_I$, where $a_i = F(i)$ is called the **ith term** of $(a_i)_I$.

Let $(S_i)_I$ be an *I*-tuple of sets. As in Exercise 3.3, we denote the union of the S_i's by $\bigcup_I S_i$. By the **Cartesian product** of $(S_i)_I$ (notation: $\prod_I S_i$) is meant the set of functions G from I into $\bigcup_I S_i$ such that $G(i) \in S_i$ for each $i \in I$. Note that any such G is an I-tuple of elements of $\bigcup_I S_i$, and can be denoted by an expression of the form $(x_i)_I$; thus $\prod_I S_i = \{(x_i)_I \mid x_i \in S_i\}$. We call the S_i's the *factors* of the product. If $I' \subseteq I$, and $(S_i)_{I'}$ is the restriction to I' of the function $(S_i)_I$, we call $\prod_{I'} S_i$ a *subproduct* of $\prod_I S_i$.

> If I has two elements, say $I = \{1, 2\}$, then there is a natural one-to-one correspondence between $\prod_I S_i$ and $S_1 \times S_2$, since any $G \in \prod_I S_i$ defines an ordered pair $(G(1), G(2)) \in S_1 \times S_2$, and conversely. From now on we shall use the notations $\prod_{\{1,2\}} S_i$ and $S_1 \times S_2$ interchangeably. More generally, if I is finite, say $I = \{1, \ldots, n\}$, we shall often write $\prod_{i=1}^{n} S_i$, or $S_1 \times \cdots \times S_n$, instead of $\prod_I S_i$, and $(x_1, \ldots, x_n)$ instead of $(x_i)_I$. Note that if $I = \varnothing$ we have $\prod_I S_i = \{\varnothing\}$.

If all the S_i's are equal, say to S, then $\prod_I S_i$ becomes simply the set of all functions from I into S (or equivalently, the set of all I-tuples of elements of S). In this case we call $\prod_I S_i$ the Ith **Cartesian power** of S, and denote it by S^I. We shall continue to abbreviate $S^{\mathbf{N}_n}$ by S^n (Section 4), and to speak of sequences and n-tuples rather than $\mathbf{N}$-tuples and $\mathbf{N}_n$-tuples. We shall omit the word "Cartesian" in speaking of products and powers when there is no danger of confusion.

The following propositions give some basic properties of product sets:

Proposition 1. *A product of one factor is in one-to-one correspondence with the factor.*

Proof: If $I = \{1\}$, evidently $\{(x_1, (x_i)_I) \mid x_1 \in S_1\}$ is a one-to-one correspondence of S_1 with $\prod_I S_i$. //

Proposition 2. *A product is empty if and only if some factor is empty.*

Proof: If $S_j = \varnothing$, there cannot exist a G such that $G(j) \in S_j$. Conversely, if every S_i is nonempty, let H be a choice function on $\bigcup_I S_i$, and define G by $G(i) = H(S_i)$ for each $i \in I$; then $G \in \prod_I S_i$, making it nonempty. //

Proposition 3. *A product of a nonempty set of factors has only one element if and only if every factor has only one element.*

Proof: If each $S_i = \{a_i\}$, then evidently $\prod_I S_i = \{(a_i)_I\}$. Conversely, if there exist a_j, b_j, distinct, in S_j, let c_i be any element of S_i (each S_i is nonempty by Proposition 2), and define $x_i = y_i = c_i$ if $i \neq j$; $x_j = a_j$, $y_j = b_j$. Then $(x_i)_I$ and $(y_i)_I$ are distinct elements of $\prod_I S_i$. //

Proposition 4. *Any product is in one-to-one correspondence with a subproduct from which factors having only one element have been omitted.*

Proof: Let $S_j = \{x_j\}$ for each $j \in J \subset I$. Let $G \in \prod_{I-J} S_i$; then $G \cup \{(j, x_j) \mid j \in J\}$ is in $\prod_I S_i$. Conversely, let $H \in \prod_I S_i$; then $H - \{(j, x_j) \mid j \in J\}$ is in $\prod_{I-J} S_i$. It is easily seen, using the corollary to Proposition 3.6, that the function $\{(G, G \cup \{(j, x_j) \mid j \in J\}) \mid G \in \prod_{I-J} S_i\}$ is a one-to-one correspondence of $\prod_{I-J} S_i$ with $\prod_I S_i$. $\parallel$

Proposition 5. *A product of subsets is a subset of the product.*

Proof: Let $A_i \subseteq S_i$ for each $i \in I$; then $\prod_I A_i$ is just the set of $G \in \prod_I S_i$ such that $G(i) \in A_i$ for each $i \in I$. $\parallel$

[In I-tuple notation: $\prod_I A_i$ is just the set of $(x_i)_I$ such that $x_i \in A_i$ for each $i \in I$.]

Proposition 6. *A permutation of a product is in one-to-one correspondence with the product.*

Proof: Let F be the I-tuple $(S_i)_I$, and let P be a permutation of I. Then $P \circ F$ is also an I-tuple; we denote it by $(S_i)_{P(I)}$. Evidently, if $G \in \prod_I S_i$, then $P \circ G \in \prod_{P(I)} S_i$, while if $H \in \prod_{P(I)} S_i$, then $P^{-1} \circ H \in \prod_I S_i$. Thus, using the corollary to Proposition 3.6, we see that $\{(G, P \circ G) \mid G \in \prod_I S_i\}$ is a one-to-one correspondence of $\prod_I S_i$ with $\prod_{P(I)} S_i$. $\parallel$

Applied to $A \times B$, this proposition yields the obvious one-to-one correspondence

$$\{((a, b), (b, a)) \mid (a, b) \in A \times B\}$$

of $A \times B$ with $B \times A$.

Proposition 7. *A product of products is in one-to-one correspondence with a product.*

Proof: Let $F = (I_j)_J$ be a J-tuple of sets, and for each $j \in J$, let $F_j = (S_i)_{I_j}$ be an I_j-tuple of sets. Let K_j be the obvious one-to-one correspondence of $\{j\} \times I_j = \{(j, x) \mid x \in I_j\}$ with I_j, and let $I = \bigcup_J (\{j\} \times I_j)$; then $\bigcup_J (K_j \circ F_j)$ is an I-tuple, call it $(S_i)_I$. [It is a function since the $\{j\} \times I_j$'s are all disjoint.] Let $T_j = \prod_{I_j} S_i$; then any element of $\prod_J T_j$ is a J-tuple whose jth term is an element of $\prod_{I_j} S_i$, that is, an I_j-tuple of elements of S's which we can write as $(x_i)_{I_j}$. Let $(x_i)_I$ be the element of $\prod_I S_i$ whose restriction to $\{j\} \times I_j$ is $(x_i)_{I_j}$. Then readily, $\{(((x_i)_{I_j})_J, (x_i)_I) \mid ((x_i)_{I_j})_J \in \prod_J T_j\}$ is a one-to-one correspondence of $\prod_J T_j = \prod_J (\prod_{I_j} S_i)$ with $\prod_I S_i$. $\parallel$

Applied to, say, $(A \times B) \times C$, this proposition can be interpreted as follows: $J = \{1, 2\}$; $I_1 = \{1, 2\}$; $I_2 = \{1\}$; $I = \{(1, 1), (1, 2), (2, 1)\}$; $((a, b), c)$ corresponds to (a, b, c). The apparent complication of introducing the sets $\{j\} \times I_j$ is necessary in order to enable us to construct a set I and an I-tuple which yield the required one-to-one correspondence. We could not simply take $I = \bigcup_J I_j$, since the I_j's—as in the example just given—are not necessarily disjoint, which means that $\bigcup_J F_j$ is not necessarily a function.

Proposition 8. *Let $(S_i)_I$ be an I-tuple of sets, and for each $i \in I$, let R_i be a relation on S_i. Let $R = \{((x_i)_I, (y_i)_I) \mid (x_i, y_i) \in R_i \text{ for each } i \in I\}$. Then R is a relation on $\prod_I S_i$, and is an equivalence if and only if each R_i is an equivalence.*

Proof: If each R_i is an equivalence, we have $(x_i, x_i) \in R_i$ for each $i \in I$, so that $((x_i)_I, (x_i)_I) \in R$ for all $(x_i)_I \in \prod_I S_i$, proving R reflexive. Conversely, let $((x_i)_I, (x_i)_I) \in R$ for all $(x_i)_I \in \prod_I S_i$. Since any $x_i \in S_i$ is the ith term of some $(x_i)_I \in \prod_I S_i$, we thus have $(x_i, x_i) \in R_i$ for all $x_i \in S_i$, proving R_i reflexive. The proofs for symmetry and transitivity are left to the reader. //

Exercise 1. *Is Proposition 8 true if "equivalence" is replaced by "order relation"?*

Proposition 9. *Let $(S_i)_I$ and $(T_i)_I$ be I-tuples of sets, and for each $i \in I$, let R_i be a relation between S_i and T_i. Let R be defined as in Proposition 8; then R is a relation between $\prod_I S_i$ and $\prod_I T_i$. Moreover, R is a function (and one-to-one, or onto) if and only if each R_i is a function (and one-to-one, or onto).*

Proof: If each R_i is a function, then for each $x_i \in S_i$ there is exactly one $y_i \in T_i$ such that $(x_i, y_i) \in R_i$; hence there is exactly one $(y_i)_I$, for any given $(x_i)_I$, such that $((x_i)_I, (y_i)_I) \in R$. The converse and the rest of the proof are left to the reader. //

Corollary. *Let $S_i \sim T_i$ for each $i \in I$; then $\prod_I S_i \sim \prod_I T_i$.*

Exercise 2. *The following statements about the sets S and A are equivalent:*
 (a) *There exists a set B such that $S \sim A \times B$*
 (b) *There exists an I-tuple $(S_i)_I$ such that $S \sim \prod_I S_i$, and $A \sim S_j$ for some $j \in I$.*

[Hint: If (a) holds, take $I = \{1, 2\}$, $S_1 = A$, $S_2 = B$ in (b). If (b) holds, take $B = \prod_{I-\{j\}} S_i$ in (a).]

PROJECTIONS AND INDEPENDENT EQUIVALENCES

In the remainder of this section we establish two useful alternative characterizations of product sets.

Proposition 10. *Let $S = \prod_I S_i$, and let $p_j = \{((x_i)_I, x_j) \mid (x_i)_I \in S\}$, where $j \in I$. Then p_j is a function from S onto S_j, and for all $(y_i)_I \in S$ we have $\bigcap_I p_i^{-1}(y_i) = \{(y_i)_I\}$.*

Proof: Clearly p_j is a function onto, and takes any I-tuple in S into its jth term. The last part of the proposition simply says that there is exactly one I-tuple in S which has the same ith term as $(y_i)_I$ for each $i \in I$—namely, $(y_i)_I$ itself.   //

The function p_j is called the **projection** of S onto S_j (or, sometimes, the jth projection of S).

Exercise 3. p_j *is constant if and only if S_j has only one element; one-to-one, if and only if S_i has only one element for every $i \neq j$ in I.*

Exercise 4. *Let R, R_i be as in Proposition 9; let p_i be the projection of S onto S_i, and q_i the projection of $T = \prod_I T_i$ onto T_i. Then $R_i = p_i^{-1} \circ R \circ q_i$ and $R = \bigcap_I (p_i \circ R_i \circ q_i^{-1})$.*

We now show that the p's "determine" $\prod_I S_i$:

Theorem 1. *Let S be a set, let $(S_i)_I$ be an I-tuple of sets, and for each $i \in I$, let p_i be a function from S onto S_i; moreover, for all $(y_i)_I \in \prod_I S_i$, let $\bigcap_I p_i^{-1}(y_i)$ have only one element y. Then $\{(y, (p_i(y))_I) \mid y \in S\}$ is a one-to-one correspondence of S with $\prod_I S_i$.*

Proof: Evidently $\bigcap_I p_i^{-1}(y_i) = \{y\}$ implies $p_i(y) = y_i$ for all $i \in I$; while y is in $\bigcap_I p_i^{-1}(p_i(y))$, which must thus $= \{y\}$, since it can have only one element. Hence the desired conclusion follows by applying the corollary to Proposition 3.6 to $\{(y, (p_i(y))_I) \mid y \in S\}$ and $\{((y_i)_I, y) \mid (y_i)_I \in \prod_I S_i\}$.   //

Since p_i is a function, the relation $E_i = p_i \circ p_i^{-1}$ is an equivalence on S (it is the relation "has the same ith projection as"). By Exercises 3 and 18.1, $E_i = S \times S$ if and only if S_i has only one element.

Proposition 11. *Let $S = \prod_I S_i$, and let E_i be as just defined. If I has just one element, the sole E_i is I_S; while if I has more than one element, then $\bigcap_I E_i = I_S$ and $E_j \circ \bigcap_{I-\{j\}} E_i = S \times S$ for each $j \in I$.*

Proof: Since E_j is just the set of pairs $((x_i)_I, (y_i)_I)$ such that $x_j = y_j$, the intersection of all the E_j's is evidently I_S. On the other hand, for any $j \in I$ and any $(x_i)_I$ and $(y_i)_I$ in S, there certainly exists a $(z_i)_I$ in S such that $z_j = x_j$, while $z_i = y_i$ for all $i \neq j$ in I. Thus $((x_i)_I, (z_i)_I) \in E_j$, while $((z_i)_I, (y_i)_I) \in \bigcap_{I-\{j\}} E_i$, so that the arbitrary element $((x_i)_I, (y_i)_I)$ of $S \times S$ is in $E_j \circ \bigcap_{I-\{j\}} E_i$.   //

Corollary 1. *The E's commute.*

Proof: For all distinct j, k in I we have $E_j \circ E_k \supseteq E_j \circ \bigcap_{I-\{j\}} E_i$, so that E_j and E_k commute by Corollary 1 to Proposition 17.5.   //

Corollary 2. *The set of those E's which $\neq S \times S$ is either empty or independent in $\mathscr{E}_S{}^{-1}$ (the complete lattice of equivalences on S, ordered by $\supseteq$), and its sup in $\mathscr{E}_S{}^{-1}$ is I_S.*

Proof: The sup in $\mathscr{E}_S{}^{-1}$ is the intersection, while the inf must contain the composite, so that $\inf\{E_j, \bigcap_{I-\{j\}} E_i\}$ in $\mathscr{E}_S{}^{-1}$ must be $S \times S$, which is the least element of $\mathscr{E}_S{}^{-1}$. //

Exercise 5. *Let $D_i = \bigcap_{I-\{i\}} E_j$. Prove that the D's commute, and that if any of them is not I_S, the set of such is independent in $\mathscr{E}_S$.*

Like the projections, the E's "determine" $\prod_I S_i$, if I is finite:

Theorem 2. *Let $E_1, \ldots, E_n$ be equivalences on the set S such that $\bigcap_{\mathbf{N}_n} E_i = I_S$ and $E_j \circ \bigcap_{\mathbf{N}_n - \{j\}} E_i = S \times S$ for each $j \in \mathbf{N}_n$. Then the E's commute, and $\{(x, ((E_1)_x, \ldots, (E_n)_x)) \mid x \in S\}$ is a one-to-one correspondence of S with $\prod_{i=1}^n S/E_i$.*

Proof: By Theorem 18.1, $F_{E_i}(S) \sim S/E_i$; it thus suffices to show that the canonical functions $F_{E_1}, \ldots, F_{E_n}$ are as in Theorem 1—in other words, that if C_i is any E_i-class, $1 \leq i \leq n$, then $C = \bigcap_{i=1}^n C_i$ contains exactly one element. In fact, it suffices to show that $C \neq \varnothing$, since it then must be an $(\bigcap_{i=1}^n E_i)$-class, and we know that $\bigcap_{i=1}^n E_i = I_S$.

In proving that $C \neq \varnothing$ we may evidently assume that no E_i is $S \times S$; in fact, we shall prove by induction on n that if the E's are independent in $\mathscr{E}_S{}^{-1}$, then $C \neq \varnothing$. This is trivial for $n = 1$; suppose it has been shown when there are only $n - 1$ E's. Then $C' = \bigcap_{i=1}^{n-1} C_i \neq \varnothing$, so that it is an $(\bigcap_{i=1}^{n-1} E_i)$-class. Let $s' \in C'$, and let s_n be any element of the E_n-class C_n. Then $(s_n, s') \in S \times S = E_n \circ \bigcap_{i=1}^{n-1} E_i$, so that there exists an $s \in S$ such that $(s_n, s) \in E_n$ and $(s, s') \in \bigcap_{i=1}^{n-1} E_i$. But this means that $s \in C_n$ and $s \in C'$, so that s is in $C_n \cap C' = C$, proving C nonempty. //

We conclude this section by introducing the concept of a "supplemented" equivalence and establishing some of its properties:

Proposition 12. *The following statements about the equivalence E on the set S are equivalent:*

(1) *There exists an equivalence D on S such that $D \circ E = S \times S$ and $D \cap E = I_S$.*

(2) *There exists an I-tuple $(E_i)_I$ of equivalences on S which is as in Proposition 11, and E is one of the E_i's.*

Proof: See the hint for Exercise 2. //

If (1–2) hold, we say that E is a **supplemented equivalence**, and call D a **supplement** of E. Note that D is also supplemented and has E as a supplement.

Exercise 6. *Let D, E be equivalences on S such that D is a supplement of E; let R be an equivalence on S which contains E; let $A \subseteq S$ be R-invariant; and let D', E' be the restrictions of D, E to A. Then D' is a supplement of E'.*

Proposition 13. *Let D, E be equivalences on S such that D is a supplement of E; then any D-class $\sim S/E$.*

Proof: Let F be the function $\{(y, E_y) \mid y \in D_x\}$. For all $z \in S$ we have $(x, z) \in S \times S = D \circ E$, so that there exists a $y \in D_x$ such that $E_y = E_z$, which proves that F is onto. On the other hand, if u, v are in D_x and $E_u = E_v$, we have $(u, v) \in D \cap E = I_S$, so that $u = v$, proving that F is one-to-one.   //

Corollary 1. *Let E be a supplemented equivalence; then any two E-classes are in one-to-one correspondence.*

Corollary 2. *Let S have n elements, and let E be a supplemented equivalence on S; then the number of elements of S/E divides n.*

Corollary 3. *Let S have p elements, where p is prime; then the only supplemented equivalences on S are I_S and $S \times S$.*

Note that, conversely, I_S and $S \times S$ are supplemented equivalences on any set S, and have each other as supplements.

20. CARDINAL NUMBERS

In this and the next section we develop parts of the theory of cardinal numbers, which will be needed in particular when we study abelian groups and vector spaces of infinite rank in Chapters IX and XI.

By the **cardinal number**, or **cardinality**, of a set S we mean the set $K(S) = \{T \mid T \sim S\}$ of sets which are in one-to-one correspondence with S. Note that $K(S)$ is also the cardinal number of any set $T \in K(S)$, since by transitivity of $\sim$ we have, for any set A, $A \sim T$ if and only if $A \sim S$.

Examples:
  (a) $K(\varnothing) = \{\varnothing\}$.
  (b) $K(\{x\})$ is the set of all one-element sets; $K(\{x, y\})$ (where $x \neq y$) is the set of all two-element sets; . . . .
  (c) $K(\{x_1, \ldots, x_n\})$ (where the x's are all different) is the set of all n-element sets. We shall denote this cardinal number by K_n; thus $K(\mathbf{N}_n) = K_n$.

   Note that K_n is not the same thing as the natural number n. We shall see in the course of this and the next section, however, that the cardinal numbers of finite sets do behave just like the corresponding natural numbers in many respects.

(d) $K(\mathbf{N})$ is the set of all denumerably infinite sets. This cardinal number is usually denoted by $\aleph_0$ ("aleph sub zero").

Let S be finite and nonempty; then $S \sim \mathbf{N}_n$ for some $n \in \mathbf{N}$, so that $K(S) = K_n$. The cardinal numbers K_n, and $\{\varnothing\}$, are called finite; all other cardinal numbers are called infinite. Note that every set in a finite (infinite) cardinal number is finite (infinite). For uniformity, we shall sometimes denote $\{\varnothing\}$ by K_0.

Exercise 1.

(a) $K_r = K_s$ if and only if $r = s$—in other words, $\{(r, K_r) \mid r \in \mathbf{N}^\circ\}$ is a one-to-one correspondence of $\mathbf{N}^\circ$ with the set of finite cardinal numbers.
(b) $K(\mathbf{N}^\circ) = \aleph_0$.

If K and L are cardinal numbers, we say that $K \le L$ ("K is not greater than L") if there exist sets $S \in K$ and $T \in L$ such that S is in one-to-one correspondence with a subset of T. [Note that the same must then be true of any $U \in K$ and any $V \in L$. Indeed, let $S \sim T' \subseteq T$. Now $U \sim S$ and $V \sim T$; let V' be the subset of V corresponding to T'. Then $U \sim S \sim T' \sim V' \subseteq V$.] Thus if $S \subseteq T$ we have $K(S) \le K(T)$.

Examples:

(a) $\{\varnothing\} \le K$ for any K.
(b) For all r, s in $\mathbf{N}^\circ$ we have $K_r \le K_s$ if and only if $r \le s$.
(c) $K_n \le \aleph_0$ for all $n \in \mathbf{N}^\circ$.
(d) K is infinite if and only if $\aleph_0 \le K$.

Exercise 2. *The one-to-one correspondence of Exercise 1 is an order isomorphism.*

Exercise 3. *For any function F defined on S we have $K(F(S)) \le K(S)$.*

Proposition 1. $\le$ *is reflexive and transitive—that is,*
(1) *For any cardinal number K we have $K \le K$*
(2) *If K, L, M are cardinal numbers such that $K \le L$ and $L \le M$, then $K \le M$.*

Proof: (1) The identity function is a one-to-one correspondence of any $S \in K$ with its improper subset S. (2) Let $T \in K$, $U \in L$, $V \in M$, and let F, G be one-to-one correspondences of T with $U' \subseteq U$ and of U with $V' \subseteq V$, respectively. Let G' be the restriction of G to U'; then $F \circ G'$ is a one-to-one correspondence of T with V'. //

As the notation "$\leq$" suggests, we would like to prove that $\leq$ is an order relation. It remains only to show that $\leq$ is weakly antisymmetric—that is, if K, L are cardinal numbers such that $K \leq L$ and $L \leq K$, then $K = L$. To do this, we need

Theorem 1 (Bernstein–Cantor). *Let A, B, C be sets such that $A \subset B \subset C$ and $A \sim C$; then $B \sim C$.*

Proof: Let $B - A = S$, $C - B = T$; then A, S, T are disjoint, and we must prove that $A \cup S \cup T \sim A \cup S$, given that $A \cup S \cup T \sim A$.

Let F be a one-to-one correspondence of $A \cup S \cup T$ with A, and let $(A_i)_\mathbf{N}$, $(S_i)_\mathbf{N}$, $(T_i)_\mathbf{N}$ be the sequences defined by $A_1 = A$, $S_1 = S$, $T_1 = T$; $A_{n+1} = F(A_n)$, $S_{n+1} = F(S_n)$, $T_{n+1} = F(T_n)$. By transitivity of $\sim$ and induction, we have $A_n \sim A$, $S_n \sim S$, $T_n \sim T$ for all $n \in \mathbf{N}$. Moreover, we have $A_{n+1} \cup S_{n+1} \cup T_{n+1} = A_n$ for all $n \in \mathbf{N}$; indeed, this is true for $n = 1$ since $A_2 \cup S_2 \cup T_2 = F(A) \cup F(S) \cup F(T) = F(A \cup S \cup T) = A = A_1$, and if it is true for k, applying F to both sides shows that it remains true for $k + 1$. Similarly, A_n, S_n and T_n are disjoint for all $n \in \mathbf{N}$, since F is one-to-one. Hence S_{n+1} and T_{n+1}, which are subsets of A_n, are each disjoint from both S_n and T_n; and by another induction argument, it follows that all the S_n's and all the T_n's are disjoint from one another.

Let $A^* = \bigcap_{\mathbf{N}-\{1\}} A_n$, and note that

$$A = A^* \cup \left(\bigcup_{\mathbf{N}-\{1\}} S_n \right) \cup \left(\bigcup_{\mathbf{N}-\{1\}} T_n \right). \qquad (\alpha)$$

[In fact, A certainly contains the right member of (α), since images under F must be $\subseteq A$. Conversely, if $x \in A$ is in no S_n or T_n, it must be in every A_n, hence in A^*.] Furthermore, A^*, the S_n's, and the T_n's are all disjoint. [Indeed, if x is in A^*, it can be in no S_n or T_n, and conversely; while the S_n's and T_n's are also all disjoint, as already pointed out.]

It follows from (α) that $A \cup S \cup T = A^* \cup \left(\bigcup_\mathbf{N} S_n \right) \cup \left(\bigcup_\mathbf{N} T_n \right)$, and that $A \cup S = A^* \cup \left(\bigcup_\mathbf{N} S_n \right) \cup \left(\bigcup_{\mathbf{N}-\{1\}} T_n \right)$. Let F_n be the restriction of F to T_n. Then evidently

$$I_{A^*} \cup \left(\bigcup_\mathbf{N} I_{S_n} \right) \cup \left(\bigcup_\mathbf{N} F_n \right)$$

is a one-to-one correspondence of $A \cup S \cup T$ with $A \cup S$. $\parallel$

Corollary 1. *Let U, V be sets each of which is in one-to-one correspondence with a subset of the other; then $U \sim V$.*

Proof: Let G, H be one-to-one correspondences of U with $V' \subseteq V$ and of V with $U' \subseteq U$, respectively. If $V' = V$ or if $U' = U$, we have nothing to prove; we may thus suppose that $U' \subset U$ and $V' \subset V$. Let H' be the restriction of H to V'; then $G \circ H'$ is a one-to-one correspondence of U with $H'(V')$, which is a proper subset of U'—call it U''. Taking U'', U', U for A, B, C in the theorem, it follows that $U \sim U'$, whence $U \sim V$. $\parallel$

Corollary 2. $\leq$ *is weakly antisymmetric.*

Proof: If K, L are cardinal numbers such that $K \leq L$ and $L \leq K$, then there exist $U \in K$ and $V \in L$ satisfying the hypothesis of Corollary 1. Hence $U \sim V$, so that by the transitivity of $\sim$, the set $K = \{W \mid W \sim U\}$ is the same as the set $L = \{W \mid W \sim V\}$. $\parallel$

Corollary 3. $\leq$ *is an order relation on any set of cardinal numbers.*

As usual, we abbreviate "$\leq$ but $\neq$" by "$<$."

Corollary 4. $K < L$ *if and only if there exist* $S \in K$, $T \in L$ *such that* $S \sim$ *a subset of T, but $T \sim$ no subset of S.*

Exercise 4. *For any set S we have $K(S) < K(\mathcal{P}_S)$.* [Hint: Proposition 5.12.]

Corollary 1. *For any set S, not every subset of S can be an element of S.*

Corollary 2. *For any set S, there exists an element not in S.*

Exercise 5. *Any nonempty subset of $\mathbf{N}$ either $\sim \mathbf{N}$ or $\sim \mathbf{N}_m$ for some $m \in \mathbf{N}$.*

Exercise 6. *K is finite if and only if $K < \aleph_0$.*

Finally, we prove that the order relation $\leq$ is total:

Theorem 2. *For any cardinal numbers K, L we have $K \leq L$ or $L \leq K$.*

Proof: Let $S \in K$, $T \in L$, and let $\mathcal{F}$ be the set of one-to-one functions from subsets of S into T. Since $\varnothing$ is trivially a one-to-one function from $\varnothing \subseteq S$ into T, the set $\mathcal{F}$ is nonempty. Given $F \in \mathcal{F}$, let d_F denote the domain of F; thus d_F is a subset of S. We define a relation $\leq$ on $\mathcal{F}$ as follows: $F \leq G$ if and only if $d_F \subseteq d_G$, and F is the restriction of G to d_F. Clearly $\leq$ is an order relation.

Let $\mathcal{F}^*$ be a chain in the ordered set $\mathcal{F}$. Then $F^* = \bigcup_{\mathcal{F}^*} F$ is readily a function defined on $d_{F^*} = \bigcup_{\mathcal{F}^*} d_F$, and its restriction to the domain of any $F \in \mathcal{F}^*$ is just F. Suppose that there existed x, y in d_{F^*} such that $x \neq y$ but $F^*(x) = F^*(y)$. Let $x \in d_{F_1}$, $y \in d_{F_2}$. Since $\mathcal{F}^*$ is a chain, we have $d_{F_1} \subseteq d_{F_2}$ or vice versa, say the former, so that x and y are both in d_{F_2}. Hence $F_2(x) = F^*(x) = F^*(y) = F_2(y)$, and since F_2 is one-to-one, this implies $x = y$, contradiction. We have thus proved that F^* is one-to-one, that is, $F^* \in \mathcal{F}$. Moreover, evidently $F \leq F^*$ for all $F \in \mathcal{F}^*$, so that F^* is an upper bound for $\mathcal{F}^*$. Since $\mathcal{F}^*$ was any chain in $\mathcal{F}$, we have thus shown that the ordered set $\mathcal{F}$ is inductive.

It follows by Zorn's lemma that $\mathcal{F}$ has a maximal element $\bar{F}$. If $d_{\bar{F}} = S$, we have S in one-to-one correspondence with a subset of T (namely, $\bar{F}(S)$), and we are done. Similarly, if $\bar{F}(d_{\bar{F}}) = T$, we have T in one-to-one correspondence with a subset of S (namely, $d_{\bar{F}}$). But if neither of these is true, let

$s \in S - d_F$ and $t \in T - \bar{F}(d_F)$, and let $G = \bar{F} \cup \{(s, t)\}$. Evidently G is one-to-one, so that $G \in \mathscr{F}$, and $\bar{F}$ is the restriction of G to d_F, so that $\bar{F} \le G$; but $\bar{F} \ne G$, contradicting the maximality of $\bar{F}$. $\parallel$

Corollary. $\le$ *is a total order relation on any set of cardinal numbers.*

21. CARDINAL ARITHMETIC

ADDITION

Proposition 1. *Let* A, B, S, T *be sets such that* $A \cap B = \varnothing$, $S \cap T = \varnothing$, $A \sim S$, $B \sim T$; *then* $A \cup B \sim S \cup T$.

Proof: Let F, G be one-to-one correspondences of A with S and B with T, respectively; then $F \cup G$ is a one-to-one correspondence of $A \cup B$ with $S \cup T$. [Compare Exercise 3.9.] $\parallel$

Proposition 2. *Let* K, L *be cardinal numbers; then there exist* $S \in K$, $T \in L$ *such that* $S \cap T = \varnothing$.

Proof: Let A, B be any sets in K, L, respectively, and let $S = \{(1, a) \mid a \in A\}$, $T = \{(2, b) \mid b \in B\}$. $\parallel$

Let $\mathscr{K}$ be any set of cardinal numbers; let K, L be in $\mathscr{K}$; and let $S \in K$, $T \in L$ be disjoint, as in Proposition 2. By Proposition 1, $K(S \cup T)$ does not depend on the particular $\mathscr{K}$, S, and T which are used, but only on K and L. Thus the relation $\{((K, L), K(S \cup T)) \mid K, L \text{ in } \mathscr{K}; S \in K, T \in L, S \cap T = \varnothing\}$ is a function defined on $\mathscr{K} \times \mathscr{K}$. We denote $K(S \cup T)$ by $K + L$, and call it the **sum** of K and L; the process of applying this function to a pair of cardinal numbers is called **addition**.

Examples:

(a) $K + \{\varnothing\} = K$ for all K—in other words, $\{\varnothing\}$ is an **identity** for addition of cardinal numbers.

(b) $K_r + K_s = K_{r+s}$ for all r, s in $\mathbf{N}$. [Hint: Proposition 4.7 and the remark following it.]

(c) $K_m + \aleph_0 = \aleph_0$ for all $m \in \mathbf{N}$. [Hint: Let $S \in K_m$, $S \cap \mathbf{N} = \varnothing$, and let G be a one-to-one correspondence of S with $\mathbf{N}_m$; then $G \cup F_m$ is a one-to-one correspondence of $S \cup \mathbf{N}$ with $\mathbf{N}$.]

Exercise 1. $\aleph_0 + \aleph_0 = \aleph_0$. [Hint: Prove that $\mathbf{N} \sim 2\mathbf{N}$ (Exercise 5.3) $\sim F^{-1}(2\mathbf{N})$; $2\mathbf{N} \cap F^{-1}(2\mathbf{N}) = \varnothing$; $2\mathbf{N} \cup F^{-1}(2\mathbf{N}) = \mathbf{N}$.]

Exercise 2. *Prove that addition of cardinal numbers is commutative and associative.*

Proposition 3. *For any cardinal numbers K, L we have $K \leq K + L$. Conversely, if $K \leq M$, there exists an L such that $M = K + L$.*

Proof: Let $A \in K$, $B \in L$, $A \cap B = \varnothing$; then $A \cup B \in K + L$, and I_A is a one-to-one correspondence of A with a subset of $A \cup B$, so that $K \leq K + L$. Conversely, let $S \in K$, $T \in M$; since $K \leq M$, we have $S \sim T'$ for some $T' \subseteq T$. Let $L = K(T - T')$; then since $T' \cap (T - T') = \varnothing$, we have $M = K(T) = K(T' \cup (T - T')) = K(T') + K(T - T') = K + L$. $\quad //$

Exercise 3. *If $K \leq L$ and $M \leq N$, then $K + M \leq L + N$.*

MULTIPLICATION

Proposition 4. *If $A \sim S$ and $B \sim T$, then $A \times B \sim S \times T$.*

Proof: This can be regarded as a special case of the corollary to Proposition 19.9. Or, directly: Let F, G be as in the proof of Proposition 1; then readily

$$\{((a, b), (F(a), G(b))) \mid (a, b) \in A \times B\}$$

is a one-to-one correspondence of $A \times B$ with $S \times T$. $\quad //$

Let $\mathscr{K}$ be any set of cardinal numbers; let K, L be in $\mathscr{K}$; and let $A \in K$, $B \in L$. By Proposition 4, $K(A \times B)$ does not depend on $\mathscr{K}$, A, or B, but only on K and L. Thus the relation $\{((K, L), K(A \times B)) \mid K, L \text{ in } \mathscr{K}; A \in K, B \in L\}$ is a function defined on $\mathscr{K} \times \mathscr{K}$. We denote $K(A \times B)$ by KL, and call it the **product** of K and L. The process of applying this function to a pair of cardinal numbers is called **multiplication.**

Examples:

(a) $K\{\varnothing\} = \{\varnothing\}$ for all K—in other words, $\{\varnothing\}$ is **absorbent** for multiplication of cardinal numbers.

(b) $K_r K_s = K_{rs}$ for all r, s in $\mathbf{N}$. [Proposition 5.8.]

(c) $K_m \aleph_0 = \aleph_0$ for all $m \in \mathbf{N}$. [Hint: $m\mathbf{N}$, $F^{-1}(m\mathbf{N})$, $F_2^{-1}(m\mathbf{N})$, ..., $F_{m-1}^{-1}(m\mathbf{N})$ are disjoint, each $\sim \mathbf{N}$, and their union is $\mathbf{N}$.]

Exercise 4. $\aleph_0 \aleph_0 = \aleph_0$. [Hint: Define the sequence $(a_i)_{\mathbf{N}}$ of elements of $\mathbf{N} \times \mathbf{N}$ by $a_1 = (1, 1)$; if $a_n = (r, s)$, then $a_{n+1} = (r + 1, s - 1)$ if $s \neq 1$, and $a_{n+1} = (1, r + 1)$ if $s = 1$. Use induction to prove that this sequence is onto—first prove that it contains all pairs of the form $(1, m)$—and apply Proposition 3.3.]

Exercise 5. *Prove that multiplication of cardinal numbers is commutative and associative, and that it distributes over addition.*

Exercise 6. *If $K \leq L$ and $M \leq N$, then $KM \leq LN$.*

Proposition 5. *Let $K(S) = K$ for each $S \in \mathscr{S}$, and let $K(\mathscr{S}) = L \neq \varnothing$; then $K(\bigcup_{\mathscr{S}} S) \leq KL$.*

Proof: Let $K(T) = K$; let F_S be a one-to-one correspondence of T with S; let F be the function from $T \times \mathscr{S}$ into $\bigcup_{\mathscr{S}} S$ which takes (t, S) into $F_S(t)$ for all $t \in T$. Clearly F is onto, so that $\bigcup_{\mathscr{S}} S$ is an image of $T \times \mathscr{S}$. $\parallel$

Corollary. *For any cardinal numbers K, L, where $L \neq \{\varnothing\}$, we have $K \leq KL$.*

Proof: $K = K(S) \leq K(\bigcup_{\mathscr{S}} S) \leq KL$. $\parallel$

Theorem 1. $KK = K$ *for any infinite cardinal number K.*

Proof: Let $S \in K$, and let $A \subseteq S$ be such that $K(A) = \aleph_0$. Let F_0 be a one-to-one correspondence of A with $A \times A$ (such exists by Exercise 4). Let $\mathscr{F} = \{F \mid A \subseteq d_F \subseteq S$, and F is a one-to-one correspondence of d_F with $d_F \times d_F\}$, where d_F is the domain of F. Since $\mathscr{F}$ contains F_0, it is nonempty. Let R be the relation on $\mathscr{F}$ consisting of the pairs (G, H) such that $d_G \subseteq d_H$ and G is the restriction of H to d_G. Readily, as in the proof of Theorem 20.2, R is an order relation, and $\mathscr{F}$ ordered by R is inductive. Thus by Zorn's lemma, there is a maximal F^* in $\mathscr{F}$; denote d_{F^*} by B.

If $K(B) = K$, we are done, since F^* is a one-to-one correspondence of B with $B \times B$. Otherwise, let $K(B) = L < K$; we thus have $LL = L$. Now by Propositions 3, 5 and Exercise 6,

$$L \leq L + L \leq L + L + L \leq K_3 L \leq LL,$$

and since $L = LL$, all of these cardinal numbers must be equal. Suppose that $K(S - B) \leq L$; then we would have $K = K(S) = K(B) + K(S - B) \leq L + L = L < K$, contradiction. Hence $K(S - B) > L$; let $T \subset S - B$ be such that $K(T) = L$.

Now $(B \cup T) \times (B \cup T) = (B \times B) \cup (B \times T) \cup (T \times B) \cup (T \times T)$, where the sets in the right member are disjoint, and each evidently has cardinality L. Since $L + L + L = L$, there exists a one-to-one correspondence F^{**} of T with $(B \times T) \cup (T \times B) \cup (T \times T)$. Hence $F^* \cup F^{**}$ is a one-to-one correspondence of $B \cup T$ with $(B \times B) \cup [(B \times T) \cup (T \times B) \cup (T \times T)] = (B \cup T) \times (B \cup T)$. Since $B \cup T \supset B$, this contradicts the maximality of F^*. $\parallel$

Corollary. *If K is infinite and $\{\varnothing\} < L \leq K$, then $K + L = KL = K$.*

Proof: $K \leq K + L \leq K + K \leq K_2 K \leq KK = K$; $K \leq KL \leq KK = K$. $\parallel$

EXPONENTIATION

Proposition 6. *If $A \sim B$ and $I \sim J$, then $A^I \sim B^J$.*

Proof: The corollary to Proposition 19.9; or, directly, if G, H are one-to-one correspondences of A with B and I with J, respectively, then $\{(F, H^{-1} \circ F \circ G) \mid F \in A^I\}$ is readily a one-to-one correspondence of A^I with B^J. $\parallel$

Let $\mathscr{K}$ be any set of cardinal numbers; let K, L be in $\mathscr{K}$, $A \in K$, $I \in L$. By Proposition 6, $K(A^I)$ does not depend on $\mathscr{K}$, A, or I, but only on K and L. Thus the relation $\{((K, L), K(A^I)) \mid K, L \text{ in } \mathscr{K}; A \in K, I \in L\}$ is a function defined on $\mathscr{K} \times \mathscr{K}$. We denote $K(A^I)$ by K^L, and call the process of applying this function to a pair of cardinal numbers **exponentiation**.

Examples:

(a) $\{\varnothing\}^K = \{\varnothing\}$ for all $K \neq \{\varnothing\}$; $K^{\{\varnothing\}} = K_1$ for all K.

(b) $K^{K_1} = K$ and $K_1^K = K_1$ for all K—in other words, K_1 is a **right identity** and **left absorbent** for exponentiation of cardinal numbers. Note that by Example (a), $\{\varnothing\}$ is also left absorbent.

(c) $K_r^{K_s} = K_{r^s}$ for all r, s in $\mathbf{N}$.

(d) $K(S)^{K_n} = K(S^n)$ for all S and all $n \in \mathbf{N}$.

Exercise 7. $K^{K_n} = K$ for all infinite K and all $n \in \mathbf{N}$. [Hint: Theorem 1 and induction.]

Exercise 8. $K < K_2^K$ for all K. [Hint: Use the proof of Proposition 5.11 to show that $K_2^K = K(\mathscr{P}_S)$ for any $S \in K$.]

Exercise 9. Generalize the laws of exponents (Exercise 5.8 (b–d)) to cardinal numbers.

Proposition 7. Let S be infinite, and let S_n be the set of n-element subsets of S; then $K(S_n) = K(S)$ for all $n \in \mathbf{N}$.

Proof: Readily $K(S) \leq K(S_n)$ (prove it!). On the other hand, let $S^{(n)}$ be the set of one-to-one functions from $\mathbf{N}_n$ into S. (These functions can be thought of as n-tuples whose terms are all distinct.) Since $S^{(n)} \subseteq S^n$, we have $K(S^{(n)}) \leq K(S^n) = K(S)^{K_n} = K(S)$ (Exercise 7). But evidently

$$\{((a_1, \ldots, a_n), \{a_1, \ldots, a_n\}) \mid (a_1, \ldots, a_n) \in S^{(n)}\}$$

is a function from $S^{(n)}$ onto S_n, so that $K(S_n) \leq K(S^{(n)})$. $/\!/$

Proposition 8. Let S be infinite, and let S^* be the set of finite subsets of S; then $K(S^*) = K(S)$.

Proof: Clearly $K(S) = K(S_1) \leq K(S^*)$. On the other hand, $S^* = \bigcup_\mathbf{N} S_n$, so that by Propositions 5 and 7 we have $K(S^*) \leq \aleph_0 K(S) \leq K(S)K(S)$ (Exercise 6) $= K(S)$ (Theorem 1). $/\!/$

V

GROUPOIDS

We are now ready to begin the study of algebra proper. In this chapter we consider the simplest possible kind of algebraic structure—a set on which a single "composition" is defined, with no special assumptions whatsoever about the composition. Such a set is called a *groupoid*. In Chapters VI ff. we will study the consequences of requiring the composition to satisfy various conditions, for example, those making the groupoid a semigroup or a group.

22. COMPOSITIONS

Let S be a set; a function F from $S \times S$ into S is called a **composition** on S. [We abbreviate $F((x, y))$ by $F(x, y)$, where $(x, y) \in S \times S$.]

Examples:

(a) $S = \mathscr{P}_{A \times A}$ is the set of relations on the set A; $F(Q, R) = Q \circ R$.

(b) $S = A^A$ is the set of functions from the set A into itself; F is the same as in Example (a).

(c) S is any lattice; $F(x, y) = x \vee y$. In particular:

    (1) $S = \mathscr{P}_A$, where A is any set; $F(B, C) = B \cup C$

    (2) $S = \mathbf{N}$; $F(m, n) =$ the greater of m and n

    (3) $S = \mathbf{N}$; $F(m, n) =$ the least common multiple of m and n

    —or the analogous examples using $\wedge$ in place of $\vee$.

(d) $S = \mathscr{P}_A$, where A is any set; $F(B, C) = B - C$.

(e) $S = \mathbf{N}$; $F(m, n) = m + n$, mn, or m^n—or analogously, if S is the set of finite cardinal numbers.

(f) S is the set of cardinal numbers $\leq K$, where K is infinite; $F(L, M) = L + M$ or LM [corollary to Theorem 21.1 and Exercises 21.3, 6].

(g) Let S be any set and F any composition on S; let $\bar{F}$ be the function from

$\mathscr{P}_S \times \mathscr{P}_S$ into $\mathscr{P}_S$ defined by $\bar{F}(A, B) = \{F(a, b) \mid a \in A, b \in B\}$, where A, B are subsets of S. Then $\bar{F}$ is a composition on $\mathscr{P}_S$. [Note that $\bar{F}$ is just the restriction of $\tilde{F}$ to the set of subsets of $S \times S$ which are of the form $A \times B$, where $A \subseteq S, B \subseteq S$. In particular, we have $\bar{F}(A, \varnothing)$ $= \bar{F}(\varnothing, B) = \varnothing$; $\bar{F}(\{a\}, \{b\}) = \tilde{F}(\{a\}, \{b\}) = \{F(a, b)\}$.]

Three remarks about this concept of a composition:

(1) We are considering here only *binary* compositions, which take *pairs* of elements (of S) into elements. One could also consider ternary compositions (taking triples of elements into elements), or even n-ary compositions; we shall make this generalization in Chapter X.

(2) There are other types of "compositions" which involve *two* sets; one important class of such compositions will be introduced in Chapter XI.

(3) "Compositions" which are defined only on a subset of $S \times S$—for example, subtraction and division of natural numbers—are also sometimes studied, but we shall not do so on any general level in this book.

As most of the examples given above suggest, it is customary to use a compact notation for the function values of a composition—"$Q \circ R$" rather than $\circ (Q, R)$, "$m + n$" rather than $+(m, n)$, and so on. In fact, it is customary to use the notation for addition or multiplication to represent the values of an arbitrary composition. Thus, if we wish to denote the composition F "multiplicatively," we write simply xy instead of $F(x, y)$, relying on the context to make it clear that F, not multiplication, is meant. Similarly, we can denote F "additively" by writing $x + y$ instead of $F(x, y)$. *From now on we will usually denote compositions multiplicatively.* [In Chapter X ff., when we study two compositions on the same set, we will denote one of them additively and the other multiplicatively.] If F is denoted multiplicatively, we will also denote $\bar{F}$ multiplicatively, writing AB instead of $\bar{F}(A, B)$; we abbreviate $\{x\}A$ by xA, and $A\{x\}$ by Ax.

A composition F on a finite set can be represented by a *composition table*, analogous to the familiar multiplication table, in which the entry in the row headed by x and column headed by y is $F(x, y)$. For example, the following is a composition table for the union composition on the set of subsets of $S = \{a, b\}$:

$\cup$	$\varnothing$	$\{a\}$	$\{b\}$	S
$\varnothing$	$\varnothing$	$\{a\}$	$\{b\}$	S
$\{a\}$	$\{a\}$	$\{a\}$	S	S
$\{b\}$	$\{b\}$	S	$\{b\}$	S
S	S	S	S	S

If F is a composition on the set S, we say that S is a **groupoid** under F.

More formally, a groupoid is a *pair* (S, F), where F is a composition on S; we say that S is the *underlying set* of the groupoid, and F is the groupoid composition. Note that a given set can be the underlying set of many different groupoids (as in Examples (c1), its "dual," and (d); Examples (c2–3) and (e)).

Exercise 1. *If $S = \varnothing$ or $S = \{x\}$, there is exactly one composition on S. How many compositions are there on a set with two elements? with n elements?*

A groupoid with only one element is called **trivial**.

23. SUBGROUPOIDS

Let S be a groupoid under F, and let A be a subset of S. We say that A is **stable** (or "closed") under F if $x \in A$, $y \in A$ imply $xy \in A$ [or, more concisely: if $AA \subseteq A$]. Trivially, $\varnothing$ and S are stable under any F. Some other examples:

(a) As Examples (a–b) of compositions show, A^A is a stable subset of the groupoid $\mathscr{P}_{A \times A}$ under $\circ$. Other stable subsets of this groupoid include
  (1) The set of one-to-one functions from A into A
  (2) The set of functions from A onto A
  (3) The set of $G \in A^A$ such that $G(B) \subseteq B$ for some given $B \subseteq A$
  (4) The set of $G \in A^A$ such that $G(b) = b$ for all b in some given $B \subseteq A$.
(b) Any sublattice of a lattice is stable under $\vee$ and $\wedge$.
(c) $m + \mathbf{N}$ (that is, $F_m(\mathbf{N})$) and $m\mathbf{N}$, for any $m \in \mathbf{N}$, are stable under addition, multiplication, and exponentiation.
(d) $A \subseteq S$ is stable under F if and only if $\mathscr{P}_A \subseteq \mathscr{P}_S$ is stable under $\bar{F}$—in other words, if and only if $B \subseteq A$, $C \subseteq A$ imply $BC \subseteq A$.

Exercise 1. $\{x\}$ *is stable if and only if $xx = x$.* [If $xx = x$, we call x **idempotent** ("with respect to F" understood). Thus the sole element of a trivial groupoid is idempotent.]

If $S' \subseteq S$ is stable under F, the restriction of F to $S' \times S'$ is a function from $S' \times S'$ into S' (and not merely into S). Thus this restriction, call it F', is a composition on S', so that S' is a groupoid under F'. Such a groupoid is called a **subgroupoid** of S.

Evidently, for a subset S'' of S', stability under F' is equivalent to stability under F; and a restriction of F' is of course also a restriction of F. Thus a subgroupoid of a subgroupoid of S is a subgroupoid of S. In fact, the subgroupoids of any given subgroupoid S' are the same as the subgroupoids of S which are contained in S'.

Proposition 1. *Any intersection of subgroupoids is a subgroupoid.*

Proof: If $\mathscr{A}$ is a set of subgroupoids, and x, y are in $\bigcap_{\mathscr{A}} A$, then x, y are in each $A \in \mathscr{A}$, so that xy is in each $A \in \mathscr{A}$ and hence in their intersection. $\parallel$

Corollary. *The set of subgroupoids of any groupoid S, ordered by inclusion, is a complete lattice with least element $\varnothing$ and greatest element S.*

We shall denote the lattice of subgroupoids of S by $\mathscr{S}_S$.

If A, B are subgroupoids of S, their inf in $\mathscr{S}_S$ is of course their intersection, while (as in the proof of Proposition 16.1) their sup is the intersection of all the subgroupoids of S which contain their union. [Note that since, in general, the sup is not the union itself, $\mathscr{S}_S$ is not necessarily a sublattice of $\mathscr{P}_S$.] More generally, if T is any subset of S, the subgroupoid (T) generated by T is the intersection of all subgroupoids of S which contain T. A more "constructive" description of (T) is provided by

Proposition 2. *Let T be a subset of the groupoid S, and define the sequence $(T_i)_N$ of subsets of S by $T_1 = T$; $T_{n+1} = \bigcup_{k=1}^{n} T_k T_{n-k+1}$. Then $(T) = \bigcup_N T_n$.*

An element of T_n can be thought of as a "composite" of n elements of T (not necessarily distinct), grouped arbitrarily by parentheses so that the composition is applied only to a pair of them at a time.

Proof: If x, y are in $\bigcup_N T_n$, say $x \in T_r$, $y \in T_s$, then evidently $xy \in T_{r+s}$, so that $\bigcup_N T_n$ is a subgroupoid. Since $T = T_1 \subseteq \bigcup_N T_n$, it remains only to show that any subgroupoid A which contains T must contain $\bigcup_N T_n$. But indeed, A contains T_1, and if it contains $T_1, \ldots, T_m$, we have $T_k T_{m-k+1} \subseteq A$ for each $k \in N_m$, so that their union T_{m+1} is also contained in A. It follows by induction that A contains every T_n, and so contains their union. $\parallel$

Exercise 2. *The subset A of the groupoid S is called a* **left ideal** *if $SA \subseteq A$ (that is, $x \in S$, $a \in A$ imply $xa \in A$); a* **right ideal**, *if $AS \subseteq A$; and a* **two-sided ideal** *(or simply an* **ideal**), *if it is both a left and a right ideal. Verify that*

(a) *$\varnothing$ and S are two-sided ideals*

(b) *A left or right ideal is a subgroupoid*

(c) *If A is a right ideal and B a left ideal, then $AB \subseteq A \cap B$*

(d) *Any union or intersection of left ideals is a left ideal, and similarly for right ideals.*

Corollary. *The set of left (or right, or two-sided) ideals of S, ordered by inclusion, is a complete lattice, in which the inf is the intersection and the sup is the union, the least element is $\varnothing$ and the greatest element is S. [Thus each of these lattices is a sublattice of $\mathscr{P}_S$ and of $\mathscr{S}_S$.]*

Exercise 3. *In $\mathscr{S}_S$, the sup of any chain is its union.*

24. HOMOMORPHISMS

In studying ordered sets we found it useful to introduce the concepts of an order preserving function and an order isomorphism. In this section we define analogous concepts for groupoids.

Let S, T be groupoids under the compositions F, G, both denoted multiplicatively. A function H from S into T is called a **homomorphism** if $H(xy) = H(x)H(y)$ for all x, y in S.

> Note that this can be restated as "$z = xy$ implies $H(z) = H(x)H(y)$," which closely parallels the definition of an order-preserving function. Note also that if we let H_2 be the function from $S \times S$ into $T \times T$ defined by $H_2(x, y) = (H(x), H(y))$, then H is a homomorphism if and only if $F \circ H = H_2 \circ G$. Strictly speaking, we should call H a homomorphism "with respect to F and G" (for short: an (F, G)-homomorphism), but we shall not do so unless there is danger of confusion as to which compositions are intended.

A homomorphism which is one-to-one is called an **isomorphism**. If H is an isomorphism defined on S, we say that S and $H(S)$ are **isomorphic** [notation: $S \cong H(S)$].

> Note that in the case of an *order* isomorphism it was not enough to assume that F was order preserving and one-to-one, because this did not guarantee that F^{-1} would be order preserving. Here, however, the inverse of an isomorphism *is* automatically "composition preserving" (Proposition 2 below). A homomorphism onto is sometimes called an **epimorphism**, and a one-to-one homomorphism a **monomorphism**, with the term "isomorphism" reserved for a homomorphism which is both one-to-one and onto.

Examples:
(a) Let S, T be lattices; then an order isomorphism of S with T is an isomorphism with respect to the sup (or inf) compositions on S and T. [Is an order-preserving function a homomorphism?]
(b') For any $k \in \mathbf{N}$, define the function G_k, from $\mathbf{N}$ into itself, by $G_k(n) = kn$; then G_k is a homomorphism of the groupoid $\mathbf{N}$ under addition into itself. Analogously for $G_k(n) = n^k$ and $\mathbf{N}$ under multiplication.

(b″) Similarly, define the function H_k, from $\mathbf{N}$ into itself, by $H_k(n) = k^n$; then H_k is a homomorphism of the groupoid $\mathbf{N}$ under addition into the groupoid $\mathbf{N}$ under multiplication.

(c) $\mathbf{N}°$ under addition is isomorphic to the groupoid of finite cardinal numbers under addition; analogously for multiplication and exponentiation.

(d) Let S, T be groupoids, and let H be a homomorphism of S into T; then $\tilde{H}$ is a homomorphism of $\mathscr{P}_S$ into $\mathscr{P}_T$ (with respect to the compositions of Example (g), Section 22).

(e) The identity function is an isomorphism of any groupoid onto itself. More generally, let S be any groupoid and S' any subgroupoid of S; then the embedding of S' in S is an isomorphism of S' into S.

(f) If H is a homomorphism of S into T, and S' is any subgroupoid of S, then the restriction of H to S' is a homomorphism of S' into T.

(g) Let S, T be groupoids, and let x be an idempotent element of T (Exercise 23.1); then the constant function which takes every element of S into x is a homomorphism of S into T (and onto its subgroupoid $\{x\}$).

A homomorphism of a groupoid into itself is called an **endomorphism**; an isomorphism of a groupoid onto itself is called an **automorphism**. Thus the identity function (Example (e)) is an automorphism, and G_k (Examples (b′)) is an endomorphism. Note that H_k (Example (b″)) is not an endomorphism, since the groupoids $(\mathbf{N}, +)$ and $(\mathbf{N}, \cdot)$ are different.

Proposition 1. *A composite of homomorphisms is a homomorphism.*

Proof: $G(F(xy)) = G(F(x)F(y)) = G(F(x))G(F(y))$. $\parallel$

Corollary 1. *If F and G are both homomorphisms onto, or both isomorphisms, so is $F \circ G$.*

If F is a homomorphism defined on S, we call $F(S)$ a *homomorphic image* of S. Thus by Corollary 1, a homomorphic image of a homomorphic image of S is a homomorphic image of S.

Corollary 2. *The set of endomorphisms $E(S)$ of any groupoid S is a groupoid under $\circ$, and the set $A(S)$ of automorphisms of S is a subgroupoid of $E(S)$.*

Proposition 2. *The inverse of an isomorphism is an isomorphism.*

Proof: $F[F^{-1}(uv)] = uv = F(F^{-1}(u))F(F^{-1}(v)) = F[F^{-1}(u)F^{-1}(v)]$; since F is one-to-one, the expressions in brackets must be equal, so that F^{-1} is a homomorphism. $\parallel$

Corollary. *"Isomorphic" is an equivalence—that is, if $\mathscr{S}$ is any set of groupoids, then $\{(S, T) \mid S, T \text{ in } \mathscr{S}; S \cong T\}$ is an equivalence on $\mathscr{S}$.*

Proof: It is reflexive by Example (e), symmetric by Proposition 2, and transitive by Corollary 1 to Proposition 1.   //

Exercise 1. *Any two trivial groupoids (=groupoids with only one element) are isomorphic.*

Proposition 3. *A homomorphic image or preimage of a subgroupoid is a subgroupoid.*

Proof: Let F be a homomorphism of S into T, and let A be a subgroupoid of S. Then for all $u = F(x)$, $v = F(y)$ in $F(A)$ we have $uv = F(x)F(y) = F(xy)$ in $F(A)$, so that $F(A)$ is a subgroupoid of T. Similarly, let B be a subgroupoid of T; then for all x, y in $F^{-1}(B)$ we have $F(xy) = F(x)F(y)$ in B since each factor is, so that xy is in $F^{-1}(B)$, proving that $F^{-1}(B)$ is a subgroupoid of S.   //

Proposition 4. *A homomorphic image of a set of generators is a set of generators.*

Proof: Let S be a groupoid, F a homomorphism defined on S, and A a subset of S; we want to prove that $F(A)$ generates $F((A))$, that is, $(F(A)) = F((A))$. But indeed, since $F((A))$ is a groupoid and contains $F(A)$, it must contain $(F(A))$. Conversely, it is not difficult to prove by induction that any element of $F(A_n)$ (Proposition 23.2) must be in $F(A)_n$, so that $(F(A)) = F(\bigcup_N A_n) = \bigcup_N F(A)_n \subseteq \bigcup_N F(A)_n = (F(A))$.   //

25. CONGRUENCES AND QUOTIENT GROUPOIDS

Let S be a groupoid under the composition F, denoted multiplicatively, and let E be an equivalence on S. We say that E is a **congruence** for F if $(a, c) \in E$ and $(b, d) \in E$ imply $(ab, cd) \in E$ for all a, b, c, d in S. The equivalence classes of a congruence are called **congruence classes.**

> Note that the definition of homomorphism can analogously be written as "$(a, c) \in H$ and $(b, d) \in H$ imply $(ab, cd) \in H$." We shall study the relationship between homomorphisms and congruences in the next section.

Examples:
  (a) The equivalences I_S and $S \times S$ are congruences for any composition on S.
  (b) If E is a congruence on the groupoid S, and A is a subgroupoid of S, then the restriction of E to A is a congruence on A ("for the restriction composition" understood).
  (c) "Congruence modulo d" (Example (d), Section 17) is a congruence on $\mathbf{N}$ for both addition and multiplication.

Exercise 1. *The equivalence E on S is a congruence if and only if $(a, b) \in E$ implies $(ac, bc) \in E$ and $(ca, cb) \in E$ for all a, b, c in S.*

Exercise 2. *If D, E are congruences on S, so is $D \circ E$, provided it is an equivalence.*

> Just as there is a natural way of defining a composition on a subset $A \subseteq S$ if A is stable, so there is a natural way of defining a composition on a quotient set S/E if E is a congruence:

Given a congruence E on S, we can define a composition F/E on the quotient set S/E as follows. If A, B are elements of S/E, let $a \in A$, $b \in B$, and define $(F/E)(A, B)$ to be the unique element of S/E which contains ab. It is easily verified that since E is a congruence, $(F/E)(A, B)$ does not depend on which a, b we use, so that F/E is indeed a function from $(S/E) \times (S/E)$ into S/E. We call F/E the **quotient** of F by E; and we call the groupoid S/E (under F/E) a **quotient groupoid** of S. Note that $AB \subseteq (F/E)(A, B)$ for all A, B in S/E.

Exercise 3. $S/(S \times S)$ *is trivial;* $S/I_S \cong S$.

Proposition 1. *The set $\mathscr{C}_S$ of congruences on the groupoid S, ordered by inclusion, is a complete lattice with least element I_S and greatest element $S \times S$.*

Proof: Clearly any intersection of congruences is a congruence. //

Exercise 4. *In $\mathscr{C}_S$, the sup of any chain is its union.*

Proposition 2. *Let D, E be congruences on the groupoid S; then the following statements are equivalent:*

(1) $D \circ E$ *is the sup of D and E in $\mathscr{C}_S$*
(2) $D \circ E$ *is a congruence*
(3) $D \circ E$ *is an equivalence*
(4) $D \circ E$ *is symmetric*
(5) $D \circ E = E \circ D$ *("D and E commute").*

Proof: Exercise 2 and Proposition 17.5. //

Theorem 1. *Let S be a groupoid such that all congruences on S commute; then $\mathscr{C}_S$ is modular.*

Proof: By Proposition 2, the sup in $\mathscr{C}_S$ is the composite. Thus to prove modularity, we must show that for all P, Q, R in $\mathscr{C}_S$ such that $P \subseteq R$, we have $(P \circ Q) \cap R \subseteq P \circ (Q \cap R)$. But indeed, let (x, y) be in $(P \circ Q) \cap R$; then $(x, y) \in R$, and there exists $z \in S$ such that $(x, z) \in P \subseteq R$ and $(z, y) \in Q$. Now $(x, y) \in R$ and $(x, z) \in R$ imply $(z, y) \in R$; thus $(z, y) \in Q \cap R$, and from this together with $(x, z) \in P$ we have $(x, y) \in P \circ (Q \cap R)$. //

> By Exercise 17.13, the equivalences on a set cannot all commute if the set has more than two elements; but it

can well happen that the congruences on a groupoid all commute—in fact, as we shall see in Chapter VII, this is always true if the groupoid is a group. Thus Theorem 1 can hold under nontrivial circumstances.

26. CONGRUENCES AND CANONICAL HOMOMORPHISMS

The relationships between functions and equivalences described in Section 18 all continue to hold if we replace "set" by "groupoid," "function" by "homomorphism," and "equivalence" by "congruence." The basis for this correspondence is established by Propositions 1, 2, and 6 below. The remaining results of this section follow immediately from their counterparts in Section 18 (one need only verify in each case that a function has the homomorphism property, or an equivalence has the congruence property, as appropriate); the proofs are left to the reader.

Proposition 1. Let E be a congruence on the groupoid S; then the canonical function F_E is a homomorphism of S onto S/E.

Proof: The fact that F_E is a homomorphism is an immediate consequence of the definition of the quotient composition. $\parallel$

We call F_E the **canonical homomorphism** of E.

Proposition 2. Let F be a homomorphism defined on the groupoid S; then $E_F = F \circ F^{-1}$ is a congruence on S.

Proof: $(a, c) \in E_F$, $(b, d) \in E_F$ imply $F(a) = F(c)$, $F(b) = F(d)$, so that $F(a)F(b) = F(c)F(d)$. Since F is a homomorphism, this implies $F(ab) = F(cd)$, so that $(ab, cd) \in E_F$, making E_F a congruence. $\parallel$

As in Exercise 18.1, the homomorphism F is an isomorphism if and only if $E_F = I_S$. As in the corollary to Proposition 18.2, every congruence is defined by its canonical homomorphism, and no two congruences can have the same canonical homomorphism.

Proposition 3. Let F, G be homomorphisms defined on the groupoid S such that $E_F \subseteq E_G$; then $F^{-1} \circ G$ is a homomorphism of $F(S)$ onto $G(S)$.

Corollary. If E is a congruence on S, and G a homomorphism defined on S such that $E \subseteq E_G$, then $F_E^{-1} \circ G$ is a homomorphism of S/E onto $G(S)$.

Theorem 1. If F is a homomorphism defined on S, then $F_{(E_F)}^{-1} \circ F$ is an isomorphism of S/E_F with $F(S)$.

Proposition 1 and Theorem 1 can be summarized as follows: Every quotient groupoid is a homomorphic image, and every homomorphic image is isomorphic to a quotient groupoid.

Corollary 1. *Any homomorphism is the composite of an onto homomorphism and an onto isomorphism.*

Corollary 2. *Let F be a homomorphism defined on S, and A a subgroupoid of S. Let F' be the restriction of F to A, and E'_F the restriction of E_F to A. Then $F^{-1}_{(E'_F)} \circ F'$ is an isomorphism of A/E'_F with $F(A)$.*

Corollary 3. *Let E be a congruence on S, and A a subgroupoid of S. Let E' be the restriction of E to A, and F'_E the restriction of F_E to A. Then $F_{E'}^{-1} \circ F'_E$ is an isomorphism of A/E' with $F_E(A)$.*

Proposition 4. *Let F be a homomorphism defined on S, and E a congruence on S such that E and E_F commute; then $F^{-1} \circ E \circ F$ is a congruence on $F(S)$. In particular, it is a congruence if $E \subseteq E_F$, or if F is an isomorphism.*

Proposition 5. *Let F be a homomorphism defined on S, and E any congruence on $F(S)$; then $F \circ E \circ F^{-1}$ is a congruence on S and contains E_F.*

Let $\mathscr{C}_{S,E_F}$ be the lattice of congruences on S which contain E_F.

Theorem 2. *Let F be any homomorphism defined on S; then*

$$\{(E, F^{-1} \circ E \circ F) \mid E \in \mathscr{C}_{S,E_F}\}$$

is an order isomorphism of $\mathscr{C}_{S,E_F}$ with $\mathscr{C}_{F(S)}$.

Corollary 1. *Let D be any congruence on S; then*

$$\{(E, F_D^{-1} \circ E \circ F_D) \mid E \in \mathscr{C}_{S,D}\}$$

is an order isomorphism of $\mathscr{C}_{S,D}$ with $\mathscr{C}_{S/D}$.

Corollary 2. *Isomorphic groupoids have order isomorphic congruence lattices.*

Theorem 3. *Let F be a homomorphism defined on S, and E a congruence on S which commutes with E_F; then $\tilde{F}$ restricted to S/E is an isomorphism of S/E with $F(S)/F^{-1} \circ E \circ F$.*

Corollary 1. *Let D, E be congruences on S which commute; then $\tilde{F}_D$ restricted to S/E is an isomorphism of S/E with $(S/D)/F_D^{-1} \circ E \circ F_D$.*

Corollary 2. *A quotient groupoid of a quotient groupoid of S is isomorphic to a quotient groupoid of S itself.*

In summary:

(1) The lattice of congruences on any homomorphic image $F(S)$ is order isomorphic to the lattice of congruences on S which contain E_F.

98 V: GROUPOIDS

(2) Congruences which correspond under (1) have isomorphic quotient groupoids.

Proposition 6. *Let E be a congruence on the groupoid S, and A a subgroupoid of S; then EA is a subgroupoid of S.*

Proof: Let x, y be in EA, say $(x, a) \in E$, $(y, b) \in E$, where a, b are in A. Then $(xy, ab) \in E$, where $ab \in A$ since A is a subgroupoid, so that $xy \in EA$. ∥

Corresponding to Corollary 4 to Proposition 18.8 we have

Theorem 4. *Let E be a congruence on S, and A a subgroupoid of S; then $A/E \cap (A \times A) \cong EA/E \cap (EA \times EA)$.*

Let $\mathscr{S}_S^{(E)}$ be the lattice of E-invariant subgroupoids of S.

Theorem 5. *Let F be a homomorphism defined on S; then the restriction of $\tilde{F}$ to $\mathscr{S}_S^{(E_F)}$ is an order isomorphism of $\mathscr{S}_S^{(E_F)}$ with $\mathscr{S}_{F(S)}$.*

In words: The lattice of subgroupoids of any homomorphic image $F(S)$ is order isomorphic to the lattice of E_F-invariant subgroupoids of S.

Corollary 1. *Let E be a congruence on S; then the restriction of $\tilde{F}_E$ to $\mathscr{S}_S^{(E)}$ is an order isomorphism of $\mathscr{S}_S^{(E)}$ with $\mathscr{S}_{S/E}$.*

Corollary 2. *Isomorphic groupoids have order isomorphic subgroupoid lattices.*

27. NORMAL SUBSETS†

Let S be a groupoid, A a subset of S. There always exist congruences E on S such that A is contained in an E-class; for example, $A \subseteq S$, which is the sole $S \times S$-class.

Proposition 1. *For any $A \subseteq S$ there exists a smallest congruence E_A on S such that A is contained in an E_A-class.*

Proof: The set of such congruences is readily closed under intersection; the intersection of all of them is the smallest one. ∥

Clearly $A \subseteq B$ implies $E_A \subseteq E_B$, so that $E_{A \cap B} \subseteq E_A \cap E_B$; and $E_\varnothing = I_S = E_{\{x\}}$ for all $x \in S$.

We call A **normal** if $A = \varnothing$ or if there exists a congruence E on S such that A is an E-class. For example, S itself is normal, since it is an $S \times S$-class, and $\{x\}$ is normal for any $x \in S$, since it is an I_S-class.

† Concepts analogous to those in this section could be formulated for any set S, using equivalences instead of congruences. However, they would be trivial, since any nonempty $A \subseteq S$ is an equivalence class (Exercise 17.10).

Exercise 1. *A is normal if and only if it is E-invariant and contained in an E-class for some congruence E on S.*

Proposition 2. *The following statements about the nonempty subset A of the groupoid S are equivalent:*

(1) *A is normal*
(2) *A is an E_A-class*
(3) *A is E_A-invariant.*

Proof: If A is normal, let A be an E-class and let $a \in A$, so that $A = E_a$. Then $A \subseteq (E_A)_a \subseteq E_a = A$, so that $A = (E_A)_a$ is an E_A-class. For the rest of the proof, use Exercise 1. $\quad \parallel$

Corollary. *If $A \neq \varnothing$ is normal, there exists a smallest congruence E_A on S such that A is an E_A-class.*

Exercise 2. *Prove that the set of congruences E on S such that A is an E-class, ordered by inclusion, is inductive if it is nonempty.*

Corollary. *If $A \neq \varnothing$ is normal, there exists a maximal congruence on S of which A is a class.*

Exercise 3. *If A is a D-class and an E-class, and $D \circ E$ is a congruence, then A is a $D \circ E$-class.*

Corollary. *If $A \neq \varnothing$ is normal, and all congruences on S commute, there is a greatest congruence on S of which A is a class.*

Proposition 3. *Any intersection of normal subsets is normal.*

Proof: Let $\mathscr{A}$ be a set of normal subsets, and let $A^* = \bigcap_{\mathscr{A}} A$. If $A^* = \varnothing$, there is nothing to prove. If not, let $x \in A^*$, so that x is in each $A \in \mathscr{A}$, and $A = (E_A)_x$ for each $A \in \mathscr{A}$. Thus $A^* = \bigcap_{\mathscr{A}} (E_A)_x = (\bigcap_{\mathscr{A}} E_A)_x$ is an $\bigcap_{\mathscr{A}} E_A$-class. $\quad \parallel$

Corollary. *The set of normal subsets of S, ordered by inclusion, is a complete lattice $\mathscr{M}_S$ with least element $\varnothing$ and greatest element S.*

Let D be any congruence on S; readily, the set of normal subsets of S which are either empty or E-classes for some $E \supseteq D$ is a sublattice of $\mathscr{M}_S$, call it $\mathscr{M}_{S,D}$.

Theorem 1. *Let F be a homomorphism defined on the groupoid S; then the restriction of $\tilde{F}$ to $\mathscr{M}_{S,E_F}$ is an order isomorphism of $\mathscr{M}_{S,E_F}$ with $\mathscr{M}_{F(S)}$.*

Proof: Clearly $A = \varnothing$ if and only if $F(A) = \varnothing$; for the rest of the proof, use Theorems 26.2–3. $\quad \parallel$

Corollary 1. *An isomorphism takes normal subsets into normal subsets.*

Corollary 2. *Isomorphic groupoids have order isomorphic lattices of normal subsets.*

Our next goal is to show, in analogy with Theorem 25.1, that if the congruences on S commute, the lattice $\mathcal{M}_S$ is "almost modular."

Proposition 4. *Let A be an E-class, and let D commute with E; then DA is a $D \circ E$-class.*

Proof: $D \circ E$ is a congruence, and $(D \circ E)(DA) = (D \circ E \circ D)A = (D \circ E)A = D(EA) = DA$, so that DA is $D \circ E$-invariant. On the other hand, let x, y be in DA, say $(x, a) \in D$, $(y, b) \in D$, where a, b are in A. Thus $(a, b) \in E$, so that (x, y) is in $D \circ E \circ D = D \circ E$, proving that DA is contained in a $D \circ E$-class.   //

Corollary. *Let A be a D-class and B an E-class, where D and E commute, and let $A \cap B \neq \varnothing$; then $EA = DB$.*

Proof: $EA = DB = $ the $D \circ E$-class containing $A \cap B$.   //

Proposition 5. *Let A, B be normal, $A \cap B \neq \varnothing$, and let E_A and E_B commute. Then $E_A B = E_B A$ is normal, and is the sup of A and B in $\mathcal{M}_S$.*

Proof: Since A is an E_A-class and B an E_B-class, by Proposition 4 and its corollary, $E_A B = E_B A$ is an $E_A \circ E_B$-class. Let C be any normal subset which contains A and B; then A and B are each contained in the E_C-class C, so that $E_A \subseteq E_C$ and we have $E_A B \subseteq E_C B \subseteq E_C C = C$.   //

Exercise 4. *In Proposition 5, $E_{(E_A B)} = E_A \circ E_B$.*

Theorem 2. *Let S be a groupoid on which all congruences commute; let A, B, C be normal subsets of S such that $A \subseteq C$ and $A \cap B \neq \varnothing$. Then A, B, C satisfy the modularity law—in other words, $A \vee (B \cap C) = (A \vee B) \cap C$ in $\mathcal{M}_S$.*

Proof: By Proposition 5, $A \vee B = E_A B$ and $A \vee (B \cap C) = E_A(B \cap C)$; thus we must show that $(E_A B) \cap C \subseteq E_A(B \cap C)$. Let $x \in (E_A B) \cap C$, say $(x, b) \in E_A$, where $b \in B$. Then $(x, b) \in E_A \subseteq E_C$, while $x \in C$, which is a C-class, so that $b \in C$, that is, $b \in B \cap C$, proving $x \in E_A(B \cap C)$.   //

By Theorem 2, the results of Section 14 about chains in a modular lattice can be applied to chains of nonempty normal subsets. In the next section we shall prove further results of a more "algebraic" nature, using the concepts which we now introduce.

Let S be a groupoid, V a subgroupoid of S, and U a normal subset of V (briefly: U is normal in V). If U is an E-class, where E is a congruence on V, we call the quotient groupoid V/E a **quotient** of $[U, V]$. Note that there may be many E's on V such that U is an E-class, so that $[U, V]$ may have many different quotients.

Proposition 6. *Let U be normal in V, and let W be any subgroupoid of S; then $U \cap W$ is normal in $V \cap W$.*

Proof: Let E be a congruence on V such that U is an E-class. Then the restriction E' of E to the subgroupoid $V \cap W$ is a congruence on $V \cap W$, and $U \cap W$ is either empty or an E'-class. ‖

Corollary. *If U is normal in V, and W is a subgroupoid such that $U \subseteq W \subseteq V$, then U is normal in W.*

Theorem 3. *Let A be a subgroupoid of S and B a normal subset of S such that $A \cap B \neq \varnothing$, and let E be a congruence on S such that B is an E-class. Then $A \cap B$ is normal in A, and there exist quotients of $[A \cap B, A]$ and $[B, EA]$ which are isomorphic.*

Proof: As in the proof of Proposition 6, the restriction E' of E to A is a congruence on A, and $A \cap B$ is an E'-class. On the other hand, EA is a subgroupoid containing B, and evidently B is an E''-class, where E'' is the restriction of E to EA. Finally, $A/E' \cong EA/E''$ by Theorem 26.4. ‖

In the light of Proposition 5, the last part of Theorem 3 can be regarded as an algebraic analog of Theorem 13.1.

28. NORMAL SUBGROUPOIDS AND NORMAL SERIES

Readily, the results of Section 27 continue to hold if we restrict ourselves to normal subsets which are also subgroupoids (in brief: to **normal subgroupoids**). In particular, analogs of Theorems 27.1–2 hold for the complete lattice $\mathcal{N}_S = \mathcal{M}_S \cap \mathcal{S}_S$ of normal subgroupoids of S. [To see this for Theorem 27.1, use Proposition 24.3.] Note that $\mathcal{N}_S$ still has $\varnothing$ as least element and S as greatest element, and that any trivial subgroupoid is normal since it is an I_S-class. Note also that if the congruences on S commute, $\mathcal{M}_S$ is a sublattice of $\mathcal{N}_S$, since the sup in $\mathcal{M}_S$ (Proposition 27.5) of two normal subgroupoids is a subgroupoid.

> Our goal in this section is to prove an algebraic analog of Theorem 14.1, to the effect that under suitable conditions, any two finite chains from $A \neq \varnothing$ to B in $\mathcal{N}_S$ have refinements of the same length whose corresponding steps (in some order) are not only order isomorphic, but have isomorphic quotients. Actually, we shall prove a more general result concerning chains of subgroupoids which are not necessarily normal in S, but only normal "in one another."

Let $\mathscr{A} = \{A_0, \ldots, A_m\}$, where $\varnothing \neq A = A_0 \subset A_1 \subset \cdots \subset A_m = B$, be a finite chain of subgroupoids of S. We call $\mathscr{A}$ a **normal series** from A to B if A_{i-1} is normal in A_i, $1 \leq i \leq m$. In particular, by the corollary to Proposition 27.6, any finite chain from A to B in $\mathscr{N}_S$ is a normal series; but the converse is not necessarily true, since the terms of a normal series need not be normal in S. If $\mathscr{B}$ is also a normal series from A to B and contains $\mathscr{A}$, it is called a **refinement** of $\mathscr{A}$; if $\mathscr{A}$ has no proper refinement (that is, no refinement except itself), it is called **unrefinable**. Thus an unrefinable normal series from A to B is a maximal element of the set of normal series from A to B, ordered by inclusion.

If there exists a normal series from A to B, we say that A is a **subnormal** subgroupoid of B. Thus in particular, a normal subgroupoid is subnormal.

Proposition 1. *If U, V are subnormal in S, so is $U \cap V$.*

Proof: If $U = U_0 \subseteq U_1 \subseteq \cdots \subseteq U_m = S$ and $V = V_0 \subseteq V_1 \subseteq \cdots \subseteq V_n = S$ are normal series, by Proposition 27.6 so is $U \cap V = U_0 \cap V_0 \subseteq U_1 \cap V_0 \subseteq \cdots \subseteq U_m \cap V_0 = V_0 \subseteq V_1 \subseteq \cdots \subseteq V_n = S$. ‖

Corollary. *A finite intersection of subnormal subgroupoids is subnormal.*

If, for example, $\mathscr{S}_S$ is finite, this makes the set of subnormal subgroupoids of S a complete lattice, and a normal series is then a special type of chain in this lattice. In general, however, an arbitrary intersection of subnormal subgroupoids need not be subnormal.

Lemma 1 (Zassenhaus' lemma). *Let A, B be subgroupoids of S such that $A \cap B \neq \varnothing$; let D, E be congruences on A, B, respectively; and suppose that all congruences on $A \cap B$ commute. Then $D \circ E \circ D$ and $E \circ D \circ E$ are congruences on $D(A \cap B)$ and $E(A \cap B)$, respectively, and their quotient groupoids are isomorphic.*

Proof: Readily $D \circ E \circ D$ and $E \circ D \circ E$ are relations on $D(A \cap B)$ and $E(A \cap B)$, respectively. Let D', E' be the restrictions of D, E to $A \cap B$; then it is easily seen that $(D \circ E \circ D) \circ (D \circ E \circ D) = D \circ E \circ D \circ E \circ D = D \circ E \circ D' \circ E \circ D = D \circ E' \circ D' \circ E' \circ D$. Since D' and E' commute, this reduces to $D \circ D' \circ E' \circ D = D \circ E' \circ D = D \circ E \circ D$, which is thus transitive and hence readily a congruence. By Theorem 26.4, $D(A \cap B)/(D \circ E \circ D)$ is isomorphic to the quotient groupoid of $A \cap B$ defined by the restriction of $D \circ E \circ D$ to $A \cap B$, which is just $D' \circ E' \circ D' = D' \circ E'$. Similarly, $E \circ D \circ E$ is a congruence on $E(A \cap B)$, and $E(A \cap B)/(E \circ D \circ E)$ is isomorphic to the quotient of $A \cap B$ by $E' \circ D' \circ E' = D' \circ E'$. ‖

Lemma 2. *Let A, B, D, E be as in Lemma 1, and let $C \subseteq A \cap B$; then $(D \circ E \circ D)C = (D \circ E)C = D(A \cap EC)$.*

Proof: Since $C \subseteq A \cap B$ we readily have $(D \circ E \circ D)C = (D \circ E' \circ D')C$, and since D' and E' commute, this reduces to $(D \circ E')C = (D \circ E)C$. Since D is a congruence on A, clearly $(D \circ E)C = D(EC) = D(A \cap EC)$.   ‖

Corollary 1. *If* A, B, D, E *are as above, and* $x \in A \cap B$, *then* $(D \circ E \circ D)_x = D(A \cap E_x)$.

Proof: Take $C = \{x\}$ in the lemma.   ‖

Corollary 2. *Let* A, B, D, E *be as above, and let* B' *be an* E-*class such that* $A \cap B' \neq \varnothing$; *then* $D(A \cap B')$ *is a* $D \circ E \circ D$-*class.*

Proof: Take $x \in A \cap B'$ in Corollary 1.   ‖

We can now prove

Theorem 1. *Let* S *be a groupoid such that all congruences on any subgroupoid of* S *commute, and let* $\varnothing \neq A \subseteq B$ *be subgroupoids of* S. *Then any two normal series from* A *to* B *have refinements of the same length whose corresponding steps* (*in some order*) *have isomorphic quotients.*

Proof: Let $\mathscr{A} = \{A_0, \ldots, A_m\}$ and $\mathscr{B} = \{B_0, \ldots, B_n\}$ be two such normal series, where $A = A_0 \subset A_1 \subset \cdots \subset A_m = B$ and $A = B_0 \subset B_1 \subset \cdots \subset B_n = B$. Let D_i be a congruence on A_i such that A_{i-1} is a D_i-class, $1 \le i \le m$, and let E_j be a congruence on B_j such that B_{j-1} is an E_j-class, $1 \le j \le n$. Let $A_{i,j} = D_i(A_i \cap B_j)$ and $B_{j,i} = E_j(A_i \cap B_j)$, $1 \le i \le m$, $1 \le j \le n$. By the first part of Lemma 1, $D_i \circ E_j \circ D_i$ is a congruence on $A_{i,j}$, and by Corollary 2 to Lemma 2, $D_i(A_i \cap B_{j-1}) = A_{i,j-1}$ is a $D_i \circ E_j \circ D_i$-class. Thus the chain

$$A = A_{0,0} \subseteq A_{0,1} \subseteq \cdots \subseteq A_{0,n} = A_1 = A_{1,0} \subseteq A_{1,1} \subseteq \cdots \subseteq A_{1,n}$$
$$= A_2 \subseteq \cdots \subseteq A_{m,n} = B$$

is a normal series refining $\mathscr{A}$, and similarly the chain $A = B_{0,0} \subseteq \cdots \subseteq B_{n,m} = B$ is a refinement of $\mathscr{B}$. Finally, by the last part of Lemma 1 we have $A_{i,j}/(D_i \circ E_j \circ D_i) \cong B_{j,i}/(E_j \circ D_i \circ E_j)$.   ‖

Corollary. *If* S, A, B *are as in the theorem, any two unrefinable normal series from* A *to* B *have the same length, and their corresponding steps* (*in some order*) *have isomorphic quotients.*

Theorem 1 is known as the **Schreier refinement theorem**, and its corollary as the **Jordan–Hölder** theorem. An unrefinable normal series is called a **composition series**.

29. DIRECT PRODUCTS

Let $S = \prod_I S_i = \{(x_i)_I \mid x_i \in S_i\}$ be the Cartesian product of the I-tuple of sets $(S_i)_I$, and let F_i be a composition on S_i. Then a composition F on S is defined by

$$F((x_i)_I, (y_i)_I) = (F_i(x_i, y_i))_I$$

for all $(x_i)_I$, $(y_i)_I$ in S. The groupoid S under this composition is called the **direct product** of the I-tuple of groupoids $(S_i)_I$. If all the S_i's are the same, we speak of *direct powers* rather than direct products. From now on we denote F and every F_i multiplicatively.

Propositions 19.1–7 readily continue to hold for direct products of groupoids, with "isomorphism" replacing "one-to-one correspondence." Thus a product of one factor is isomorphic to the factor; any product is isomorphic to a subproduct from which trivial factors have been omitted; a product of subgroupoids is a subgroupoid of the product; a product of products is isomorphic to a product; and a permutation of a product is isomorphic to the product. By this last result, we can speak of "the" direct product of a set $\mathscr{S}$ of groupoids, since if $(S_i)_I$ and $(S_i)_J$ are one-to-one correspondences of I, J, respectively, with $\mathscr{S}$, then $\prod_I S_i \cong \prod_J S_i$. We also have (proofs are left to the reader):

Proposition 1. *Let R_i and R be as in Proposition* 19.8; *then R is a congruence if and only if each R_i is a congruence.*

Proposition 2. *Let R_i and R be as in Proposition* 19.9; *then R is a homomorphism if and only if each R_i is a homomorphism.*

Corollary. *Let $S_i \cong T_i$ for each $i \in I$; then $\prod_I S_i \cong \prod_I T_i$.*

Proposition 3. *The following statements about the groupoids S and A are equivalent:*

    (1) *There exists a groupoid B such that $S \cong A \times B$*
    (2) *There exists an I-tuple of groupoids $(S_i)_I$ such that $S \cong \prod_I S_i$ and $A \cong S_j$ for some $j \in I$.*

If the conditions of Proposition 3 hold, we say that A is a **direct factor** of S. By the corollary to Proposition 2, an isomorphic image of a direct factor is a direct factor. If T is a direct factor of S and V a direct factor of T, then V is a direct factor of S; indeed, $S \cong T \times U$ and $T \cong V \times W$ readily imply $S \cong V \times (W \times U)$. In short: a direct factor of a direct factor is a direct factor. Note that S is always a direct factor of itself, since $S \cong S \times \{x\}$, where $\{x\}$ is a trivial groupoid. In fact, we can even have $S \cong S \times S$ (Examples: $S = \varnothing$; S trivial; $S = A^N$, where A is any groupoid [Hint: Use Exercise 21.1].)

For each $j \in I$, the projection $p_j = \{((x_i)_I, x_j) \mid (x_i)_I \in S\}$ is readily a homomorphism. It follows by Propositions 2 and 26.2 and Theorem 26.1 that $E_j = p_j \circ p_j^{-1}$ is a congruence on S, and that $S_j \cong S/E_j$. In analogy with Theorems 19.1–2 we also have

Theorem 1. *Let $(p_i)_I$ be an I-tuple of homomorphisms of the groupoid S onto groupoids S_i which are as in Theorem* 19.1; *then $\{(y, (p_i(y))_I) \mid y \in S\}$ is an isomorphism of S with $\prod_I S_i$.*

Theorem 2. *Let $E_1, \ldots, E_n$ be congruences on the groupoid S which are as in Theorem 19.2; then the E's commute, and $\{(x, ((E_1)_x, \ldots, (E_n)_x)) \mid x \in S\}$ is an isomorphism of S with $\prod_{i=1}^{n} S/E_i$.*

Proposition 4. *The following statements about the congruence E on the groupoid S are equivalent:*

(1) *There exists a congruence D on S such that $D \circ E = S \times S$ and $D \cap E = I_S$*

(2) *There exists an I-tuple $(E_i)_I$ of congruences on S which is as in Proposition 19.11, and $E = E_j$ for some $j \in I$.*

If the conditions of Proposition 4 hold, we say that E is a **supplemented congruence** on S, and call D a **supplement** of E.

Corollary. *A is a direct factor of S if and only if $A \cong S/E$, where E is a supplemented congruence on S.*

Proof: Theorem 2 and its converse. //

INDECOMPOSABLE GROUPOIDS

If all congruences on S commute, the lattice $\mathscr{C}_S$ is modular, hence so is the lattice $\mathscr{C}_S{}^{-1}$. We can thus apply the results of Section 15 to the independent E's. In fact, we can prove further results of a more "algebraic" nature. To do this, we must first develop a characterization of unrefinability (of an independent set) in terms of direct products.

We call the groupoid S **indecomposable** if $S \cong A \times B$ implies that A is trivial and $B \cong S$, or vice versa. [We could have defined an analogous property for sets, using one-to-one correspondence in place of isomorphism; readily, a set has this property if and only if it is finite and has a prime number of elements.]

Proposition 5. *S is indecomposable if and only if $S \cong \prod_I S_i$ implies that all but one of the S_i's are trivial, and that one $\cong S$.*

Proof: For "if," take $I = \{1, 2\}$, $S_1 = A$, $S_2 = B$. Conversely, if S is indecomposable and $S \cong \prod_I S_i$, then for each $j \in I$ we have $S \cong S_j \times \prod_{I-(j)} S_i$, so that one of these factors must be trivial. If there exists $j \in I$ such that the second factor is trivial, then every S_i except S_j must be trivial, and we have $S \cong S_j$. If not, S_j itself must be trivial for every $j \in I$, so that S is trivial. //

Proposition 6. *The following statements about the groupoid S are equivalent:*

(1) *S is indecomposable*

(2) *The only supplemented congruences on S are I_S and $S \times S$*

(3) *$\{I_S\}$ is the only independent subset of $\mathscr{C}_S{}^{-1}$ whose sup is I_S.*

Proof: If S is indecomposable and D, E are supplemented congruences, by Theorem 2 we must have S/D trivial, $S/E \cong S$, or vice versa, say the former, so that $D = S \times S$, whence $E = I_S$, proving (2). Conversely, if (2) holds and $S \cong A \times B$, the congruences on S defined by the projections of $A \times B$ on A and B are supplemented, hence must be $S \times S$ and I_S (in some order), so that A is trivial and $B \cong A \times B \cong S$ or vice versa, proving (1). The equivalence of (2) and (3) follows immediately from the definitions of supplementedness and independence.   //

Theorem 3. *Let $S = \prod_{i=1}^{n} S_i$; let $E_i = p_i \circ p_i{}^{-1}$, $1 \leq i \leq n$; and let $\mathscr{C}_S$ be modular and finite dimensional. Then $\{E_1, \ldots, E_n\}$ is an unrefinable independent set in $\mathscr{C}_S{}^{-1}$ if and only if each S_i is nontrivial and indecomposable.*

Proof: The set of E_i's is independent provided each S_i is nontrivial, so that no E_i is $S \times S$. If it is refinable, some $\{E_j\}$ must be refinable, so that there exist congruences E_{j1} and E_{j2} on S, neither of them $S \times S$, such that $E_{j1} \cap E_{j2} = E_j$ and $E_{j1} \circ E_{j2} = S \times S$. Let $D_{j1} = F_{E_j}{}^{-1} \circ E_{j1} \circ F_{E_j}$ and $D_{j2} = F_{E_j}{}^{-1} \circ E_{j2} \circ F_{E_j}$ be the corresponding congruences on S/E_j (Corollary 1 to Theorem 26.2). Then readily neither of D_{j1}, D_{j2} is $(S/E_j) \times (S/E_j)$, but $D_{j1} \cap D_{j2} = I_{S/E_j}$ and $D_{j1} \circ D_{j2} = (S/E_j) \times (S/E_j)$. Thus by Proposition 6, S/E_j cannot be indecomposable, and the same is then true for S_j since $S_j \cong S/E_j$.

Conversely, if some S_j—or equivalently, some S/E_j—fails to be indecomposable, by Proposition 6 there exist congruences D_{j1} and D_{j2} on S/E_j, neither of them $(S/E_j) \times (S/E_j)$, such that $D_{j1} \cap D_{j2} = I_{S/E_j}$ and $D_{j1} \circ D_{j2} = (S/E_j) \times (S/E_j)$. Let E_{j1} and E_{j2} be the corresponding congruences on S; then readily neither E_{j1} nor E_{j2} is $S \times S$, but $E_{j1} \circ E_{j2} = S \times S$ and $E_{j1} \cap E_{j2} = E_j$, so that $\{E_j\}$ is refinable.   //

Corollary. *If $\mathscr{C}_S$ is modular and finite dimensional, S is isomorphic to a finite direct product of indecomposable groupoids.*

Proof: $\{I_S\}$ has a finite unrefinable refinement.   //

We can now prove, as an "algebraic" analog of Theorem 15.1:

Theorem 4. *Let $S \cong \prod_{i=1}^{m} A_i \cong \prod_{i=1}^{n} B_i$, where the A's and B's are nontrivial and indecomposable; and let $\mathscr{C}_S$ be modular and finite dimensional. Then $m = n$, and for each i there exists j $(1 \leq i \leq n, 1 \leq j \leq n)$ such that*

$$S \cong A_1 \times \cdots \times A_{i-1} \times B_j \times A_{i+1} \times \cdots \times A_n$$
$$\cong B_1 \times \cdots \times B_{j-1} \times A_i \times B_{j+1} \times \cdots \times B_n.$$

Proof: Let $D_1, \ldots, D_m$ and $E_1, \ldots, E_n$ be the congruences on S corresponding to the A's and B's, respectively. By Theorem 3, $\{D_1, \ldots, D_m\}$ and $\{E_1, \ldots, E_n\}$ are unrefinable independent sets in $\mathscr{C}_S^{-1}$, and each has I_S as its sup. Hence by Theorem 15.1 we have $m = n$, and each D_i is interchangeable with some E_j. Thus

$$S \cong (S/D_1) \times \cdots \times (S/D_{i-1}) \times (S/E_j) \times (S/D_{i+1}) \times \cdots \times (S/D_n)$$
$$\cong (S/E_1) \times \cdots \times (S/E_{j-1}) \times (S/D_i) \times (S/E_{j+1}) \times \cdots \times (S/E_n);$$

and $S/D_k \cong A_k$, $S/E_k \cong B_k$, $1 \leq k \leq n$. $\quad //$

Note that we are not asserting that each A_i is isomorphic to the corresponding B_j; this requires an additional assumption about S (see Section 39).

VI

SEMIGROUPS AND GROUPS

In this chapter we study groupoids in which special assumptions of various kinds are made about the composition. The first kind of assumption involves the existence of elements on which the composition "operates" especially simply.

30. IDEMPOTENT ELEMENTS

Every groupoid has a trivial quotient groupoid (namely, $S/(S \times S)$); but a groupoid has a trivial subgroupoid if and only if it has an idempotent element (Exercise 23.1). In all of the examples of groupoids given in Section 22, idempotent elements do exist. [In fact, $\varnothing$, I_A, and $A \times A$ are all idempotent for $\circ$; any element of a lattice is idempotent for both sup and inf; $\varnothing$ is idempotent for relative complement; 0 (or $\{\varnothing\}$, the cardinal number of $\varnothing$) is idempotent for addition and multiplication, as is any infinite cardinal number; 1 (or K_1) is idempotent for multiplication and exponentiation; and if e is idempotent for F, so is $\{e\}$ for $\bar{F}$.] In this section we study groupoids which have an idempotent element or, equivalently, a trivial subgroupoid.

Let S be a groupoid, A a subgroupoid of S. Clearly, if A contains an idempotent element, so does S; but S may contain one even though A does not. Thus the property of containing an idempotent element does not "pass" from a groupoid to its subgroupoids, but does pass in the opposite direction. For quotient groupoids this situation is exactly reversed. On the one hand, we have

Proposition 1. *If e is idempotent, so is $F(e)$, where F is a homomorphism.*

Proof: $F(e)F(e) = F(ee) = F(e)$. $\parallel$

Corollary. *If S has an idempotent element, so does any homomorphic image or quotient groupoid of S.*

108

On the other hand, a homomorphic preimage of a groupoid with an idempotent element need not have an idempotent element. [For example, any S has the trivial homomorphic image $S/(S \times S)$, so that S is the preimage of a groupoid whose sole element is idempotent; but S itself, being arbitrary, need not have an idempotent.] However, with regard to preimages of idempotent elements we have the very important

Proposition 2. *If e is idempotent and F is a homomorphism, then $F^{-1}(F(e))$ is a subgroupoid and an E_F-class.*

Proof: $F^{-1}(F(e)) = (E_F)_e$, and it is a subgroupoid since $\{F(e)\}$ is. //

Corollary 1. *If $e \in S$ is idempotent and E is any congruence on S, then E_e is a subgroupoid.*

Corollary 2. *If S has an idempotent element, and E is any congruence on S, then S has a normal subgroupoid which is an E-class.*

We call E_e a **kernel** of E, and $(E_F)_e$ a kernel of F. Thus a kernel of a homomorphism (or congruence) is a normal subgroupoid.

Finally, regarding products of groupoids with an idempotent element we have

Proposition 3. $S = \prod_I S_i$ *has an idempotent element if and only if every S_i has an idempotent element.*

Proof: In fact, $(e_i)_I$ is idempotent if and only if e_i is idempotent for each $i \in I$. //

Exercise 1. *Give an example of a groupoid which is isomorphic to a proper subgroupoid of itself.* [Hint: Let $S = A^N$, where A has an idempotent element, and consider the proper subgroupoid of S which corresponds, under an isomorphism of S with $S \times S$, to the proper subgroupoid $S \times \{e\}$ of $S \times S$, where $e \in S$ is idempotent.]

> The theory of direct products can be significantly sharpened in the case of groupoids with idempotent elements, but we shall defer doing this until Section 39.

31. IDENTITIES AND ABSORBENT ELEMENTS

The element e of the groupoid S is called a **left identity** if $ex = x$ for all $x \in S$; a **right identity**, if $xe = x$ for all $x \in S$; a **two-sided identity** (or in brief: an **identity**), if it is both a left and a right identity. Similarly, $a \in S$ is called **left absorbent** if $ax = a$ for all $x \in S$; **right absorbent**, if $xa = a$ for all $x \in S$; and **(two-sided) absorbent**, if it is both left and right absorbent. Note that any left or right identity or absorbent element is idempotent.

For the examples of compositions given in Section 22, we have the following examples of identities and absorbent elements:

(a) For composition of relations on the set A, I_A is the only (left or right) identity and $\varnothing$ the only (left or right) absorbent element. For composition of functions from A into itself, I_A is still the only identity; if $A \neq \varnothing$, the constant functions are the only right absorbent elements, and there are no left absorbent elements.

(b) The only possible (left or right) identity for the sup composition on a lattice is the least element, if there is one, and the only possible (left or right) absorbent element is the greatest element, if any; vice versa for the inf composition. For example, for the union composition on $\mathscr{P}_A$, $\varnothing$ is the only identity and A the only absorbent element; vice versa for the intersection composition.

(c) For relative complement on $\mathscr{P}_A$, $\varnothing$ is the only right identity and the only left absorbent element; there is no left identity or right absorbent element unless $A = \varnothing$.

(d) For addition on $\mathbf{N}°$, 0 is the only identity and there are no absorbent elements; for multiplication, 1 is the only identity and 0 the only absorbent element. For exponentiation on $\mathbf{N}$, 1 is the only right identity and the only left absorbent element; there are no left identities and no right absorbent elements. Similarly for addition, multiplication, and exponentiation of finite cardinal numbers. For addition on the set of cardinal numbers $\leq K$, where K is infinite, $\{\varnothing\}$ is the only identity and K the only absorbent element. [What happens in the case of multiplication on this set?]

(e) If e is a left or right identity, or left or right absorbent, for the composition F on S, then $\{e\}$ is the same for $\bar{F}$ on $\mathscr{P}_S$.

Exercise 1. *For any x in the groupoid S, define the function $L_x \in S^S$ ("left multiplication by x") by $L_x(y) = xy$ for all $y \in S$. Then x is a left identity if and only if $L_x = I_S$, and x is left absorbent if and only if L_x is the constant function $\{(y, x) \mid y \in S\}$.*

Exercise 2. *x is left absorbent if and only if $\{x\}$ is a right ideal (Exercise 23.2); right absorbent, if and only if $\{x\}$ is a left ideal.*

Exercise 3. *Any set of left (or right) identities is a subgroupoid. Any set of left absorbent elements is a right ideal, any set of right absorbent elements a left ideal.*

Exercise 4. *A left absorbent element must be in any nonempty left ideal, a right absorbent element in any nonempty right ideal.*

Exercise 5. *Let A be a subset of the groupoid S which contains a left (or right) identity; then $AA \supseteq A$.*

Corollary 1. *If A is also a subgroupoid, then* $AA = A$.

Corollary 2. *In a groupoid with a left (or right) identity, the composition is onto.*

Proposition 1. *If d and e are left and right identities, respectively, then* $d = e$ *is the only left, right, or two-sided identity; and analogously for absorbent elements.*

Proof: $de = e$ since d is a left identity, and $de = d$ since e is a right identity; thus $d = e$ is a two-sided identity. If e' is any left identity, we then have $e'e = e' = e$ by the same argument, and similarly if e'' is any right identity we have $ee'' = e = e''$. The proof for absorbent elements is left to the reader. //

Exercise 6. *If e is both a left identity and left absorbent, or both a right identity and right absorbent, the groupoid is trivial. Conversely, if* $S = \{e\}$ *is trivial, e is both an identity and absorbent.* [But note that by Examples c–d above, an element can be both a right identity and left absorbent without S being trivial.]

If S is a groupoid and A a subgroupoid of S, there evidently may be an identity or absorbent element in S but not in A. Conversely, there may be an element of A which is an identity or absorbent in A (that is, $ex = x$, or $= e$, for all $x \in A$), but not in S ($ey \neq y$, or $\neq e$, for some $y \in S - A$). The most we can say is that if $e \in A$ is a (left or right) identity or absorbent element in S, it is certainly the same in A.

For homomorphic images or quotient groupoids, on the other hand, we have immediately

Proposition 2. *Let e be a right or left identity or absorbent element in the groupoid S; then so is F(e) in F(S), where F is a homomorphism.*

Corollary. *Let e be a right or left identity or absorbent element in S; then so is* E_e *in* S/E, *where E is a congruence.*

A homomorphic preimage of an identity or absorbent element need not be an identity or absorbent. However, we have

Exercise 7. *If e is a right or left identity or absorbent element, and F is a homomorphism, then* $F^{-1}(F(e))$ *is a subgroupoid and an* E_F*-class. Moreover, if e is left (right) absorbent, this subgroupoid is a right (left) ideal.*

Finally, for product groupoids we have

Proposition 3. $(e_i)_I$ *is a right or left identity or absorbent element in* $\prod_I S_i$ *if and only if* e_i *is the same in* S_i *for each* $i \in I$.

32. CANCELLABLE AND INVERTIBLE ELEMENTS

The element x of the groupoid S is called **left cancellable** if $xy = xz$ implies $y = z$ for all y, z in S; **right cancellable**, if $yx = zx$ implies $y = z$ for all y, z in S; **cancellable**, if it is both left and right cancellable.

Exercise 1. x *is left cancellable if and only if* L_x (*Exercise* 31.1) *is one-to-one*.

Exercise 2. *A left identity is left cancellable, a right identity right cancellable*.

Exercise 3. *A left absorbent element is left cancellable, or a right absorbent element right cancellable, if and only if the groupoid is trivial*.

Let $e \in S$ be an identity (left, right, or two-sided). If $x'x = e$, we call x' a **left e-inverse** of x, and x a **right e-inverse** of x'. An element which has a left (right) e-inverse is called left (right) **e-invertible**. If $x'x = xx' = e$, we call x and x' (two-sided) e-invertible, and say that they are (two-sided) e-inverses of each other.

> One could also study "a-invertibility," where a is absorbent; evidently "a-invertible element" would be a generalization of "divisor of zero."

Exercise 4. *A left identity e is its own two-sided e-inverse and its own only right e-inverse*.

Exercise 5. *If d, e are left identities, d is a right d-inverse and a left e-inverse of e*.

Exercise 6. *A left absorbent element has a right e-inverse, where e is a left identity, if and only if the groupoid is trivial*.

["Left" and "right" can, of course, be interchanged throughout these exercises.]

The following examples of cancellable and invertible elements are provided by our standard examples of compositions. [In (a–d) we need not specify e, since there is only one identity.]

(a') The following statements about $F \in A^A$ are equivalent:

    (1) F is left cancellable for $\circ$ on $\mathscr{P}_{A \times A}$
    (2) F is left invertible for $\circ$ on $\mathscr{P}_{A \times A}$
    (3) F is left cancellable for $\circ$ on A^A
    (4) F is onto.

[Proof: (4) implies (2) by Proposition 3.2, while (2) implies (1) since $\circ$ is associative (see Proposition 34.5). Conversely, let $x \notin F(A)$, and let $G = I_A - \{(x, x)\} \cup \{(x, y)\}$, where $y \neq x$; then $G \in A^A$, and $F \circ I_A = F \circ G$, so that F is not left cancellable for $\circ$ on A^A.]

(a″) The following statements about $F \in A^A$ are equivalent:
(1) F is right cancellable for ∘ on $\mathscr{P}_{A \times A}$
(2) F is right invertible for ∘ on $\mathscr{P}_{A \times A}$
(3) F is right cancellable for ∘ on A^A
(4) F is one-to-one.
[Proof: Analogous, using Proposition 3.5.]

(b) There are no left or right cancellable or invertible elements, except for the identities, for the sup and inf compositions on a lattice. [Proof: Let S be a lattice, $x \in S$, $x \neq 0$; then $x \vee 0 = x \vee x = 0 \vee x = x$, so that x is neither left nor right cancellable. Similarly, $x' \vee x = 0$ implies $x = x' = 0$, so that if $x \neq 0$ it is neither left nor right invertible. The proofs for inf are analogous.]

(c) For relative complement on $\mathscr{P}_A$, A is the only left cancellable element and $\varnothing$ the only right cancellable element. Any $C \supseteq B$ is a right inverse of B, and any $C \subseteq B$ is a left inverse of B, for any $B \subseteq A$.

(d) Any $n \in \mathbf{N}°$ is cancellable for addition, and any $n \neq 0$ cancellable for multiplication. Any $n \in \mathbf{N}$ is right cancellable, and any $n \neq 1$ left cancellable, for exponentiation. There are no invertible elements for addition or multiplication except for the identities. Any $n \in \mathbf{N}$ has 1 as a unique left inverse for exponentiation, so that 1 has every element as a right inverse, and no other element has a right inverse. [What happens on the cardinals $\leq K$?]

(e) If x is left or right cancellable for the composition F on S, then $\{x\}$ is the same for $\bar{F}$ on $\mathscr{P}_S$. If x' is a left (right) inverse of x, then $\{x'\}$ is a left (right) inverse of $\{x\}$.

If S is a groupoid and A a subgroupoid of S, an element of A may be cancellable in A (that is, $xy = xz$ implies $y = z$ for all y, z in A) but not in S. Similarly, $a \in A$ may be e-invertible in S but may not have an e-inverse in A even if $e \in A$; and conversely, a may have an e-inverse in A, where e is an identity in A, but e may not be an identity in S. The most we can say is that if $a \in A$ is (left or right) cancellable in S, it is the same in A, and that if $a \in A$ has a (left or right) e-inverse a' in A, where $e \in A$ is an identity for all of S, then a' is a (left or right) e-inverse of a in S.

Proposition 1. *If x is left or right cancellable in the groupoid S, then so is $F(x)$ in $F(S)$, where F is an isomorphism. If $x \in S$ is (right or left) e-invertible, then $F(x)$ is (right or left) $F(e)$-invertible, where F is a homomorphism; in fact, if $x'x = e$, then $F(x')F(x) = F(e)$, and similarly on the right.*

Corollary. *If x is (right or left) e-invertible in S, then E_x is (right or left) E_e-invertible in S/E, where E is a congruence.*

Exercise 7. *Give an example showing that "isomorphism" cannot be replaced by "homomorphism" in the first part of Proposition 1.*

Proposition 2. $(x_i)_I$ *is (left or right) cancellable in* $\prod_I S_i$ *if and only if* x_i *is the same in* S_i *for each* $i \in I$. *Also,* $(x_i)_I$ *is (left or right)* $(e_i)_I$-*invertible in* $\prod_I S_i$ *if and only if* x_i *is (left or right)* e_i-*invertible in* S_i *for each* $i \in I$; *in fact,* $(x_i')_I(x_i)_I = (e_i)_I$ *if and only if* $x_i'x_i = e_i$ *for each* $i \in I$, *and similarly on the right.*

33. ASSOCIATIVITY AND COMMUTATIVITY

Another important type of property which a composition can have involves not special elements, but rather relationships expressible in terms of the composition which hold for *all* elements of the groupoid. The two most frequently encountered properties of this type are the familiar commutativity and associativity.

The composition F on S is called **commutative**, if $xy = yx$ for all x, y in S; **associative**, if $(xy)z = x(yz)$ for all x, y, z in S.

Examples:

(a) sup and inf, addition and multiplication are both commutative and associative

(b) ∘ is associative but not commutative

(c) Relative complement and exponentiation are neither commutative nor associative

(d) If F is associative or commutative, so is $\bar{F}$, and conversely.

Exercise 1. *F is associative if and only if* $L_{ab} = L_b \circ L_a$ *for all a, b in S.* [Thus if F is associative, $\{(a, L_a) \mid a \in S\}$ is a homomorphism of S into S^S under composition of functions *in reverse order.*]

Exercise 2. *Give an example of a composition which is commutative but not associative.*

If F is commutative, the left-handed, right-handed, and two-sided types of identities, absorbent elements, cancellable elements, invertible elements and inverses need, of course, no longer be distinguished. Useful simplifications in the properties of these special types of elements also result if F is associative, as we shall see in Section 34.

Commutativity and associativity pass to both subgroupoids and quotient groupoids, as well as to direct products:

Proposition 1. *If the composition F on the groupoid S is associative (commutative), so is the restriction of F to any subgroupoid of S.*

Proposition 2. *Let S, T be groupoids under the compositions F, G, and let H be a homomorphism of S into T. If F is associative (commutative), so is the restriction of G to $H(S)$.*

Corollary. *Let S be a groupoid under the composition F, and let E be a congruence on S. If F is associative (commutative), so is the quotient composition F/E on S/E.*

Proposition 3. *Let $S = \prod_I S_i$; let F_i be the composition on the groupoid S_i, for each $i \in I$, and let F be the direct product composition on S. Then F is associative (commutative) if and only if F_i is associative (commutative) for each $i \in I$.*

Let F be a composition on S, and let $(a_1, \ldots, a_n)$ be an n-tuple of elements of S. We define the F-composite of $(a_1, \ldots, a_n)$, denoted by $\prod_{i=1}^{n} a_i$, as follows: $\prod_{i=1}^{1} a_i = a_1$; $\prod_{i=1}^{m+1} a_i = (\prod_{i=1}^{m} a_i)a_{m+1}$.

There should be no confusion with the notation used for product sets and direct products, where we always use capital letters for the "factors." If we were denoting F additively rather than multiplicatively, we would use $\sum$ instead of $\prod$; compare the definition at the end of Section 4.

Theorem 1 (the general associative law). *Let F be a composition on S; let $(s_1, \ldots, s_n)$ be an n-tuple of elements of S; and let $(n_1, \ldots, n_k)$ be a k-tuple of natural numbers such that $1 = n_1 < n_2 < \cdots < n_k = n + 1$. Then F is associative if and only if for any such $(s_1, \ldots, s_n)$ and $(n_1, \ldots, n_k)$ we have*

$$\prod_{j=1}^{k-1} \left(\prod_{i=n_j}^{n_{j+1}-1} s_i \right) = \prod_{i=1}^{n} s_i.$$

Proof: For "if" take $n = 3$, $k = 3$, $n_2 = 2$ and 3. For "only if" we use induction on n; the assertion is trivial if $n = 1$. Suppose $n > 1$ and the assertion true for all $m < n$; then by definition of $\prod$ and induction hypothesis we have

$$\prod_{j=1}^{k-1} \left(\prod_{i=n_j}^{n_{j+1}-1} s_i \right) = \left(\prod_{j=1}^{k-2} \left(\prod_{i=n_j}^{n_{j+1}-1} s_i \right) \right) \left(\prod_{i=n_{k-1}}^{n} s_i \right)$$

$$= \left(\prod_{i=1}^{n_{k-1}-1} s_i \right) \left(\prod_{i=n_{k-1}}^{n} s_i \right). \tag{*}$$

If $n - n_{k-1} + 1 = 1$, the right member of (*) is just $(\prod_{i=1}^{n-1} s_i)s_n$, which $= \prod_{i=1}^{n} s_i$ by definition of $\prod$. But if $n - n_{k-1} + 1 > 1$, the right member of (*) becomes, using associativity,

$$\left(\prod_{i=1}^{n_{k-1}-1} s_i \right) \left[\left(\prod_{i=n_{k-1}}^{n-1} s_i \right) s_n \right] = \left[\left(\prod_{i=1}^{n_{k-1}-1} s_i \right) \left(\prod_{i=n_{k-1}}^{n-1} s_i \right) \right] s_n,$$

where the bracket in the new right member is equal to $\prod_{i=1}^{n-1} s_i$ by induction hypothesis, so that the conclusion follows as in the case $n - n_{k-1} + 1 = 1$.   //

> This theorem says that if F is associative, the "composite" of an n-tuple is the same no matter how the n-tuple is broken up into subtuples—in other words, no matter how its terms are "grouped by parentheses." By virtue of this theorem, if F is associative we can safely write xyz instead of $(xy)z$ or $x(yz)$, and $x_1 \cdots x_n$ instead of $\prod_{i=1}^{n} x_i$. Similarly, if F is denoted additively, we can use expressions such as $x + y + z$ and $x_1 + \cdots + x_n$. If all the x_i's are the same, we write x^n instead of $\prod_{i=1}^{n} x_i$, and nx instead of $\sum_{i=1}^{n} x_i$, where $x_i = x$ for each i.

Exercise 3. *Prove that the* **laws of exponents**

$$x^{m+n} = x^m x^n; \qquad x^{mn} = (x^m)^n$$

for all m, n in $\mathbf{N}$ hold for any associative composition. [Note that these laws can be restated as follows:

(a) For any $x \in S$, the function $H_x = \{(n, x^n) \mid n \in \mathbf{N}\}$ is a homomorphism of $\mathbf{N}$, under addition, into S;

(b) Let G_n be the function $\{(x, x^n) \mid x \in S\}$; then $\{(n, G_n) \mid n \in \mathbf{N}\}$ is a homomorphism of $\mathbf{N}$, under multiplication, into the groupoid S^S under $\circ$.]

Theorem 2 (the general commutative law). *Let F be an associative composition on S; let $(s_1, \ldots, s_n)$ be an n-tuple of elements of S, and let G be a permutation of $\mathbf{N}_n$. Then F is commutative if and only if $\prod_{i=1}^{n} s_{G(i)} = \prod_{i=1}^{n} s_i$ for any such $(s_1, \ldots, s_n)$ and any such G.*

Proof: For "if" take $n = 2$, $G(1) = 2$, $G(2) = 1$. For "only if" we again use induction; the case $n = 1$ is trivial. If $n > 1$ and the assertion is true for $n - 1$, let $G(k) = n$ and let the permutation H of $\mathbf{N}_{n-1}$ be defined by $H(i) = G(i)$, $1 \le i < k$; $H(i) = G(i + 1)$, $k \le i < n$. Then by Theorem 1 and commutativity we have

$$\prod_{i=1}^{n} s_{G(i)} = \left(\prod_{i=1}^{k-1} s_{G(i)} \right) \left(\prod_{i=k+1}^{n} s_{G(i)} \right) s_{G(k)} = \left(\prod_{i=1}^{n-1} s_{H(i)} \right) s_{G(k)}.$$

By induction hypothesis, the parenthesis in the last member is equal to $\prod_{i=1}^{n-1} s_i$, while $s_{G(k)} = s_n$.   //

Exercise 4. *Prove that for any associative, commutative composition we have* $(xy)^n = x^n y^n$ *for all $n \in \mathbf{N}$—in other words, that for any $n \in \mathbf{N}$, $G_n = \{(x, x^n) \mid x \in S\}$ is an endomorphism of S.* [What are the analogs of the laws in Exercises 3–4 in additive notation?]

Exercise 5. *For any associative, commutative composition we have*

$$\prod_{i=1}^{m} \left(\prod_{j=1}^{n} a_{ij} \right) = \prod_{j=1}^{n} \left(\prod_{i=1}^{m} a_{ij} \right).$$

Exercise 6. *If F is a homomorphism, then* $F(\prod_{i=1}^{n} x_i) = \prod_{i=1}^{n} F(x_i)$ *for all* $x_1, \ldots, x_n$.

Corollary: $F(x^n) = F(x)^n$ *for all x.*

34. SEMIGROUPS AND GROUPS

A groupoid whose composition is associative is called a **semigroup**. If the composition is also commutative, we call the semigroup commutative; if there is an identity element, we say that the semigroup "is with identity" (or "has identity"). A semigroup with identity is sometimes called a **monoid**.

Examples:

(a) The set of relations on any set is a semigroup with identity under ∘

(b) Any lattice is a commutative semigroup under sup (or inf)

(c) $\mathbf{N}^\circ$ is a commutative semigroup with identity under addition (or multiplication).

Note that the trivial groupoid is a commutative semigroup with identity.

By Propositions 33.1–3, any subgroupoid, homomorphic image, or quotient groupoid of a semigroup is a semigroup, and any direct product of semigroups is a semigroup. We can therefore speak of the *subsemigroups* and *quotient semigroups* of a semigroup, and of the *product semigroup* of an *I*-tuple of semigroups. The results obtained earlier in this chapter can be restated in this new terminology—for example, we can say that any quotient semigroup of a semigroup with identity is a semigroup with identity (corollary to Proposition 31.2); that any subsemigroup of a commutative semigroup is commutative (Proposition 33.1); and so on.

As remarked in Section 33, the special types of elements studied in Sections 30–32 are especially well-behaved in a semigroup:

Proposition 1. *A left cancellable idempotent element of a semigroup is a left identity.*

Proof: If e is such an element of the semigroup S, then for all $x \in S$ we have $e(ex) = (ee)x = ex$, so that (cancelling e) $ex = x$. ∥

Corollary. *A semigroup can contain at most one cancellable idempotent element.*

Proposition 2. *If S is a semigroup and x, y in S are left cancellable, so is xy.*

Proof: $(xy)u = (xy)v$ implies $x(yu) = x(yv)$ implies $yu = yv$ implies $u = v$ for all u, v in S. ∥

Corollary 1. *The set of left cancellable elements of a semigroup is a subsemigroup.*

Corollary 2. *If x is left cancellable in a semigroup, so is x^n for all $n \in \mathbf{N}$.*

Proposition 3. *Let S be a semigroup and let $x \in S$ be left d-invertible, $y \in S$ left e-invertible, where d, e are left or right identities in S; then xy is left e-invertible. In fact, let $x'x = d$, $y'y = e$; then $(y'x')(xy) = e$.* [Note the inversion of order!]

    Proof: $(y'x')(xy) = y'(x'x)y = y'dy = y'y = e.$ ∥

Corollary 1. *The set of left invertible elements of a semigroup is a subsemigroup.*

Corollary 2. *If x is left invertible in a semigroup, so is x^n for all $n \in \mathbf{N}$; in fact, if $x'x = e$, then $(x')^n x^n = e$.*

Proposition 4. *Let $ex = x$ in the semigroup S, where x is right cancellable; then e is a right identity.*

    Proof: For all $y \in S$ we have $(ye)x = y(ex) = yx$, so that (cancelling x) $ye = y.$ ∥

Corollary. *If S also contains a left cancellable element, e is a two-sided identity.*

Proposition 5. *Let S be a semigroup and let $x \in S$ be left e-invertible, where e is a left identity in S; then x is left cancellable.*

    Proof: Let $x'x = e$; then $xy = xz$ implies $x'(xy) = x'(xz)$ implies $(x'x)y = (x'x)z$ implies $ey = ez$ implies $y = z.$ ∥

Proposition 6. *Let S be a semigroup and let $x \in S$ have left and right e-inverses, where e is a two-sided identity in S; then x has a unique two-sided inverse which is its only left or right inverse.*

    Proof: Let $x'x = xx'' = e$; then $x'' = ex'' = (x'x)x'' = x'(xx'') = x'e = x'$. By the same argument, any left e-inverse of x must equal any right e-inverse of x; and e is unique by Proposition 31.1.   ∥

Corollary. *Let S, x be as in the proposition, and let x^{-1} be the unique inverse of x; then x is the unique inverse of x^{-1}. (In short: $(x^{-1})^{-1} = x$.)*

    Proof: x^{-1} has x as a left and right inverse, and so satisfies the hypothesis of the proposition.   ∥

Evidently "left" and "right" can be interchanged throughout Propositions 1–6.

Exercise 1. *If S is a semigroup, and $x \in S$ has a right e-inverse, where e is a left identity, then L_x is onto. Conversely, if L_x is onto, x has a right e-inverse for any (left or right) identity e in S.*

Proposition 7. *The following statements about the semigroup S are equivalent:*
(1) *There exists an $x \in S$ such that $Sx = xS = S$*
(2) *S has identity.*

Proof: If $e \in S$ is an identity, we have $Se = eS = S$. Conversely, let $Sx = xS = S$. Since $x \in S = Sx$, there exists $d \in S$ such that $dx = x$; and since any $y \in S$ is in xS, say $y = xz$, we have $dy = d(xz) = (dx)z = xz = y$, so that d is a left identity. Similarly, there exists a right identity, hence a unique two-sided identity. $\;//$

In a semigroup we also have a simpler description (compare Proposition 23.2) of the subsemigroup generated by a subset:

Proposition 8. *In a semigroup, $(A) = \{\prod_{i=1}^{k} y_i \mid k \in \mathbf{N}; \text{ the } y_i\text{'s in } A\}$.*

Proof: This set of composites is readily a subsemigroup (use the general associative law) and contains A (take $k = 1$). On the other hand, any subsemigroup which contains A must (induction on k) contain all of these composites. $\;//$

Corollary 1. $(x) = \{x^k \mid k \in \mathbf{N}\}$.

Corollary 2. (x) *is commutative.*

Corollary 3. *Let $ab = ba$ for all a, b in A; then (A) is commutative.*

Proof: Use the general associative and commutative laws. $\;//$

Proposition 9. *In a commutative semigroup, $(A) = \{\prod_{i=1}^{k} y_i^{k_i} \mid k \text{ and the } k_i\text{'s}$ in $\mathbf{N}$; the y_i's distinct elements of $A\}$.*

Proof: Proposition 8 and the general commutative law. $\;//$

Corollary 1. *If $\mathscr{A}$ is a set of subsemigroups, then $(\bigcup_{\mathscr{A}} A) = \{\prod_{i=1}^{k} a_i \mid k \in \mathbf{N};$ $a_1, \ldots, a_k$ in distinct elements of $\mathscr{A}\}$.*

Corollary 2. *Let S be a semigroup, A a commutative subsemigroup of S, and let $x \in S$ be such that $xa = ax$ for all $a \in A$. Then*

$$(A \cup \{x\}) = A \cup (x) \cup \{ax^r \mid a \in A, r \in \mathbf{N}\}.$$

Corollary 3. *Let S be a commutative semigroup with identity e; then for all $x_1, \ldots, x_n$ in S we have $(x_1, \ldots, x_n) = \{\prod_{i=1}^{n} x_i^{r_i} \mid r_i \in \mathbf{N}^\circ, 1 \le i \le n;$ some $r_i \ne 0\}$, where $x_i^0 = e$.*

The following exercises treat ideals in the semigroup S:

Exercise 2. *For any $A \subseteq S$, SA is a left ideal and AS a right ideal.*

Exercise 3. *If S has a left identity, SA is the left ideal generated by A (that is, the smallest left ideal containing A), and similarly on the right. [Hint: $SA \supseteq eA = A$.]*

Exercise 4. *For any* $x \in S$, Sx *is called a* **principal left ideal**, *and* xS *a* **principal right ideal**. *Prove that if* S *has a left* (*right*) *identity, any left* (*right*) *ideal is a union of principal left* (*right*) *ideals.* [Hint: $I = \bigcup_{x \in I} Sx$.]

Exercise 5. *If* $x \in S$ *is not left cancellable, neither is* zx *for any* $z \in S$, *and similarly on the right.*

Corollary. *The set of elements of* S *which are not left* (*right*) *cancellable is a left* (*right*) *ideal.*

Exercise 6. *Let* $a \in S$ *be absorbent; then for any* $x \in S$ *and* $A \subseteq S$, *we say that* x **annihilates** A *on the left if* $xA = \{a\}$. *Prove that the set of* $x \in S$ *which annihilate a given* $A \subseteq S$ *on the left is a left ideal, and that it is also a right ideal if* A *is a left ideal.*

Exercise 7. *Let* $a \in S$ *be absorbent; we call* $x \in S$ **nilpotent** *if* $x^n = a$ *for some* $n \in \mathbb{N}$. *Prove that if* S *is commutative and* x *is nilpotent, so is* zx *for any* $z \in S$, *so that the set of nilpotent elements of* S *is an ideal.*

Exercise 8. *Continuing Exercise 7. we call* $A \subseteq S$ *nilpotent if* $A^n = \{a\}$ *for some* $n \in \mathbb{N}$—*in other words, if* $a_1 \cdots a_n = a$ *for all* $a_1, \ldots, a_n$ *in* A. *Note that* $\{x\}$ *is nilpotent if and only if* x *is nilpotent; prove that every element and subset of a nilpotent set is nilpotent.*

Exercise 9. *If* A *is a nilpotent left ideal, then* AS *is a nilpotent two-sided ideal, and similarly on the right.*

CANCELLATION SEMIGROUPS AND GROUPS

A semigroup in which every element is cancellable is called a **cancellation semigroup**. A semigroup with identity e in which every element is e-invertible is called a **group**. By Proposition 5, a group is a cancellation semigroup. Evidently the trivial groupoid is a group. Note that since a group must have an identity element, it cannot be empty. A commutative group is usually called **Abelian**.

Examples:
  (a) The set of permutations of any set, and the set of automorphisms of any groupoid, are groups under $\circ$.
  (b) $\mathbb{N}^\circ$ is a cancellation semigroup under addition; $\mathbb{N}$ is a cancellation semigroup under both addition and multiplication.

Proposition 10. *Let* S *be a semigroup with identity* e; *then the set of* e-*invertible elements of* S *is a group.*

Proof: It is a semigroup by Corollary 1 to Proposition 3; it contains e by Exercise 32.4; and the inverse of an invertible element is invertible by the corollary to Proposition 6. //

This group is called the **group of units** of S.

Note that by Propositions 6 and 31.1, the identity in any group is unique, and the inverse of any element is unique. From now on we denote the unique inverse of x in any group by x^{-1} (or by $-x$, when we use additive notation).

Exercise 10. *A group in which $x^2 = e$ (or equivalently, $x^{-1} = x$) for all x is Abelian.*

Exercise 11. *Let G be a group; then $F = \{((x, y), xy^{-1}) \mid x, y$ in $G\}$ is a composition on G. Prove that*

(a) *The following statements are equivalent:*
 (1) *F is associative*
 (2) *F is commutative*
 (3) *F is the same as the group composition*
 (4) *$x^2 = e$ for all $x \in G$*
(b) *The group identity e is the only right identity for F; there is no left identity unless F is commutative, and no left or right absorbent element unless G is trivial*
(c) *Any element of G is cancellable for F, and is its own two-sided e-inverse for F.*

Exercise 12. *Let S be a groupoid under the composition F, and define the "reverse composition" F^* by $F^*(x, y) = F(y, x)$ for all x, y in S. We denote the groupoid S under F^* by S^*. Verify that*

(a) *$(S^*)^* = S$*
(b) *A subset of S is stable under F^* if and only if it is stable under F*
(c) *A function from S into the groupoid T (under the composition G) is an (F^*, G^*)-homomorphism if and only if it is an (F, G)-homomorphism; in particular, if $S \cong T$ then $S^* \cong T^*$.*
(d) *An equivalence on S is a congruence for F^* if and only if it is a congruence for F*
(e) *$\prod_I (S_i)^* = (\prod_I S_i)^*$*
(f) *$e \in S$ is idempotent (a (left, right) identity, (left, right) absorbent) for F^* if and only if it is idempotent (a (right, left) identity, (right, left) absorbent) for F*
(g) *$x \in S$ is (left, right) cancellable or invertible for F^* if and only if it is (right, left) cancellable or invertible for F*
(h) *F^* is associative if and only if F is associative*

(i) F^* *is commutative if and only if* $F^* = F$

(j) *If* G *is a group, then* $G^* \cong G$. [Hint: Use $\{(x, x^{-1}) \mid x \in G\}$.]

We conclude this section with two propositions which provide useful criteria for a semigroup to be a group.

Proposition 11. *Let* S *be a semigroup with left identity* e, *and let every element of* S *be left* e-*invertible; then* S *is a group.*

Proof: Let x' be a left e-inverse of $x \in S$; then $x'x = e = ee = (x'x)e = x'(xe)$. Since x' is left invertible, by Proposition 5 it is also left cancellable, so that (cancelling it) we have $x = xe$, and since x was arbitrary, this makes e a right identity. Since x' has a left inverse and also has the right inverse x, by Proposition 6 and its corollary x has x' as its unique two-sided inverse. $/\!/$

Corollary. *Let* S *be a semigroup with left identity, and let* $Sx = S$ *for all* $x \in S$; *then* S *is a group.*

Proposition 12. *The following statements about the semigroup* S *are equivalent:*

(1) S *is a group*

(2) $Sx = xS = S$ *for all* $x \in S$, *and* $S \neq \varnothing$

(3) $Sx = S$ *for all* $x \in S$, *and* $aS = S$ *for some* $a \in S$.

Proof: If S is a group, for any $y \in S$ we have $y = (yx^{-1})x \in Sx$ and $y = x(x^{-1}y) \in xS$, proving (2). Conversely, if (3) holds, S has identity e by Proposition 7; and since $e \in Sw$ for any $w \in S$, there exists $w' \in S$ such that $w'w = e$, so that any $w \in S$ has a left e-inverse, making S a group by Proposition 11. $/\!/$

Left and right can, of course, be interchanged in Proposition 11 and in (3) of Proposition 12.

Exercise 13. *Let* S *be a semigroup with identity* e *in which every element has either a left* e-*inverse or a right* e-*inverse; then* S *is a group.*

35. DIVISION IN SEMIGROUPS

If x, y are elements of the groupoid S, and there exists an $a \in S$ such that $y = ax$, we say that x divides y on the right. Similarly, if there exists $b \in S$ such that $y = xb$, we say that x divides y on the left. If S is commutative, these relations are the same, and we say simply that x **divides** y (notation: $x \mid y$); we call y a **multiple** of x, and x a **divisor** (or sometimes a **factor**) of y. Note that in a semigroup with identity e, u is a unit (=invertible) if and only if it divides e on both right and left.

Proposition 1. *If* S *has identity, the* "*divides*" *relations on* S *are reflexive; if* S *is a semigroup, they are transitive.*

Proof: If $e \in S$ is an identity, any $x \in S$ divides itself on both right and left, since $x = ex = xe$. If S is a semigroup, $y = ux$ and $z = vy$ imply $z = v(ux) = (vu)x$, and similarly on the left. //

Exercise 1. *Let S be a cancellation semigroup with identity e, and no units other than e; then the "divides" relations on S are weakly antisymmetric, and thus are order relations.* [Note that **N** under multiplication and **N**° under addition have these properties; compare Exercise 5.2 and Propositions 4.11, 13.]

The set of $y \in S$ such that x divides y on the right is just Sx, so that if S is a semigroup, this set is a principal left ideal (Exercise 34.4); and analogously with "left" and "right" interchanged.

Proposition 2. *If S has identity, and $Sx \supseteq Sy$, then x divides y on the right. If S is a semigroup, and x divides y on the right, then $Sx \supseteq Sy$.*

Proof: If $Sy \subseteq Sx$, and $e \in S$ is an identity, we have $y = ey \in Sy \subseteq Sx$, so that $y = ax$ for some $a \in S$. If S is a semigroup and $y = ax$, let $z \in Sy$; say $z = wy$; then $z = w(ax) = (wa)x \in Sx$. //

Corollary 1. *In a semigroup with identity, x divides y on the right if and only if $Sx \supseteq Sy$. In particular, $Sx = Sy$ if and only if x and y divide each other on the right.*

Corollary 2. *In a semigroup with identity, if $y = ux$, where u is left invertible, then $Sx = Sy$.*
Proof: Let $u'u = e$; then $x = u'y$. //

If $Sx = Sy$, y is sometimes called a left **associate** of x, and analogously on the right. Clearly "is a left (right) associate of" is an equivalence on S.

Proposition 3. *Let S be a semigroup with identity, let $x \in S$ be right cancellable, and let $Sx = Sy$; then $y = ux$, where u is left invertible.*
Proof: Let $x = ay$, $y = bx$; then $x = abx$, so that (cancelling x) $ab = e$, proving that b is left invertible. //

A similar argument shows that if S, x are as in Proposition 3 and $Sx = Scx$, then c is left invertible. "Left" and "right" can, of course, be interchanged throughout all the foregoing.

Exercise 2. *If some element of the semigroup S divides every element on both left and right, S has identity, and any such element is a unit.* [Hint: Proposition 34.7.]

Corollary 1. *In a semigroup S, u is a unit if and only if $Su = uS = S$.*

Corollary 2. *In a semigroup, any left and right divisor of a unit is a unit.*

In the remainder of this section we assume, unless specified otherwise, that S is a commutative cancellation semigroup with identity e. [Exercise: What happens if any of these assumptions is relaxed?]

IRREDUCIBLE AND PRIME ELEMENTS

We call $x \in S$ **irreducible** if $x = ab$ implies $x \mid a$ or $x \mid b$ for all a, b in S. Similarly, we call x **prime** if $x \mid ab$ implies $x \mid a$ or $x \mid b$ for all a, b in S. Clearly prime implies irreducible.

Since a unit divides any element (Exercise 2), any unit is trivially irreducible and prime. [The case where x is a unit is often ruled out in these definitions, but we shall not do so here.] If S is **N** under multiplication, it turns out, as we shall see below, that "prime" and "irreducible" are equivalent, and that $x \neq 1$ is prime if and only if it is prime in the sense of Exercise 5.4.

Exercise 3. *x is prime if and only if* $x \mid \prod_{i=1}^{n} x_i$ *implies* $x \mid x_i$ *for some i,* $1 \leq i \leq n$.

Exercise 4. *If x is irreducible or prime, so is any associate of x.*

Proposition 4. *The following statements are equivalent:*

(1) *x is irreducible*

(2) *If* $x = ab$, *then a or b is a unit*

(3) *If* $y \mid x$, *then* $x \mid y$ *or y is a unit.*

Proof: If x is irreducible and $x = ab$, then $x \mid a$ or $x \mid b$. Suppose that $x \mid a$, say $a = xw$; then $xe = x = ab = (xw)b = x(wb)$, so that $wb = e$, making b a unit and proving (2). If (2) holds and $y \mid x$, say $x = yz$, then y or z is a unit, but if z is a unit, we have $y = ye = y(zz^{-1}) = (yz)z^{-1} = xz^{-1}$, so that $x \mid y$, proving (3). If (3) holds and $x = ab$, then $x \mid a$ or a is a unit, and in the latter case we have $a^{-1}x = a^{-1}(ab) = (a^{-1}a)b = eb = b$, so that $x \mid b$, proving (1). ‖

Exercise 5. *The following statements are equivalent:*

(a) *x is irreducible*

(b) *If* $x = \prod_{i=1}^{n} x_i$, *then at most one of the x_i's is not a unit*

(c) *If* $x = \prod_{i=1}^{n} x_i$, *then* $x \mid x_i$ *for some i,* $1 \leq i \leq n$.

Let $\mathscr{I}_S$ be the set of principal ideals of S, ordered by inclusion; thus $\mathscr{I}_S$ has $S = Se$ as greatest element. Let $\mathscr{I}'_S = \mathscr{I}_S - \{S\}$ be the set of *proper* principal ideals of S. The maximal elements of $\mathscr{I}'_S$, if any, are called **maximal principal ideals.**

Proposition 5. *x is an irreducible nonunit if and only if Sx is a maximal principal ideal.*

Proof: By Corollary 1 to Exercise 2, Sx is proper if and only if x is a nonunit. If x is also irreducible and $Sx \subseteq Sy$, then $y \mid x$, so that y is a unit or $x \mid y$. But if y is a unit we have $Sy = S$, while if $x \mid y$ we have $Sy \subseteq Sx$, whence $Sy = Sx$; thus Sx is maximal. The proof of the converse is left to the reader. $\parallel$

The ideal $A \subseteq S$ is called **prime** if $S - A$ is a subsemigroup. This terminology is justified by

Proposition 6. *x is prime if and only if Sx is a prime ideal.*

Proof: If Sx is not prime, let a, b be in $S - Sx$ but ab in Sx; then $x \mid ab$ but neither $x \mid a$ nor $x \mid b$, so that x is not prime, and conversely. $\parallel$

Corollary. *A proper prime principal ideal is maximal.*

GAUSSIAN SEMIGROUPS

Proposition 7. *If $\mathscr{I}_S$ satisfies the maximum condition, then any element of S is a composite of irreducible elements.*

Proof: If x is itself irreducible, there is nothing to prove. If not, the set of proper principal ideals which contain Sx is nonempty, so has a maximal element Sx_1; thus x_1 is an irreducible nonunit and $x_1 \mid x$. Let $x = x_1 x_1^*$, where $Sx \subset Sx_1^*$ since x_1 is not a unit (see the remark following Proposition 3). If x_1^* is irreducible, we are done; if not, we can repeat the same argument to find an irreducible nonunit x_2 such that $x_1^* = x_2 x_2^*$ (say), where $Sx_1^* \subset Sx_2^*$. Repeating this process yields an ascending chain $Sx \subset Sx_1^* \subset Sx_2^* \subset \cdots$ —which is impossible—unless x_n^* is irreducible for some n, so that we have $x = x_1 x_1^* = x_1 x_2 x_2^* = \cdots = (\prod_{i=1}^{n} x_i) x_n^*$, where the x_i's and x_n^* are all irreducible. $\parallel$

Proposition 8. *Let $u \prod_{i=1}^{r} x_i$ divide $v \prod_{i=1}^{s} y_i$, where u, v are units and the x's and y's are prime nonunits. Then $r \leq s$, and there exists a one-to-one function G from $\mathbf{N}_r$ into $\mathbf{N}_s$ such that $Sx_i = Sy_{G(i)}$, $1 \leq i \leq r$.*

Proof: If $s = 1$, by Exercise 5 at most one of the x's is not a unit; but the x's are all nonunits, so that we must have $r = 1$ and $Sx_1 = Sy_1$. Let $s > 1$ and suppose the assertion true for $s - 1$. By Exercise 3, $x_1 \mid \prod_{i=1}^{s} y_i$ implies $x_1 \mid y_j$ for some j, $1 \leq j \leq s$. Since y_j is irreducible and x_1 is not a unit, this implies that $y_j \mid x_1$, so that $Sx_1 = Sy_j$ and $x_1 = u_1 y_j$, where u_1 is a unit (Proposition 3). Cancelling y_j thus gives

$$uu_1 \prod_{i=2}^{r} x_i = v\left(\prod_{i=1}^{j-1} y_i \right)\left(\prod_{i=j+1}^{s} y_i \right),$$

where uu_1 is a unit and there are now only $s - 1$ y's, so that the induction hypothesis applies. //

Note that, conversely, if such a G exists, then $u \prod_{i=1}^{r} x_i$ divides $v \prod_{i=1}^{s} y_i$.

Corollary 1. *Let* $u \prod_{i=1}^{r} x_i = v \prod_{i=1}^{s} y_i$, *where* u, v *are units and the* x's *and* y's *are prime nonunits. Then* $r = s$, *and there exists a permutation* G *of* $\mathbf{N}_r$ *such that* $Sx_i = Sy_{G(i)}$, $1 \leq i \leq r$.

This corollary tells us that an element of S can be a composite of prime elements in "essentially only one way."

Corollary 2. *Let* $u \prod_{i=1}^{r} x_i^{h_i} = v \prod_{i=1}^{s} y_i^{k_i}$, *where* u, v *are units; the* x's *and* y's *are prime nonunits such that* $Sx_1, \ldots, Sx_r$ *are all distinct and* $Sy_1, \ldots, Sy_s$ *are all distinct; and the* h's *and* k's *are in* $\mathbf{N}$. *Then* $r = s$, *and there exists a permutation* G *of* $\mathbf{N}_r$ *such that* $Sx_i = Sy_{G(i)}$ *and* $h_i = k_i$, $1 \leq i \leq r$.

Combining Proposition 7 and Corollary 1 to Proposition 8, we obtain

Theorem 1. *If* $\mathscr{I}_S$ *satisfies the maximum condition and every maximal principal ideal is prime* (*or equivalently: every irreducible element is prime*), *then every nonunit of* S *is a composite of irreducible nonunits in essentially only one way* (that is, in the sense of Corollary 1 to Proposition 8).

A commutative cancellation semigroup with identity in which the conclusion of Theorem 1 holds is called **Gaussian**. The next two propositions give us the converse of Theorem 1:

Proposition 9. *If* S *is Gaussian, every irreducible element of* S *is prime.*

Proof: Let x be irreducible and divide ab, say $ab = xy$. Let $x = x_1$, $y = \prod_{i=2}^{m} x_i$, $a = \prod_{i=1}^{k} a_i$, $b = \prod_{i=k+1}^{n} a_i$, where the x's and a's are all irreducible. Then since S is Gaussian, $Sx = Sa_j$ for some $j \in \mathbf{N}_n$, so that if $1 \leq j \leq k$ we have $x \mid a$, while if $k < j \leq n$ we have $x \mid b$. //

Proposition 10. *Let* S *be Gaussian, and let* $x \mid y$, *where* $x = \prod_{i=1}^{k} x_i$, $y = \prod_{i=1}^{s} y_i$, *with the* x's *and* y's *irreducible nonunits. Then* $k \leq s$, *and* $k = s$ *if and only if* $Sx = Sy$.

Proof: Let $y = xz$; if z is a unit, we have $k = s$ by the Gaussian property. If not, let $z = \prod_{i=k+1}^{r} x_i$, where the x's are irreducible nonunits; then $r = s$, so that $k < s$. //

Corollary. *If* S *is Gaussian,* $\mathscr{I}_S$ *satisfies the maximum condition.*

Proof: Let $Sx_1 \subset Sx_2 \subset \cdots$ be an ascending chain in $\mathscr{I}_S$, and let $x_i = \prod_{j=1}^{r_i} x_{ij}$, where the x_{ij}'s are irreducible nonunits; then $r_1 > r_2 > \cdots$ would be a descending chain in $\mathbf{N}$, which is impossible. //

An Abelian group is trivially Gaussian, since every element is a unit. We shall show below that **N** under multiplication is Gaussian; this is, of course, the familiar "fundamental theorem of arithmetic." In the remainder of this section we establish two useful conditions for a semigroup to be Gaussian.

CONDITIONS FOR A SEMIGROUP TO BE GAUSSIAN

We call S a **GCD semigroup** if any two principal ideals of S have a sup in $\mathscr{I}_S$. [Note that they must have a sup in the complete lattice of *all* ideals of S (Exercise 23.2), but this sup is not necessarily in $\mathscr{I}_S$.]

Proposition 11. *A Gaussian semigroup is a GCD semigroup.*

Proof: Given a, b in S, if either is a unit then sup $\{Sa, Sb\} = S$. If not, there exists a set $\{x_1, \ldots, x_n\}$ of irreducible nonunits such that $a = \prod_{i=1}^{n} x_i^{r_i}$, $b = \prod_{i=1}^{n} x_i^{s_i}$, where the r's and s's are in **N**°. (To see this, take the union of sets of irreducible nonunits of which a and b are composites.) Let $t_i = \inf\{r_i, s_i\}$, $1 \le i \le n$, and let $c = \prod_{i=1}^{n} x_i^{t_i}$; then readily $Sc = \sup\{Sa, Sb\}$. ∥

Proposition 12. *S is a GCD semigroup if and only if any a, b in S have a* **greatest common divisor**—*this is, for any a, b in S there exists $d \in S$ such that*

(1) $d \mid a$ *and* $d \mid b$
(2) *If* $d^* \mid a$ *and* $d^* \mid b$, *then* $d^* \mid d$.

Proof: Clearly if such a d exists, $Sd = \sup \{Sa, Sb\}$, and conversely. ∥

Corollary 1. *If d_1 and d_2 are both greatest common divisors of a and b, then $Sd_1 = Sd_2$. Conversely, if d_1 is a greatest common divisor of a and b, and $Sd_1 = Sd_2$, then d_2 is also a greatest common divisor of a and b.*

Corollary 2. **N** *under multiplication is a GCD semigroup.*

Proof: Proposition 11.1. ∥

In the case of **N**, we can speak of *the* greatest common divisor of a and b, since 1 is the only unit (see Exercise 1).

Exercise 6. *If S is a GCD semigroup, any finite set of principal ideals of S has a sup in $\mathscr{I}_S$. Moreover, for all a, b, c in S we have* sup $\{Sa,$ sup $\{Sb, Sc\}\} =$ sup $\{$sup $\{Sa, Sb\}, Sc\} =$ sup $\{Sa, Sb, Sc\}$. *[Hint: See Propositions 11.2–3.]*

Note that d is a greatest common divisor of $a_1, \ldots, a_n$ if and only if it divides each of them, and is divisible by any d^* which divides each of them.

Exercise 7. *In any semigroup S we have* $\sup \{Sx, Syx\} = Sx$ *for all x, y in S. In any groupoid S with identity, if* $\sup \{Sa, Sb\} = Sa$, *then a divides b on the right.*

Lemma 1. *If S is a GCD semigroup, and* $\sup \{Sa, Sb\} = Sd$, *then* $\sup \{Sca, Scb\} = Scd$ *for all $c \in S$.*

Proof: Let $\sup \{Sca, Scb\} = Sz$; then $z|ca$, $z|cb$, say $ca = zx$, $cb = zy$. Since $Sa \subseteq Sd$, we have $Sca = cSa \subseteq cSd = Scd$, and similarly $Scb \subseteq Scd$; thus their sup must also be contained in Scd, so that $cd|z$, say $z = cdw$. Hence $ca = cdwx$, $cb = cdwy$, and (cancelling c) $a = dwx$, $b = dwy$. Since dw divides both a and b, it must divide their greatest common divisor d, say $d = dwt$. Cancelling d thus shows that w is a unit, and since $z = cdw$ we have $Sz = Scd$. $\parallel$

We say that a and b are **relatively prime** (or that a is relatively prime to b, and b to a) if $\sup \{Sa, Sb\} = S$. Note that a unit is relatively prime to any element.

Exercise 8. *a and b are relatively prime if and only if $x|a$, $x|b$ imply that x is a unit.*

Exercise 9. *Let S be Gaussian, and let $x \in S$ not be a power of an irreducible element; then there exist nonunits a, b in S, relatively prime, such that $x = ab$.*

Proposition 13. *Let S be Gaussian, and let $a = \prod_{i=1}^{r} a_i$, $b = \prod_{i=1}^{s} b_i$ be elements of S, where the a_i's and b_i's are irreducible nonunits. Then a and b are relatively prime if and only if $Sa_i \neq Sb_j$ for all i, j, $1 \leq i \leq r$, $1 \leq j \leq s$.*

Proof: If $Sa_i = Sb_j$, it contains both Sa and Sb, so that their sup cannot be S. Conversely, if their sup is $Sc \subset S$, let $c = \prod_{i=1}^{t} c_i$, where the c_i's are irreducible nonunits; then by Proposition 8, since c divides both a and b, any Sc_k is both an Sa_i and an Sb_j. $\parallel$

Corollary 1. *In a Gaussian semigroup S, a and b are relatively prime if and only if $a|bc$ implies $a|c$ for all $c \in S$.*

Proof: If $a|bc$, every Sa_i is either an Sb_j or an Sc_k; but no Sa_i can be an Sb_j. Conversely, if we had $Sa_1 = Sb_j$ (say), let $c = \prod_{i=2}^{r} a_i$; then a divides bc but not c. $\parallel$

Corollary 2. *In a Gaussian semigroup S, a and b are relatively prime if and only if whenever a and b both divide c, then ab divides c—in other words, if and only if $\inf \{Sa, Sb\} = Sab$ for all a, b in S.*

Proof: If $a|c$ and $b|c$, every Sa_i and every Sb_j is an Sc_k, and no Sc_k can be both. Conversely, if $Sa_1 = Sb_j$ (say), then a and b both divide $(\prod_{i=2}^{r} a_i)(\prod_{i=1}^{s} b_i)$, but ab does not divide it. $\parallel$

Corollary 3. *Let a, b be elements of a Gaussian semigroup, and let $a = a'd$, $b = b'd$; then a' and b' are relatively prime if and only if d is a greatest common divisor of a and b.*

Corollary 4. *An element of a Gaussian semigroup is prime if and only if it is relatively prime to every element which it does not divide.*

Lemma 2. *In a GCD semigroup, if a is relatively prime to both b and c, it is relatively prime to bc.*

Proof: If sup $\{Sa, Sb\} = S$, then by Lemma 1, sup $\{Sac, Sbc\} = Sc$. Hence (using Exercises 6–7) sup $\{Sa, Sbc\}$ = sup $\{$sup $\{Sa, Sac\}, Sbc\}$ = sup $\{Sa,$ sup $\{Sac, Sbc\}\}$ = sup $\{Sa, Sc\}$ = S. //

Proposition 14. *In a GCD semigroup, every irreducible element is prime (equivalently; every maximal principal ideal is prime).*

Proof: Let x be irreducible and $x \mid ab$, so that by Exercise 7, sup $\{Sx, Sab\}$ = Sx. If x is a unit, there is nothing to prove; if not, Sx is a maximal principal ideal, so that we have sup $\{Sx, Sa\}$ = Sx or S, and sup $\{Sx, Sb\}$ = Sx or S. By Lemma 2, they cannot both be S; thus at least one of them, say sup $\{Sx, Sa\}$, is Sx, proving that $x \mid a$. //

Corollary 1. *Let S be a GCD semigroup, and let $\mathscr{I}_S$ satisfy the maximum condition; then S is Gaussian.*

Corollary 2. *N under multiplication is Gaussian.*

Proof: Let $\mathscr{A} = \{kN \mid k \in A \subseteq N\}$ be any nonempty subset of $\mathscr{I}_N$; then A is a nonempty subset of **N**, and so has a minimal element m, which readily makes mN maximal in $\mathscr{A}$. //

Exercise 10. *Call S an "LCM semigroup" if any two principal ideals of S have an inf in $\mathscr{I}_S$. Verify that this is equivalent to any two elements of S having a least common multiple, that is, for all a, b in S there exists an $m \in S$ such that $a \mid m$ and $b \mid m$, and if $a \mid m^*$, $b \mid m^*$, then $m \mid m^*$. Prove analogs of Exercises 6–7 and Lemma 1 for LCM semigroups. Call a "relatively coprime" to b if inf $\{Sa, Sb\}$ = Sab, and prove an analog of Lemma 2 for LCM semigroups.*

We call S a **PL-semigroup** if $\mathscr{I}_S \cup \{\varnothing\}$ is closed under intersection and under union of chains. Since closedness under intersection makes $\mathscr{I}_S \cup \{\varnothing\}$ a complete lattice, a PL-semigroup is a GCD semigroup.

Exercise 11. *N under multiplication is a PL-semigroup.*

Proposition 15. *If S is a PL-semigroup, $\mathscr{I}_S$ satisfies the maximum condition.*

Proof: By Proposition 16.3, an *I*-lattice satisfies the maximum condition if it is closed under union of chains and every element of it is finitely generated.

But in fact every element of $\mathscr{I}_S$ is monogenic, since Sx is the ideal generated by $\{x\}$ (Exercise 34.3).   //

Corollary. *A PL-semigroup is Gaussian.*

Exercise 12. $\mathbf{N}^\circ$ *under addition is a PL-semigroup.* [Note, however, that in this semigroup the only unit is 0 and the only irreducible nonunit is 1, so that the Gaussian property means only that any $n \neq 0$ is the sum of a unique number of 1's.]

Exercise 13. *For all* x, y *in* S *we have* $(Sx)(Sy) = Sxy$, *so that* $\mathscr{I}_S$ *is also a commutative cancellation semigroup with identity* $S = Se$ *which is its only unit. Call* Sx *irreducible if* $Sx = SaSb$ *implies* $Sx = Sa$ *or* $Sx = Sb$; *prove that* Sx *is irreducible if and only if* x *is irreducible.* [*Prove also that* Sx *is prime if and only if* $Sx \supseteq SaSb$ *implies* $Sx \supseteq Sa$ *or* $Sx \supseteq Sb$.] *Conclude that if* $\mathscr{I}_S$ *satisfies the maximum condition, any element of* $\mathscr{I}_S$ *is a composite of irreducible elements. Prove further that an element of* $\mathscr{I}_S$ *can be a composite of prime elements in only one way* (*no "essentially" needed here, except for the order of the factors in the composite*).

36. GROUPS OF QUOTIENTS; INTEGERS AND RATIONAL NUMBERS

In this section we show that any commutative cancellation semigroup can be "embedded" in an Abelian group. Applying this construction to the semigroup **N** under addition, we obtain the group of integers; applying it to **N** under multiplication yields the group of positive rational numbers.

Theorem 1. *If* S *is a nonempty commutative cancellation semigroup, there exists an Abelian group* A, *and an isomorphism* F *of* S *into* A, *such that* $\{xy^{-1} \mid x, y \text{ in } F(S)\} = A$—*in other words, every element of* A *is a quotient of elements of* $F(S)$. [For this reason, A is called the **group of quotients** of S.]

Proof: Consider the relation on $S \times S$

$$E = \{((a, b), (c, d)) \mid a, b, c, d \text{ in } S; \ ad = bc\}.$$

It is easily verified that E is an equivalence, and a congruence for the direct product composition on $S \times S$. Let A be the quotient groupoid $(S \times S)/E$; thus A is a commutative semigroup. By cancellation, we have $((a, b), (x, x)) \in E$ if and only if $a = b$; hence $\{(y, y) \mid y \in S\}$ is an E-class (that is, an element of A), call it $\bar{e}$. Moreover, for all x, a, b in S we have $(x, x)(a, b) = (xa, xb)$, where $((xa, xb), (a, b)) \in E$; thus $\bar{e}$ is an identity for the composition on A.

For all a, b in S we also have $(a, b)(b, a) = (ab, ab) \in \bar{e}$, so that every element of A has an $\bar{e}$-inverse, making A a group.

Note next that for all a, b, c in S we have $((ab, b), (ac, c)) \in E$, and conversely $((ab, b), (d, c)) \in E$ implies $d = ac$; hence $\bar{a} = \{(ay, y) \mid y \in S\}$ is an E-class. Readily, $\bar{a} = \bar{b}$ if and only if $a = b$; while $(ay, y)(bz, z) = (abyz, yz) \in \overline{ab}$, so that $\bar{a}\bar{b} = \overline{ab}$. Thus $\{(x, \bar{x}) \mid x \in S\}$ is an isomorphism of S into A. Finally, for all a, b in S we have $((a, b), (ax, x)(y, by)) \in E$, so that the E-class containing (a, b) is $\bar{a}\bar{b}^{-1}$. $/\!/$

THE INTEGERS

Let S be $\mathbf{N}$ under addition; then the group obtained by the construction of Theorem 1 (translated into additive notation!) is called the group of **integers** under addition. We denote this group by $\mathbf{I}$, its identity by 0 (see Exercise 1 below), and the inverse of $x \in \mathbf{I}$ by $-x$. [It is often denoted by $\mathbf{Z}$ (for "Zahlen") rather than $\mathbf{I}$.]

Proposition 1. $\mathbf{I} = \{0\} \cup F(\mathbf{N}) \cup [-F(\mathbf{N})]$ (where F is as in Theorem 1, and $-F(\mathbf{N})$ means $\{-x \mid x \in F(\mathbf{N})\}$), and these three sets are disjoint.

Proof; By Propositions 4.12–13, for any m, n in $\mathbf{N}$ exactly one of the following is true: $m = n$; $m = n + r$ for some $r \in \mathbf{N}$; or $n = m + s$ for some $s \in \mathbf{N}$. In the first case, the E-class containing (m, n) is 0 ("$\bar{e}$" of the proof of Theorem 1); in the second case we have $(n + r, n) \in \bar{r}$; and in the third case, $(m, m + s) = -(m + s, m) \in -\bar{s}$. $/\!/$

An integer in $F(\mathbf{N})$ is called **positive**, while one in $-F(\mathbf{N})$ is called **negative**. From now on we shall denote the positive integer $F(n)$ by n, and its inverse by $-n$. (There is little danger of confusion even if we fail to mention whether we are regarding n as an element of $\mathbf{N}$ or of $F(\mathbf{N}) \subset \mathbf{I}$, since $F(\mathbf{N})$ is isomorphic to $\mathbf{N}$.) We abbreviate $x + (-y)$ by $x - y$. Note that **subtraction** (that is, $\{((x, y), x - y) \mid x, y \text{ in } \mathbf{I}\}$) is a composition on $\mathbf{I}$ (see Exercise 34.11).

Exercise 1. $F(\mathbf{N}) \cup \{0\}$ is a subsemigroup of $\mathbf{I}$ and is isomorphic to $\mathbf{N}^{\circ}$ under addition.

An integer which is in $F(\mathbf{N}) \cup \{0\}$ is called **nonnegative**.

Exercise 2. Let R be the following relation on $\mathbf{I}$: $\{(m, n) \mid m, n \text{ in } F(\mathbf{N}), m \leq n\} \cup \{(-m, n) \mid m, n \text{ in } F(\mathbf{N}) \cup \{0\}\} \cup \{(-m, -n) \mid m, n \text{ in } F(\mathbf{N}), n \leq m\}$. Verify that R is a total order relation. [Note that $F(\mathbf{N})$ under the restriction of R to it is order isomorphic to $\mathbf{N}$ under $\leq$, so that R "extends" $\leq$ from $\mathbf{N}$ to $\mathbf{I}$; from now on we denote R by $\leq$. Verify that $x \in \mathbf{I}$ is positive if and only if $x > 0$, and negative if and only if $x < 0$.]

Exercise 3. *Let G be the composition on* **I** *defined, for all m, n in* **N**, *by* $G(m, n)$ $= G(-m, -n) = mn$; $G(-m, n) = G(m, -n) = -mn$; $G(0, x) = G(x, 0)$ $= 0$ *for all* $x \in$ **I**. *Verify that*

  (a) *G is associative and commutative, and distributes over addition and subtraction on* **I**
  (b) 1 *is an identity for G, and* -1 *is the only other unit*
  (c) *Every integer except* 0 *is cancellable for G*
  (d) **I** $- \{0\}$ *and* $F(\mathbf{N})$ *are stable under G.*

[Note that $F(\mathbf{N})$ under the restriction of G to it is isomorphic to **N** under multiplication, so that G "extends" multiplication from **N** to **I**. From now on we denote G multiplicatively.]

Exercise 4. *Extend Exercise 5.6 from* **N°** *to* **I** *by showing that for all a, b in* **I**, *where* $b \neq 0$, *there exist q, r in* **I** *such that* $a = qb + r$ *and* $0 \le r < b$ *if* $b > 0$, $0 \le r < -b$ *if* $b < 0$.

Proposition 2. *The following statements about a, b, d in* **N** *are equivalent:*

  (1) *d is the greatest common divisor of a and b*
  (2) *d is a common divisor of a and b, and there exist m, n in* **I** *such that* $ma + nb = d$.

Proof: If (2) holds and d^* divides a and b, say $a = xd^*$, $b = yd^*$, then $d = (mx + ny)d^*$, so that d^* divides d, proving (1). Conversely, let $T = \{ma + nb \mid m, n \text{ in } \mathbf{I}\}$, and let d be the smallest positive integer in T. Let $a = qd + r$, where $0 \le r < d$; then $r = a - qd$ is still in T, contradicting the minimality of d unless $r = 0$, that is, $d \mid a$. Similarly, $d \mid b$, so that d is a common divisor of a and b, and thus must be their greatest common divisor by the first part of the proof. //

Corollary. *a, b in* **N** *are relatively prime if and only if there exist m, n in* **I** *such that* $ma + nb = 1$.

Exercise 5. *The following statements about* $a_1, \ldots, a_k$, *d in* **N** *are equivalent:*

  (a) *d is the greatest common divisor of* $a_1, \ldots, a_k$
  (b) *d is a common divisor of* $a_1, \ldots, a_k$, *and there exist* $m_1, \ldots, m_k$ *in* **I** *such that* $m_1 a_1 + \cdots + m_k a_k = d$.

THE POSITIVE RATIONALS

Let S be **N** under multiplication; then the group obtained by the construction of Theorem 1 is called the group of **positive rationals** (or positive rational numbers) under multiplication, and will be denoted by $\mathbf{R}^+$. From now on we denote $\bar{n}$ (in $\mathbf{R}^+$) by n, and $\bar{n}^{-1}$ by n^{-1}; note that 1 is the identity of $\mathbf{R}^+$. We sometimes denote n^{-1} by $1/n$, and mn^{-1} by m/n; the expression m/n is called a **fraction**, m its **numerator**, and n its **denominator**. By the theorem, every $\rho \in \mathbf{R}^+$ is a fraction, that is, there exist m, n in $\mathbf{N}$ such that $\rho = m/n$. Note that **division** (that is, $\{((x, y), x/y) \mid x, y$ in $\mathbf{R}^+\}$) is a composition on $\mathbf{R}^+$.

Proposition 3. *For any $\rho \in \mathbf{R}^+$ there exist unique m, n in $\mathbf{N}$ such that $m/n = \rho$ and m is relatively prime to n.*

Proof: Let k be the least element of $\{r + s \mid r/s = \rho\}$, and let m/n be such that $m/n = \rho, m + n = k$. If $d \mid m$ and $d \mid n$, say $m = ad, n = bd$, then $a/b = \rho$, while $(a + b)d = m + n = k$, so that $a + b < k$ (contradiction) unless $d = 1$. For the uniqueness, let $u/v = \rho$, so that $nu = mv$. Then (Corollary 1 to Proposition 35.13) $n \mid v$ and $m \mid u$, say $v = nx, u = my$, and we have $nmy = mnx$, that is, $x = y$. Thus x divides both u and v, so that they cannot be relatively prime unless $x = 1$ and they are just m and n.   //

This m/n is called the **lowest-terms fraction** of ρ.

Exercise 6. *Let $\le$ be the relation $\{(\rho, \sigma) \mid ad \le bc$ for some a, b, c, d in $\mathbf{N}$ such that $a/b = \rho, c/d = \sigma\}$ on $\mathbf{R}^+$. Verify that this is independent of the choice of a, b, c, d, and that $\le$ is a total order relation.* [Note that $F(\mathbf{N})$ under the restriction of $\le$ is order isomorphic to $\mathbf{N}$ under $\le$, so that the new $\le$ "extends" the old one from $\mathbf{N}$ to $\mathbf{R}^+$.]

Exercise 7. *Let ρ, σ be in $\mathbf{R}^+, a/b = \rho, c/d = \sigma$, and let $\rho + \sigma = (ad + bc)/bd$. Verify that $\rho + \sigma$ is independent of the choice of a, b, c, d, so that $+$ is a composition on $\mathbf{R}^+$. Prove also that*

   (a) *$+$ is associative and commutative, and the multiplicative composition on $\mathbf{R}^+$ distributes over it*
   (b) *Every element of $\mathbf{R}^+$ is cancellable for $+$*
   (c) *$F(\mathbf{N})$ is stable under $+$.*

[Note that $F(\mathbf{N})$ under the restriction of $+$ is isomorphic to $\mathbf{N}$ under addition, so that the new $+$ "extends" the old one from $\mathbf{N}$ to $\mathbf{R}^+$.]

EXAMPLE 3: THE RATIONALS

Let S be $\mathbf{R}^+$ under $+$; then the group obtained by the construction of Theorem 1 is called the group of **rationals** (or rational numbers) under addition, and will be denoted by $\mathbf{R}$. [$\mathbf{R}$ is often denoted by $\mathbf{Q}$ (for "quotients"), and $\mathbf{R}^+$ by $\mathbf{Q}^+$.] From now on we denote $F(\rho)$ by ρ and $-F(\rho)$ by $-\rho$. Readily, if $m/n = \rho$, then $(-m)(-n) = \rho$, while $(-m)/(n) = m/(-n) = -\rho$.

Exercise 8. *State and prove analogs of Exercises 1–3 for $\mathbf{R}$. Prove also that every element of $\mathbf{R}$ except 0 is invertible for multiplication, so that $\mathbf{R} - \{0\}$ is an Abelian group under multiplication.*

Exercise 9. *Let S be $\mathbf{I} - \{0\}$ under multiplication, and let $\mathbf{R}'$ be the group obtained from it by the construction of Theorem 1. Verify that we can "adjoin"* *an element* 0 *to* $\mathbf{R}'$, *and "extend" addition and multiplication to* $\mathbf{R}' \cup \{0\}$ *(from* $\mathbf{I} - \{0\}$ *and* R', *respectively) in such a way that* $\mathbf{R}' \cup \{0\}$ *is isomorphic to* $\mathbf{R}$ *with respect to both addition and multiplication.*

Exercise 10. $\mathbf{I}$, $\mathbf{R}^+$, *and* $\mathbf{R}$ *all have cardinality* $\aleph_0$. [Hint: Use Exercise 21.4.]

We conclude this section with

Proposition 4. *Let G be a group, and S a nonempty commutative subsemigroup of G; then S is a cancellation semigroup, and G has a subsemigroup isomorphic to the group of quotients of S.*

Proof: S is a cancellation semigroup by Proposition 34.5. Let $S^{-1} = \{s^{-1} \mid s \in S\}$. If $xy = yx$, then $xy^{-1} = y^{-1}yxy^{-1} = y^{-1}xyy^{-1} = y^{-1}x$; also $(yx)^{-1} = (xy)^{-1}$, that is, $x^{-1}y^{-1} = y^{-1}x^{-1}$. Thus since S is commutative, so is $(S \cup S^{-1})$ (Corollary 3 to Proposition 34.8). Moreover, we readily have $(S \cup S^{-1}) = \{xy^{-1} \mid x, y \text{ in } S\}$, which immediately yields an isomorphism of $(S \cup S^{-1})$ with the group of quotients of S.   //

Exercise 11. *Isomorphic commutative cancellation semigroups have isomorphic groups of quotients.*

Exercise 12. *An Abelian group is isomorphic to its own group of quotients.*

VII

SUBGROUPS, FACTOR GROUPS, PRODUCTS OF GROUPS

The theory of groupoids developed in Chapter V can be significantly improved if the groupoids are groups. The primary purpose of this chapter is a description of these improvements. In particular, we derive basic properties of subgroups, homomorphisms on groups, and direct products of groups.

37. SUBGROUPS

By the remarks in Section 31–32 about identities and inverses in sub-groupoids, a subsemigroup of a group need not be a group, although it must be a cancellation semigroup. For example, any group has the subsemigroup $\varnothing$, which is not a group since it is empty; the group $\mathbf{I}$ under addition has many subsemigroups (that isomorphic to $\mathbf{N}$, as in Theorem 36.1, for instance) which are not groups. If a subsemigroup *is* a group, we call it a **subgroup**. Evidently any group G has G and $\{e\}$ as subgroups; a subgroup other than these is called **proper**. It follows immediately from the definition of a sub-group that a subgroup of a subgroup of G is a subgroup of G; and con-versely, that if $K \subseteq H \subseteq G$, and K, H are subgroups of G, then K is a subgroup of H.

Proposition 1. *Let S be a groupoid in which every element is right cancellable and e is a left identity; then e is the only idempotent element of S.*

Proof: If d is idempotent we have $dd = d = ed$, so that by cancellation, $d = e$. //

Corollary 1. *Such an S has no left or right identities or absorbent elements except (possibly) e.*

135

Corollary 2. *No subgroupoid of such an S has a left or right identity or absorbent element other than e.*

This also follows from the corollary to Proposition 34.1.

Corollary 3. *The identity of a group is its only idempotent element.*

Corollary 4. *Let G be a group with identity e, and let H be any subgroup of G; then e is the identity of H. Moreover, let $x \in H$, and let x^{-1} be the inverse of x in G; then x^{-1} is the inverse of x in H.*

Corollary 5. *Any intersection of subgroups is a subgroup.*

By Corollary 5, the set of subgroups of any group G, ordered by inclusion, is a complete lattice, which we denote by $\mathscr{S}_G^*$. By Corollary 4, $\{e\}$ is the least element of $\mathscr{S}_G^*$, while G is, of course, its greatest element. Note that since there are always subgroupoids which are not subgroups ($\varnothing$, for instance), we always have $\mathscr{S}_G^* \subset \mathscr{S}_G$.

Proposition 2. *Let G be a group; then $H \subseteq G$ is a subgroup if and only if $H \neq \varnothing$ and x, y in H imply $xy^{-1} \in H$.*

Proof: If H is a subgroup, it is nonempty, and for any $y \in H$ we have $y^{-1} \in H$ by Corollary 4 above; thus since H is stable, we have $xy^{-1} \in H$ for any $x \in H$. Conversely, for any $z \in H$ we have $zz^{-1} = e$ in H, so that $ey^{-1} = y^{-1}$ is in H for any $y \in H$; thus x, y in H implies x, y^{-1} in H, so that $x(y^{-1})^{-1} = xy$ is in H, proving H stable. Hence H is a subgroupoid with identity e, and every $y \in H$ has an e-inverse y^{-1} in H, proving that H is a subgroup.   //

Exercise 1. *The only left or right ideals of a group are itself and $\varnothing$.*

Exercise 2. *Let S be a semigroup with left identity e, and let $A \subseteq S$ be such that every $x \in A$ has a left e-inverse in A, but no $x \notin A$ has a left e-inverse in S; then A is a subgroup of S.*

As descriptions of the subgroup generated by a subset we have, in analogy with Propositions 34.8–9:

Proposition 3. *In a group, the subgroup generated by A is*

$$(A) = \left\{ \prod_{i=1}^{k} y_i \mid k \in \mathbf{N}; \ y_i = e \text{ or } y_i \in A \text{ or } y_i^{-1} \in A \text{ for each } i \right\}.$$

Corollary 1. *$(x) = \{x^k \mid k \in \mathbf{I}\}$, where x^0 denotes e, and x^{-n} $(n > 0)$ denotes the composite of n x^{-1}'s.*

Corollary 2. *(x) is Abelian.*

Corollary 3. *$\mathscr{S}_G^*$ is a sublattice of $\mathscr{S}_G$.*

Proposition 4. *In an Abelian group,* $(A) = \{\prod_{i=1}^{k} y_i^{k_i} \mid k \in \mathbf{N};$ *the* k_i*'s in* $\mathbf{I}$*; the* y_i*'s distinct elements of* $A\}$.

Corollary 1. *If* $\mathscr{A}$ *is a set of subgroups, then* $(\bigcup_{\mathscr{A}} A) = \{\prod_{i=1}^{k} a_i \mid k \in \mathbf{N};$ *the* a_i*'s in distinct elements of* $\mathscr{A}\}$.

Corollary 2. *Let* G *be a group,* A *an Abelian subgroup of* G, *and let* $x \in G$ *be such that* $xa = ax$ *for all* $a \in A$. *Then* $(A \cup \{x\}) = \{ax^k \mid a \in A, k \in \mathbf{I}\}$.

Corollary 3. *In an Abelian group,* $(x_1, \ldots, x_n) = \{\prod_{i=1}^{n} x_i^{r_i} \mid$ *the* r_i*'s in* $\mathbf{I}\}$.

Exercise 3. *Extend the laws of exponents* (*Exercises* 33.3–4) *to integer exponents.*

We conclude this section by describing the subgroups of $\mathbf{I}$, the group of integers under addition. Let $H \neq \{0\}$ be any such subgroup, and let m be the smallest positive integer in H. (H must contain a nonzero integer, and if $k \in H$, then $-k \in H$, where either k or $-k$ is positive, so that H must contain a positive integer.) Since $m \in H$, we have $(m) = \{km \mid k \in \mathbf{I}\} = m\mathbf{I} \subseteq H$. On the other hand, for any $n \in H$ we have $n = qm + r$, where $0 \leq r < m$, so that $r = n - qm$ is in H, contradicting the minimality of m unless $r = 0$; thus $n = qm \in (m)$, so that $H = (m)$ and we have proved

Proposition 5. *If* H *is any subgroup of* $\mathbf{I}$, *then* $H = m\mathbf{I}$ *for some* $m \in \mathbf{I}$, *where* $m \geq 0$.

Note that $m = 0$ gives $H = \{0\}$; $m = 1$ gives $H = \mathbf{I}$.

Corollary. *If* H *is a nontrivial subgroup of* $\mathbf{I}$, *then* $H \cong \mathbf{I}$.

Proof: If $m > 0$, $\{(k, km) \mid k \in \mathbf{I}\}$ is readily an isomorphism of $\mathbf{I}$ with $m\mathbf{I}$.   //

38. CONGRUENCES ON GROUPS

By Sections 31–33, a homomorphic image or quotient groupoid of a group is a group. [A "quotient group" is usually called a **factor group**, to avoid confusion with the "group of quotients" of Section 36.] We also have

Proposition 1. *If* G *is a group and* F *is a homomorphism defined on* G, *then the preimage of a subgroup of* $F(G)$ *is a subgroup of* G.

Proof: If H is any subgroup of $F(G)$, then $F^{-1}(H)$ is a subsemigroup of G, and it contains e since H must contain the identity $F(e)$ of $F(G)$. Moreover, for any $h \in F^{-1}(H)$ we have $F(h^{-1})F(h) = F(h^{-1}h) = F(e)$, so that $F(h^{-1})$ must be the unique inverse of $F(h)$ in $F(G)$. Hence $F(h^{-1})$ is in the subgroup H, since $F(h)$ is, and we have $h^{-1} \in F^{-1}(H)$.   //

Corollary. *If S is a group, the order isomorphism of Theorem* 26.5 *takes subgroups into subgroups.*

CONGRUENCES AND NORMAL SUBGROUPS

The main result of this section is a complete description of the congruences on a group in terms of its normal subgroups.

Let S be a groupoid, A any subset of S. For any $x \in S$, the set xA is called a **left coset** of A, and the set Ax is called a **right coset** of A. In terms of the cosets of A we can define two relations on S: $L_A = \{(x, y) \mid y \in xA\}$, and $R_A = \{(x, y) \mid y \in Ax\}$. Note that if S is commutative, we have $xA = Ax$ and $L_A = R_A$ for all $A \subseteq S$.

Exercise 1. *If x is left cancellable, then $xA \sim A$.*

Corollary. *All left cosets of A by left cancellable elements have the same cardinality.*

Proposition 2. *If S is a semigroup with identity e, and A a subgroup of S which contains e, then L_A and R_A are equivalences on S, and $A = (L_A)_e = (R_A)_e$.*

Proof: Since $e \in A$, they are reflexive; since any element of A has an inverse in A, they are symmetric; since A is stable, they are transitive; while $(L_A)_e = eA = A$ and $(R_A)_e = Ae = A$. //

Note that by definition of L_A and R_A we have $(L_A)_x = xA$ and $(R_A)_x = Ax$ for any $x \in S$. Note also that if $A = S$ we have $L_A = R_A = S \times S$, while if $A = \{e\}$ we have $L_A = R_A = I_S$.

Corollary 1. *If L_A is a congruence, A is normal.*

Proof: It is an L_A-class. //

Corollary 2. *For any u, v in S, uA and vA are either disjoint or equal.*

Proof: They are L_A-classes. //

Corollary 3. $xA = A$ *if* $x \in A$; $xA \cap A = \varnothing$ *if* $x \notin A$.

Proposition 3. *Let S, A be as in Proposition* 2; *then L_A is a congruence if and only if $L_A \supseteq R_A$.*

Proof: For all x, y in S and all a, b in A we have $(x, xa) \in L_A$ and $(y, yb) \in L_A$, so that if L_A is a congruence this implies $(xy, xayb) \in L_A$, that is, $xayb = xyc$ for some $c \in A$. Set $x = b = e$ to obtain $ay = yc$; since a, y are arbitrary, this means that $Ay \subseteq yA$ for any $y \in S$, so that $R_A \subseteq L_A$. Conversely, let (x, y) and (u, v) be in L_A, say $y = xa, v = ub$, where a, b are in A; then $yv = xaub$. But $au \in Au \subseteq uA$, say $au = ua^*$, so that $yv = xu(a^*b)$, that is, $(yv, xu) \in L_A$, making L_A a congruence. //

Corollary 1. *If S is a commutative semigroup with identity e, any subgroup A of S which contains e is normal.*

Proof: $L_A = R_A$ is a congruence. $\quad \|$

Corollary 2. *Any subgroup of an Abelian group is normal.*

Corollary 3. *If S/L_A has only two elements, L_A is a congruence.*

Proof: By the last part of Proposition 2, the elements must be A and $S - A$. Thus for any $x \in A$ we have $(R_A)_x = Ax = A = (L_A)_x$, while for any $x \in S - A$ we have $(R_A)_x \subseteq S - A$ (Corollary 3 to Proposition 2) $= (L_A)_x$, so that $L_A \supseteq R_A$. $\quad \|$

> If G is a group and A is any subset of G, we have $(x, y) \in L_A$ if and only if $x^{-1}y \in A$, while $(x, y) \in R_A$ if and only if $yx^{-1} \in A$. Thus L_A and R_A can be thought of as relations of "congruence modulo A" (to see the resemblance more clearly, rewrite them in additive notation!). We now show that *any congruence on a group* must be of this special "congruence modulo A" type.

Proposition 4. *Let G be a group with identity e, and let E be any congruence on G; then $E = L_{(E_e)} = R_{(E_e)}$, and E_e is a normal subgroup of G.*

Proof: Let $(x, y) \in E$; since $(x^{-1}, x^{-1}) \in E$, we have $(e, x^{-1}y) \in E$, that is, $x^{-1}y \in E_e$, so that $y \in xE_e$, that is, $(x, y) \in L_{(E_e)}$, proving that $E \subseteq L_{(E_e)}$. Conversely, if $(x, y) \in L_{(E_e)}$ we have $x^{-1}y \in E_e$, that is, $(e, x^{-1}y) \in E$, and since $(x, x) \in E$, this implies $(xe, x(x^{-1}y)) = (x, y) \in E$, proving that $L_{(E_e)} \subseteq E$. The proof for $R_{(E_e)}$ is exactly analogous. By Corollary 1 to Proposition 30.2, E_e is a normal subgroupoid; furthermore, for all x, y in E_e we have $(y, x) \in E = R_{(E_e)}$, so that $x \in E_e y$, that is, $xy^{-1} \in E_e$, making E_e a subgroup by Proposition 37.2. $\quad \|$

> Since the only idempotent in G is e, E_e is the unique kernel of E. By Proposition 4, E is in fact *determined* by its kernel—namely, it is "congruence modulo its kernel," and the E-classes are just the cosets of the kernel.

Note that the quotient composition on G/E satisfies $(xE_e)(yE_e) = xyE_e$, since the composite of xE_e and yE_e must be the E-class containing $(xe)(ye) = xy$.

Corollary 1. *A nonempty normal subset of a group is a class of exactly one congruence.*

Proof: If E_x is an E-class we have $E_x = xE_e$, so that $E_e = x^{-1}E_x$; thus $E = L_{(E_e)}$ is determined by specifying E_x. $\quad \|$

By Corollary 1, if $U \neq \varnothing$ is normal in V, where V is a group, we can speak of *the* quotient (or, rather, factor) of $[U, V]$; in particular, we can speak of *the* factors of a normal series of groups.

Corollary 2. *A nonempty normal subgroupoid of a group is a subgroup.*

Proof: If $E_x = xE_e$ is a subgroupoid, we have $E_x E_x \subseteq E_x$, so that E_x is an idempotent element of the factor group G/E; thus E_x must be E_e, the identity of G/E. $\parallel$

Corollary 3. *The set of normal subgroups of a group, ordered by inclusion, is a complete lattice.*

Proof: They are just the nonempty normal subgroupoids, and all contain $\{e\}$, so that they are still closed under intersection. $\parallel$

We shall denote the lattice of normal subgroups of G by $\mathcal{N}_G^*$ (that is, $\mathcal{N}_G^* = \mathcal{N}_G - \{\varnothing\}$). Clearly $\mathcal{N}_G^*$ is a sublattice of $\mathcal{N}_G$.

Corollary 4. *Let F be any homomorphism defined on the group G, and let $H = (E_F)_e$ be the kernel of F; then H is a normal subgroup, and $E_F = L_H$.*

Exercise 2. *If E is any congruence on a group, any two E-classes have the same cardinality.* [Hint: Exercise 1.]

Exercise 3. *If E is a congruence on the group G, then $(x, y) \in E$ implies $(x^{-1}, y^{-1}) \in E$ for all x, y in G.*

Exercise 4. *If E is a congruence on a group, and A is a subgroup, then EA is a subgroup.* [Hint: Exercise 3.]

Exercise 5. *Let G be a group, let A generate E_e, and let $\{bE_e \mid b \in B\}$ generate G/E_e; then $A \cup B$ generates G.*

Conversely to Proposition 4 we next have

Proposition 5. *Let H be any normal subgroup of the group G; then $L_H = R_H$ is a congruence on G, and $(L_H)_e = H$.*

Proof: Let H be an E-class; since $e \in H$ we have $H = E_e$, so that by Proposition 4, $L_H = R_H = E$. $\parallel$

It is customary to denote the factor group G/L_H by G/H.

Corollary 1. *A nonempty subset of a group is normal if and only if it is a coset of a normal subgroup.*

Proof: The cosets of H are just the L_H-classes, so are normal if H is by Proposition 5. Conversely, by Proposition 4, any E-class is an $L_{(E_e)}$-class, that is, a coset of E_e. $\parallel$

Corollary 2. *The following statements about the subgroup H of the group G are equivalent:*

(1) $L_H = R_H$

(2) $L_H \supseteq R_H$

(3) L_H *is a congruence*

(4) *H is normal.*

Proof: (2) implies (3) is Proposition 3; (3) implies (4) is Corollary 1 to Proposition 2; (4) implies (1) by Proposition 5. ∥

Corollary 3. *The subgroup H of the group G is normal if and only if $xHx^{-1} \subseteq H$ for all $x \in G$.*

Proof: This is equivalent to $xH \subseteq Hx$ for all $x \in G$, that is, to $L_H \subseteq R_H$. ∥

Exercise 6. *Let G be a group, and let F_x be the function $\{(y, xyx^{-1}) \mid y \in G\}$; prove that F_x is an automorphism of G. Such an automorphism is called an* **inner automorphism**. [Thus by Corollary 3 to Proposition 5, a subgroup is normal if and only if it is "stable" under every inner automorphism.] *Prove further that the set of all inner automorphisms of G is a normal subgroup of the group of all automorphisms of G.*

Exercise 7. *Let A be any subgroup of G; prove that $\bigcap_{x \in G} F_x(A)$ is the greatest normal subgroup of G contained in A.*

THE LATTICE OF NORMAL SUBGROUPS

By Propositions 4–5, a subset of a group is the kernel of a congruence (or homomorphism) if and only if it is a normal subgroup. Furthermore, we have

Theorem 1. $\{(H, L_H) \mid H \in \mathcal{N}_G^*\}$ *is an order isomorphism of $\mathcal{N}_G^*$ with $\mathcal{C}_G$.*

Proof: Using Propositions 4–5 and the corollary to Proposition 3.6, it is easily seen that this function is a one-to-one correspondence. Moreover, if $H \subseteq K$ we evidently have $L_H \subseteq L_K$, while if $D \subseteq E$ we have $D_e \subseteq E_e$, so that both this function and its inverse are inclusion-preserving. ∥

Note that under this order isomorphism, $\{e\}$ corresponds to I_G and G to $G \times G$.

Corollary 1. *A homomorphism defined on a group is an isomorphism if and only if its kernel is $\{e\}$.*

We shall denote by $\mathcal{N}_{G,T}^*$ the complete lattice of normal subgroups of G which contain a given subset T. [Note that if $T \neq \varnothing$ we have $\mathcal{N}_{G,T}^* = \mathcal{N}_{G,T}$.]

Corollary 2. *Let F be a homomorphism defined on the group G, and let $H =$*

$(E_F)_e$ be its kernel; then $\mathcal{N}^*_{G,H}$ is order isomorphic with $\mathcal{N}^*_{F(G)}$. In particular, if K is any normal subgroup of G, then $\mathcal{N}^*_{G,K}$ is order isomorphic with $\mathcal{N}^*_{G/K}$.

Proof: Theorem 26.2.   //

Corollary 3. *Isomorphic groups have order isomorphic lattices of normal subgroups.*

We can also prove a group version of Theorem 26.5:

Proposition 6. *Let E be a congruence on the group G, and let A be a subsemigroup of G which contains the identity e; then A is E-invariant if and only if it contains E_e.*

Proof: If A is E-invariant and contains e, it contains the E-class E_e. Conversely, let $A \supseteq E_e$ and let $(x, a) \in E$, where $a \in A$; then $a^{-1}x \in E_e \subseteq A$, so that $x = a(a^{-1}x) \in A$, proving that A is E-invariant.   //

We denote by $\mathcal{S}^*_{G,T}$ the complete lattice of subgroups of G which contain a given subset T.

Corollary 1. *Let F be a homomorphism defined on the group G, and let H be its kernel; then the restriction of $\tilde{F}$ to $\mathcal{S}^*_{G,H}$ is an order isomorphism of $\mathcal{S}^*_{G,H}$ with $\mathcal{S}^*_{F(G)}$. In particular, if K is any normal subgroup of G, then the restriction of $\tilde{F}$ to $\mathcal{S}^*_{G,K}$ is an order isomorphism of $\mathcal{S}^*_{G,K}$ with $\mathcal{S}^*_{G/K}$. Moreover, these order isomorphisms take $\mathcal{N}^*_{G,H}$ onto $\mathcal{N}^*_{F(G)}$ and $\mathcal{N}^*_{G,K}$ onto $\mathcal{N}^*_{G/K}$, respectively.*

Proof: Theorem 26.5.   //

[The last part of Corollary 1 supersedes Corollary 2 to Theorem 1.] In words: There is an inclusion-preserving one-to-one correspondence between the subgroups of any homomorphic image or factor group of G and the subgroups of G which contain the kernel; and this correspondence takes normal subgroups into normal subgroups.

Corollary 2. *Isomorphic groups have order isomorphic subgroup lattices.*

We also have explicit descriptions of the sups in the lattices $\mathcal{N}^*_G$ and $\mathcal{C}_G$:

Theorem 2. *Let A, B be subgroups of the group G such that $xAx^{-1} \subseteq A$ for all $x \in B$; then AB is the sup of A and B in $\mathcal{S}^*_G$, and A is normal in AB. If A is normal in G, we also have $AB = L_A B$. If A and B are both normal in G, so is AB, making it the sup of A and B in $\mathcal{N}^*_G$.*

Proof: Since e is in both A and B we have $AB \supseteq A \cup B$; and any subsemigroup of G which contains A and B must contain AB. Thus to prove the first part it suffices to show that AB is a subgroup, since it must then be the smallest one containing A and B. But indeed, for all x, y in A and all u, v in B we have $(xu)(yv)^{-1} = x[(uv^{-1})y^{-1}(uv^{-1})^{-1}]uv^{-1} \in AB$. Note next that for all ab in AB and all $x \in A$ we have $(ab)x(ab)^{-1} = a(bxb^{-1})a^{-1} \in A$, so that

A is normal in AB. If A is normal in G, say $A = E_e$, then $b \in B$ and $(z, b) \in E$ imply $zb^{-1} \in E_e = A$, so that $z \in AB$, and conversely. Finally, if A and B are both normal, then for all $ab \in AB$ and all $w \in G$ we have $w(ab)w^{-1} = (waw^{-1})(wbw^{-1}) \in AB$, proving AB normal.   //

Corollary 1. *If A and B are normal subgroups of the group G, then $AB = BA$.*

Corollary 2. $\mathcal{N}_G^*$ *is a sublattice of* $\mathcal{S}_G^*$.

Proof: The sup of A and B in $\mathcal{S}_G$ must contain AB; but this is already a normal subgroup, hence in particular is a subsemigroup and a subgroup.   //

Corollary 3. *Let $\mathcal{A}$ be any subset of $\mathcal{N}_G^*$; then* $\sup \mathcal{A} = \{\prod_{i=1}^k a_i \mid k \in \mathbf{N};$ *the a_i's in distinct elements of $\mathcal{A}\}$. In particular, let $A_1, \ldots, A_n$ be normal subgroups of G; then* $\sup \{A_1, \ldots, A_n\}$ *in $\mathcal{N}_G^*$ is $\{\prod_{i=1}^n a_i \mid a_i \in A_i, 1 \le i \le n\}$.*

Corollary 4. *Let G be Abelian, and let $\mathcal{A}$ be any subset of $\mathcal{S}_G^*$; then* $\sup \mathcal{A} = \{\prod_{i=1}^k a_i \mid k \in \mathbf{N};$ *the a_i's in distinct elements of $\mathcal{A}\}$.*

Proof: Since G is Abelian, we have $\mathcal{N}_G^* = \mathcal{S}_G^*$.   //

Theorem 3. *Let D, E be congruences on the group G with kernels A, B, respectively; then $D \circ E$ is a congruence on G and its kernel is AB.*

Proof: $(x, y) \in D \circ E$ implies that for some $z \in G$ we have $x^{-1}z \in A$ and $z^{-1}y \in B$; hence $x^{-1}y = (x^{-1}z)(z^{-1}y) \in AB$, so that $D \circ E \subseteq L_{AB}$. Conversely, let $x^{-1}y \in AB$, say $= ab$, and let $z = yb^{-1}$; then $x^{-1}z = x^{-1}yb^{-1} = abb^{-1} = a \in A$, and $z^{-1}y = by^{-1}y = b \in B$, so that $L_{AB} \subseteq D \circ E$.   //

Corollary 1. *All congruences on a group commute.*

Corollary 2. *If G is a group, $\mathscr{C}_G$ and $\mathcal{N}_G^*$ are modular.*

It follows that the results of Section 28 are all true for groups.

We conclude this section with a description of the congruences on, and factor groups of, the group $\mathbf{I}$ of integers under addition. Since $\mathbf{I}$ is Abelian, any subgroup $m\mathbf{I}$ of $\mathbf{I}$ is normal; and the congruence $L_{m\mathbf{I}}$ is evidently just congruence modulo m. [Note that if $m = 0$ we have $L_{m\mathbf{I}} = I_{\mathbf{I}}$, while if $m = 1$ we have $L_{m\mathbf{I}} = \mathbf{I} \times \mathbf{I}$.] The elements of $\mathbf{I}/m\mathbf{I}$, where $m \ne 0$, are just the sets $\{k + mx \mid x \in \mathbf{I}\}$, $0 \le k < m$. Let $\mathbf{I}_m = \mathbf{N}_{m-1}^\circ = \{0, \ldots, m-1\}$, and define the composition $\underset{m}{+}$ ("**addition modulo m**") on $\mathbf{I}_m$ by $x \underset{m}{+} y = x + y$ if $x + y < m$; $= x + y - m$ if $x + y \ge m$. It is easily verified that $\mathbf{I}_m$ under $\underset{m}{+}$ is isomorphic to $\mathbf{I}/m\mathbf{I}$. We have thus proved

Proposition 7. *Any congruence on $\mathbf{I}$ is congruence modulo m for some $m \in \mathbf{I}$, $m \ge 0$. Any factor group of $\mathbf{I}$ is isomorphic to $\mathbf{I}$ or to $\mathbf{I}_m$ for some $m \in \mathbf{I}, m > 0$.*

Corollary. *For every $m \in \mathbf{N}$, there exists an Abelian group with m elements.*

Exercise 8. *Define* $\underset{m}{\cdot}$ **(multiplication modulo** *m***)** *on* $\mathbf{I}_m$ *by* $x \underset{m}{\cdot} y =$ *the remainder of xy on division by m. Prove that* $\underset{m}{\cdot}$ *is commutative, associative, and distributes over* $\underset{m}{+}$, *and that* 0 *is absorbent and* 1 *an identity for it. Prove also that the following statements about* $k \in \mathbf{I}_m$, *where* $k \neq 0$, *are equivalent:*

(a) k *is cancellable for* $\underset{m}{\cdot}$

(b) k *is invertible for* $\underset{m}{\cdot}$

(c) k *is relatively prime to m.*

Corollary 1. *The set of* $k \in \mathbf{I}_m$ *which are relatively prime to m is a group under* $\underset{m}{\cdot}$.

Corollary 2. $\mathbf{I}_m - \{0\}$ *is a group under* $\underset{m}{\cdot}$ *if and only if m is prime.*

Exercise 9 (the Chinese remainder theorem). *If r, s in* **N** *are relatively prime, then for any m, n in* **I** *there exists some* $k \in \mathbf{I}$ *such that* $r \mid k - m$ *and* $s \mid k - n$. [Hint: Let r^*, s^* be the remainders of r, s on division by s, r, respectively; let $r^* \underset{s}{\cdot} r' = s^* \underset{r}{\cdot} s' = 1$; let $k = nrr' + mss'$.] *More generally, prove that if* $r_1, \ldots, r_t$ *in* **N** *are pairwise relatively prime (in other words, for all distinct i, j in* $\mathbf{N}_t$, r_i *and* r_j *are relatively prime), then for any* $m_1, \ldots, m_t$ *in* **I** *there exists some* $k \in \mathbf{I}$ *such that* $r_i \mid k - m_i$, $1 \leq i \leq t$.

39. DIRECT PRODUCTS OF GROUPOIDS WITH IDEMPOTENT ELEMENTS

As we have just seen, one can say much more about congruences on groups than about congruences on arbitrary groupoids. The same is true for direct products; in fact, we can make significant improvements in their theory even if we assume only that the groupoids in question have idempotent elements.

Proposition 1. *Let* $S = \prod_I S_i$ *have the idempotent element* $e = (e_i)_I$; *then for any* $J \subset I$ *we have* $(\bigcap_{I-J} E_i)_e \cong \prod_J S_i$, *where* E_i *is the congruence on S corresponding to the projection onto* S_i.

Proof: $(\bigcap_{I-J} E_i)_e$ is just the set of $(x_i)_I \in S$ such that $x_i = e_i$ for all $i \in I - J$. Since each e_i is idempotent, this set is a subgroupoid, and readily $\{((x_i)_I, (x_i)_J) \mid (x_i)_I \in (\bigcap_{I-J} E_i)_e\}$ is an isomorphism of this subgroupoid with $\prod_J S_i$. //

From now on we abbreviate $(\bigcap_{I-J} E_i)_e$ by S_J^*.

Corollary 1. *For each* $j \in I$ *we have* $S/E_j \cong S_j \cong S_{(j)}^*$.

Evidently Proposition 1 remains valid if S is isomorphic, rather than equal, to $\prod_I S_i$, provided that we interpret the E's as the congruences on S which correspond, under the given isomorphism, to the congruences on $\prod_I S_i$ defined by the projections on the S_i's. We have thus shown that if S_i is any direct factor of S, there exists a normal subgroupoid $S^*_{(i)}$ of S which is isomorphic to S_i (so that $S^*_{(i)}$ is also a direct factor of S). Consequently, we can assume without loss of generality, given $S \cong \prod_I S_i$, that the S_i's are subgroupoids of S.

Corollary 2. *Let S have idempotent element e, and let $E_1, \ldots, E_n$ be congruences on S which are as in Theorem 19.2; then for each $j \in I$ we have*

$$S/E_j \cong (E_1 \cap \cdots \cap E_{j-1} \cap E_{j+1} \cap \cdots \cap E_n)_e.$$

By Corollary 2, if $E_1, \ldots, E_{j-1}, D, E_{j+1}, \ldots, E_n$ are also as in Theorem 19.2, we have $S/E_j \cong S/D$. As an immediate consequence we have, as promised at the end of Section 29:

Theorem 1. *In Theorem 29.4, let S have an idempotent element; then $A_i \cong B_j$.*

This result, together with Theorem 29.4, is known as the **Krull–Schmidt theorem.**

As a further consequence of Proposition 1 we have

Proposition 2. *A kernel of a supplemented congruence is a direct factor.*

Proof: Corollary 2 to Proposition 1 and the corollary to Proposition 29.4.   //

Note, in fact, that if D, E are congruences on S, and E is a supplement of D, then the direct factor $D_e \cong S/E$ has S/D as a direct supplement; thus the direct decomposition has nontrivial factors unless $D = I_S$ or $S \times S$. A kernel of a supplemented congruence on S will be called a **supplemented subgroupoid** of S; thus a supplemented subgroupoid is a special type of normal subgroupoid. Incidentally, the converse of Proposition 2 is false; a subgroupoid which is a direct factor need not be supplemented. [An example of this will be given in Section 47 (Corollary 2 to Proposition 3).] However, by Corollary 2 to Proposition 1, any direct factor is *isomorphic* to a supplemented subgroupoid.

Exercise 1. *All kernels of a given supplemented congruence are isomorphic.* [Hint: Use Corollary 2 to Proposition 1.]

Just as the E_i's are independent in $\mathscr{C}_S{}^{-1}$ (by the groupoid analog of Corollary 2 to Proposition 19.11), so the $S^*_{(i)}$'s are independent in $\mathcal{N}_{S,\langle e \rangle}$, the complete lattice of normal subgroupoids of S which contain e:

Proposition 3. $S_{(j)}^* \cap \sup \{S_{(i)}^* \mid i \in I - \{j\}\} = \{e\}$ *for each* $j \in I$, *where the* sup *is in* $\mathcal{N}_{S,\{e\}}$.

Proof: For all $i \neq j$ we have $S_{(i)}^* \subseteq (E_j)_e$, which is a normal subgroupoid, so that their sup also $\subseteq (E_j)_e$; and $(E_j)_e \cap S_{(j)}^* = \{e\}$, since $E_j \cap (\bigcap_{I-\{j\}} E_i) = I_S$. //

Corollary. *The set of nontrivial* $S_{(j)}^*$'s, *if any, is independent in* $\mathcal{N}_{S,\{e\}}$.

Proof: Since $\{e\}$ is a normal subgroupoid, it is the least element of $\mathcal{N}_{S,\{e\}}$. //

The following proposition introduces an important normal subgroupoid of an arbitrary direct product of groupoids with idempotent elements:

Proposition 4. *Let* $S = \prod_I S_i$ *have idempotent element* $e = (e_i)_I$; *then* $\prod_I^* S_i = \{(x_i)_I \mid x_i \in S_i; x_i = e_i$ *for all but finitely many* i's$\}$ *is a normal subgroupoid of* S.

Proof: Since the e_i's are idempotents, and the union of two finite sets is finite, this set is readily a subgroupoid. Let $E = \{((x_i)_I, (y_i)_I) \mid (x_i)_I, (y_i)_I$ in S; $x_i = y_i$ for all but finitely many i's$\}$; then readily E is a congruence on S and $\prod_I^* S_i = E_e$. //

We call $\prod_I^* S_i$ a **weak direct product** of $(S_i)_I$. Note that if I is finite we have $\prod_I^* S_i = S$ and $E = S \times S$. Note also that for each $j \in I$ we have $p_j(\prod_I^* S_i) = S_j$. [Weak direct products are sometimes called *direct sums*, but we shall use "direct sum" as the equivalent of "direct product" in cases where the compositions are denoted additively.]

We can improve slightly on these results if e is an identity and not merely idempotent:

Proposition 5. *Let* $S = \prod_I S_i$ *have an identity element* e; *then for all* $J, K \subseteq I$, sup S_J^*, S_K^* *in* $\mathcal{N}_{S,\{e\}}$ *is* $S_{J\cup K}^*$.

Proof: Evidently $S_{J\cup K}^*$ is a normal subgroupoid containing S_J^* and S_K^*, and so contains their sup. On the other hand, since e is an identity, readily $S_{J\cup K}^* \subseteq S_J^* S_K^*$, which must be contained in any subgroupoid containing S_J^* and S_K^*—in particular, in their sup. //

Corollary 1. sup $\{S_{J_1}^*, \ldots, S_{J_n}^*\} = S_{J_1 \cup \cdots \cup J_n}^*$.

Corollary 2. *If* I *is finite,* sup $\{S_{(i)}^* \mid i \in I - \{j\}\} = S_{I-\{j\}}^*$ *and* sup $\{S_{(i)}^* \mid i \in I\} = S$.

Exercise 2. *In general,* sup $\{S_{(i)}^* \mid i \in I\} = \prod_I^* S_i$ *(Proposition 4), where* S *is as in Proposition 5.*

40. DIRECT PRODUCTS OF GROUPS

We now consider direct products of groups. Note first that since associativity, identities, and inverses all "pass between" a direct product and its direct factors, a direct product of groups is a group, and a direct factor of a group must be a group (in other words, if a group is isomorphic to a direct product of groupoids, they must be groups).

For groupoids with an identity element e, we have just seen that if $S \cong \prod_I S_i$, then there exist normal subgroupoids $S^*_{(i)}$ of S such that $S^*_{(i)} \cong S_i$, and the set of $S^*_{(i)}$ (discarding trivial ones) is independent in $\mathcal{N}_{S,\{e\}}$ and, if finite, has S as its sup. If $S = G$ is a group, these normal subgroupoids must be normal subgroups, so that the set of nontrivial ones is independent in $\mathcal{N}^*_G$ and, if finite, has G as its sup. In this section we show, conversely, that given any such set of independent normal subgroups, its sup is isomorphic to its weak direct product; thus if the set is finite and its sup is G, we have G isomorphic to its direct product. [We can speak of "the" (weak) direct product since e is the only idempotent.]

Proposition 1. *Let $\mathcal{A}$ be a set of normal subgroups of the group G; then the following statements are equivalent:*

(1) $A \cap \sup \{\mathcal{A} - \{A\}\} = \{e\}$ *for all $A \in \mathcal{A}$*

(2) *If $\prod_{i=1}^r a_i = e$, where the a_i's are in distinct elements of $\mathcal{A}$, then every $a_i = e$.*

(3) *If $\prod_{i=1}^r a_i = \prod_{i=1}^r b_i$, where the a_i's are in distinct elements of $\mathcal{A}$ and b_i is in the same element of $\mathcal{A}$ as a_i, $1 \leq i \leq r$, then $a_i = b_i$, $1 \leq i \leq r$.*

Proof: (2) is the special case of (3) in which all the b_i's are e. If (2) holds and $x \in A \cap \sup \{\mathcal{A} - \{A\}\}$, then $x = a \in A$, and (Corollary 3 to Theorem 38.2) x is a composite of a_i's which are in distinct elements of $\mathcal{A} - \{A\}$. Thus $e = a^{-1}x$ is a composite of a_i's which are as in (2), so that by (2) these a_i's must all be e; in particular, $a^{-1} = e$, so that $x = e$, proving (1). Conversely, if (1) holds, and $\prod_{i=1}^r a_i = \prod_{i=1}^r b_i$ are as in (3) but not all the a_i's are equal to the corresponding b_i's, let k be the first subscript for which $a_k \neq b_k$; then we can cancel $a_1, \ldots, a_{k-1}$ and transpose to obtain $b_k^{-1}a_k = (\prod_{i=k+1}^r b_i)(\prod_{i=r}^{k+1} a_i^{-1}) = x$ (say). Let a_i, b_i be in $A_i \in \mathcal{A}$, $1 \leq i \leq r$; then x is in $A_k \cap \sup \{A_i \mid k + 1 \leq i \leq r\} \subseteq A_k \cap \sup \{\mathcal{A} - \{A_k\}\} = \{e\}$, so that $b_k^{-1}a_k = x = e$ and we have $a_k = b_k$, contradiction, which proves (3). //

Note that (1) implies (3) implies (2) even if the A's are not assumed to be normal.

Proposition 2. *Let $\mathcal{A}$ be as in Proposition 1, and let A, B be distinct elements of $\mathcal{A}$; then for all $a \in A$, $b \in B$ we have $ab = ba$.*

Proof: Since A is normal we have $b^{-1}ab \in A$, say $= a^*$, so that $ab = ba^*$, and similarly $ba^* = a^*b^*$ for some $b^* \in B$. Applying (3) of Proposition 1 to $ab = a^*b^*$ we thus have $a = a^*$, so that $ab = ba^* = ba$.   //

Corollary 1. *Let* $a_1, \ldots, a_r$ *be in distinct elements of* $\mathscr{A}$; *then for all permutations* F *of* $\mathbf{N}_r$ *we have* $\prod_{i=1}^{r} a_i = \prod_{i=1}^{r} a_{F(i)}$.

Corollary 2. *Let* $\prod_{i=1}^{r} a_i = \prod_{i=1}^{s} b_i$, *where the* a_i's *are in distinct elements of* $\mathscr{A}$, *and where the* b_i's *are in distinct elements of* $\mathscr{A}$, *and where no* a_i *or* b_i *is* e; *then* $r = s$, *and there exists a permutation* H *of* $\mathbf{N}_r$ *such that* $a_i = b_{H(i)}$, $1 \le i \le r$.

Proof: Rewrite each of the two composites as a composite of elements of $A_1, \ldots, A_t$, where every a_i and b_i is in one of these distinct A's; use e's for the missing factors, if any. Now apply Corollary 1 and (3) of Proposition 1.   //

In short: Any element of sup $\mathscr{A}$ is a composite of elements of distinct A_i's in only one way (up to order).

We can now prove

Theorem 1. *Let* $\mathscr{A}$ *be as in Proposition* 1; *then* sup $\mathscr{A}$ *is isomorphic to the weak direct product of* $\mathscr{A}$.

Proof: Let $\mathscr{A} = \{A_i \mid i \in I\}$, and let F be the function which takes any element of $\prod_{I}^{*} A_i$ other than $(e)_I$ into the composite of those of its terms which $\ne e$, while $F((e)_I) = e$. By Corollary 3 to Theorem 38.2, F is onto sup $\mathscr{A}$, and by Corollary 2 to Proposition 2, F is one-to-one. Furthermore, using Proposition 2 we have $\prod_{i=1}^{r} a_i b_i = (\prod_{i=1}^{r} a_i)(\prod_{i=1}^{r} b_i)$, where the a's and b's are as in (3) of Proposition 1; thus F is a homomorphism.   //

Exercise 1. *If* $I = \mathbf{N}_n$ *is finite, then* (1–3) *of Proposition* 1 *are also equivalent to*

(a) $\prod_{i=1}^{n} a_i = e$ *(where* $a_i \in A_i$, $1 \le i \le n$*) if and only if every* a_i *is* e.
(b) $\prod_{i=1}^{n} a_i = \prod_{i=1}^{n} b_i$ *(where* a_i *and* b_i *are in* A_i, $1 \le i \le n$*) if and only if* $a_i = b_i$, $1 \le i \le n$.

Exercise 2. *Let* H, K *be subgroups of the group* G; *prove that the following statements are equivalent:*

(a) $H \cap K = \{e\}$
(b) $hk = e$ *implies* $h = k = e$ *for all* $h \in H$, $k \in K$
(c) $hk = h^*k^*$ *implies* $h = h^*$, $k = k^*$ *for all* h, h^* *in* H *and all* k, k^* *in* K.

[Note that this is just Proposition 1 with $I = \{1, 2\}$, but that here the subgroups are not necessarily normal. Can normality be dispensed with if I has more than two elements?]

Exercise 3. *Let* $\mathscr{A}$ *be a set of subgroups of the group* G, *and let* $A \in \mathscr{A}$ *be such that* $A \cap$ sup $(\mathscr{A} - \{A\}) = \{e\}$, *and* $\mathscr{A} - \{A\}$ *satisfies* (2) *of Proposition* 1; *then* $\mathscr{A}$ *also satisfies* (2) *of Proposition* 1.

Exercise 4. *Let S be a commutative semigroup with identity e which is its only unit, and let $\mathscr{A}$ be a set of subsemigroups of S which contain e and are as in Corollary 2 to Proposition 2; then* sup $\mathscr{A}$ *is isomorphic to its weak direct product.* [Hint: Let F be as in the proof of Theorem 1; to see that F is onto, use Corollary 1 to Proposition 34.9.] Note that if the subsemigroups in $\mathscr{A}$ are cancellation semigroups, so is sup $\mathscr{A}$.

Corollary 1. *Let S be a Gaussian semigroup whose identity e is its only unit; let the set of maximal principal ideals of S be $\{a_i S \mid i \in I\}$; and for each $i \in I$, let A_i be the subsemigroup of S generated by $\{e, a_i\}$; then $S \cong \prod_I^* A_i$.* [Hint: Use Corollary 2 to Proposition 35.8.]

Corollary 2. *Let S be a Gaussian semigroup, U its group of units; since S is commutative, $L_U = R_U$ is a congruence. Verify that S/L_U is Gaussian, that $U = (L_U)_e$ is its identity and its only unit, and that xU is an irreducible element of S/L_U if and only if x is an irreducible element of S. Let $\{a_i U \mid i \in I\}$ be the set of irreducible nonunits of S/L_U; conclude, using Corollary 1, that $S/L_U \cong \prod_I^* (a_i U)$.*

SUPPLEMENTED SUBGROUPS

The properties of Proposition 1 are actually necessary and sufficient to make the subgroups in $\mathscr{A}$ supplemented (and not merely direct factors, as in Theorem 1), as we see from

Proposition 3. *A is a supplemented subgroup of the group G if and only if it is a normal subgroup, and there exists a normal subgroup B such that $A \cap B = \{e\}$ and $AB = G$.*

Proof: If A is normal and such a B exists, let (x, y) be in $L_A \cap L_B$; then $x^{-1}y \in A \cap B = \{e\}$, i.e., $x = y$, so that $L_A \cap L_B = I_G$. On the other hand, since $AB = G$, for any x, y in G we have $x = ab$, $y = a^*b^*$, where a, a^* are in A, and b, b^* in B. Let $z = ab^*$; then $x^{-1}z = b^{-1}b^* \in B$ and $yz^{-1} = a^*a^{-1} \in A$, so that $(x, z) \in L_B$ and $(z, y) \in L_A$, proving $(x, y) \in L_B \circ L_A$, which thus $= G \times G$.

Conversely, let A be supplemented, and let E be a supplement of L_A; thus $E = L_B$ for some normal subgroup B, and we have $L_A \cap L_B = I_G$, $L_A \circ L_B = G \times G$. Then $z \in A \cap B$ implies $(z, e) \in L_A \cap L_B$, so that $z = e$, proving $A \cap B = \{e\}$. Finally, for all $x \in G$ and all $b \in B$ we have $(x, b) \in G \times G = L_A \circ L_B$, so that $w^{-1}x \in A$ and $b^{-1}w \in B$ for some $w \in G$; but $b^{-1}w \in B$ implies $w \in B$, so that $x = w(w^{-1}x) \in BA = AB$, proving $AB = G$. //

Such a B is called a **supplement** of A in G.

Note that in the first part of the proof we have actually shown, as the desired strengthening of Theorem 1, that if A, B are normal subgroups of G such that $A \cap B = \{e\}$, then A is a supplemented subgroup of AB.

As applications of Proposition 3 we have

Proposition 4. *A normal subgroup of a supplemented subgroup of the group G is a normal subgroup of G.*

Proof: Let $K \subseteq H \subseteq G$ with K normal in H and H supplemented in G, say $G = HH^*$, $H \cap H^* = \{e\}$. Thus for any $x \in G$ there exist $h \in H$, $h^* \in H^*$ such that $x = hh^*$, so that for all $k \in K$ we have $xkx^{-1} = hh^*kh^{*-1}h^{-1}$. Since $k \in K \subseteq H$ and $h^* \in H^*$, we know by Proposition 2 that k and h^* commute, so that this reduces to hkh^{-1}; and since K is normal in H, this is in K, proving K normal in G.   ∥

Proposition 5. *A supplemented subgroup of a supplemented subgroup of the group G is a supplemented subgroup of G.*

Proof: Let $HH^* = G$, $H \cap H^* = \{e\}$, $KK^* = H$, $K \cap K^* = \{e\}$. Since H^* and (by Proposition 4) K^* are normal in G, so is H^*K^*, and $K(K^*H^*) = (KK^*)H^* = HH^* = G$. On the other hand, if $k = k^*h^*$, where $k \in K$, $k^* \in K^*$, $h^* \in H^*$, then $k^{*-1}k = h^*$ is in $H \cap H^* = \{e\}$. Thus $h^* = e$ and we have $k = k^*$ in $K \cap K^*$, so that $k = e$, proving that $K \cap (K^*H^*) = \{e\}$, which makes K^*H^* a supplement of K in G.   ∥

Thus, just as a subgroup of a subgroup of G is a subgroup of G, so a supplemented subgroup of a supplemented subgroup of G is supplemented in G; on the other hand, a normal subgroup of a normal subgroup of G is not necessarily normal in G. Note that "conversely," if K, H are subgroups of G and $K \subseteq H$, then K is a subgroup of H; if it is normal in G, it is normal in H; and if it is supplemented in G, it is supplemented in H. [To see this last, let $KK' = G$, $K \cap K' = \{e\}$, and let $K^* = K' \cap H$; then $K \cap K^* = \{e\}$, while for any $h \in H$ we have $h = kk'$ for some $k \in K$, $k' \in K'$, where k' is in H (hence in K^*) since h and k are, so that $KK^* = H$.]

Proposition 6. *Let A be a nontrivial supplemented subgroup of the group G; then $\{A\}$ is an unrefinable independent subset of $\mathcal{N}_G^*$ if and only if A is indecomposable.*

This is not a special case of Theorem 29.3, since we are not assuming finite dimensionality.

Proof: If A were decomposable, by Proposition 29.6 it would have a pair of proper supplemented subgroups B and C. By Proposition 4, B and C are normal in G, so that $\{B, C\}$ is an independent subset of $\mathcal{N}_G^*$, and its sup is A, making $\{A\}$ refinable. Conversely, if $\{A\}$ is refinable, let $A = \sup \{B, C\}$, where $\{B, C\}$ is independent; then by Theorem 1, $A \cong B \times C$ is decomposable. //

Corollary. *Let A be a nontrivial subgroup of the Abelian group G; then $\{A\}$ is an unrefinable independent subset of $\mathcal{S}_G^*$ if and only if A is indecomposable.*

Proposition 7. *An independent subset of $\mathcal{N}_G^*$ is unrefinable if and only if every one-element subset of it is unrefinable.*

> This is not a special case of Proposition 15.3, since we are not assuming finite dimensionality.

Proof: Let $\mathcal{A} \subseteq \mathcal{N}_G^*$ be independent, and let $\{A\} \subseteq \mathcal{A}$ be refinable, say $A = BC$, where B, C are nontrivial normal subgroups of G and $B \cap C = \{e\}$. Let $b \in B \cap \sup (\mathcal{A} - \{A\} \cup \{C\})$; thus $b = c \prod_{i=1}^k a_i$, where $c \in C$ and each a_i is in an element of $\mathcal{A}$ other than A. Hence $c^{-1}b = \prod_{i=1}^k a_i$ is both in $BC = A$ and in $\sup (\mathcal{A} - \{A\})$; this contradicts the independence of $\mathcal{A}$ unless $c^{-1}b = e$, that is, $c = b$, and since $B \cap C = \{e\}$, this implies $c = b = e$. We have thus shown that $B \cap \sup (\mathcal{A} - \{A\} \cup \{C\}) = \{e\}$, and similarly $C \cap \sup (\mathcal{A} - \{A\} \cup \{B\}) = \{e\}$, while trivially

$$A^* \cap \sup (\mathcal{A} - \{A\} \cup \{B, C\} - \{A^*\}) = A^* \cap \sup (\mathcal{A} - \{A^*\}) = \{e\}$$

for all A^* in $\mathcal{A} - \{A\}$ by the independence of $\mathcal{A}$. Consequently $\mathcal{A} - \{A\} \cup \{B, C\}$ is independent, making it a proper refinement of $\mathcal{A}$. //

41. COMMUTATIVITY IN GROUPS

In the course of this chapter we have made a number of remarks about the case of an Abelian group. In particular, we have seen that the description of the subgroup generated by a subset can be somewhat sharpened (Proposition 37.4 and corollaries), and that every subgroup of an Abelian group is normal, so that for Abelian groups, "normal subgroup" can be replaced by "subgroup" throughout Sections 38 and 40. For example, if G is Abelian, we have $\sup \{A, B\} = AB$ in $\mathcal{S}_G^*$, which is modular (Theorems 38.2–3).

We will study Abelian groups further in Chapter IX, primarily with reference to direct products of subgroups. In this section we introduce three concepts, related to commutativity, which can be defined for an arbitrary group.

CENTRALIZERS

Let x, y be elements of the groupoid G; if $xy = yx$, we say that x and y **commute** (and that x commutes with y, and y with x). The set $C(x)$ of elements of G which commute with x is called the **centralizer** of x. Note that $x \in C(x)$, and that $y \in C(x)$ if and only if $x \in C(y)$.

Proposition 1. *For any* $x \in G$, *if* G *is a semigroup,* $C(x)$ *is a subsemigroup, and if* G *is a group,* $C(x)$ *is a subgroup.*

Proof: If $xy = yx$ and $xz = zx$, then $x(yz) = (xy)z = (yx)z = y(xz) = y(zx) = (yz)x$. If G has identity e, then $ex = xe = x$, so that $e \in C(x)$. Finally, if $xy = yx$ and y^{-1} is a two-sided inverse of y, then $y^{-1}(xy)y^{-1} = y^{-1}(yx)y^{-1}$, so that $y^{-1}x = xy^{-1}$. //

If A is any subset of G, we define the centralizer of A as $C(A) = \bigcap_{x \in A} C(x)$—that is, as the set of elements of G which commute with every element of A. If G is a (semi)group, this is an intersection of sub(semi)groups, so that it too is a sub(semi)group. In particular, $C(G)$ is called the **center** of G. Note that $C(G)$ is commutative; that $x \in C(G)$ if and only if $C(x) = G$; and that G is commutative if and only if $C(G) = G$.

Exercise 1. *If G is a group, any subgroup of $C(G)$—in particular, $C(G)$ itself— is normal in G, and the factor group $G/C(G)$ is isomorphic to the group of inner automorphisms of G (Exercise 38.6). Prove also that $F(C(G)) \subseteq C(G)$ for any homomorphism F of G onto itself.* [By Exercise 38.6, normality is a special case of this last property.]

CONJUGATES

Let G be a groupoid, and let R be the relation on G

$$\{(x, y) \mid x, y \text{ in } G; \ yz = zx \text{ for some } z \in G\}.$$

Proposition 2. *If G is a group, R is an equivalence.*

Proof: To see that R is reflexive, take $z = e$. To see symmetry, note that if $yz = zx$, then $xz^{-1} = z^{-1}y$. For transitivity, note that if $ya = ax$ and $zb = by$, then $z(ba) = (zb)a = (by)a = b(ya) = b(ax) = (ba)x$. //

Note that if G is a group, (x, y) is in R if and only if $y = zxz^{-1}$ for some $z \in G$. We assume in what follows that G is a group.

If $(x, y) \in R$, we say that x and y are **conjugates**; the R-classes are called **conjugate classes**. Note that if x is in the center of G, the only possible conjugate of x is itself, since any $z \in G$ commutes with x; and conversely. Thus G is Abelian if and only if $R = I_G$. Note also that a subgroup is normal if and only if it is R-invariant.

Exercise 2. $zxz^{-1} = wxw^{-1}$ *if and only if* $(z, w) \in L_{C(x)}$.

Proposition 3. *For any $x \in G$ we have $R_x \sim G/L_{C(x)}$.*

Proof: If A is any $L_{C(x)}$-class, by "if" of Exercise 2 we have $zxz^{-1} = wxw^{-1}$

for any z, w in A; thus $\{(A, axa^{-1}) \mid A \in G/L_{C(x)}, a \in A\}$ is a function from $G/L_{C(x)}$ into R_x. By the "only if" of Exercise 2, this function is one-to-one, and since any $y \in G$ is in some $L_{C(x)}$-class, any conjugate yxy^{-1} of x can be obtained in this way, so that the function is onto.   //

COMMUTATORS

Let a, b be elements of the group G; then $aba^{-1}b^{-1}$ is called the **commutator** of a and b (notation: $[a, b]$).

Exercise 3. $[a, b] = e$ *if and only if a and b commute;* $[a, b]^{-1} = [b, a]$ *for all a, b in G.*

The subgroup G' of G generated by $\{[a, b] \mid a, b \text{ in } G\}$ is called the **derived group** of G.

Proposition 4. G' *is normal.*

Proof: Note first that

$$x[a, b]x^{-1} = xaba^{-1}b^{-1}x^{-1} = (xax^{-1})(xbx^{-1})(xa^{-1}x^{-1})(xb^{-1}x^{-1})$$
$$= (xax^{-1})(xbx^{-1})(xax^{-1})^{-1}(xbx^{-1})^{-1} = [xax^{-1}, xbx^{-1}],$$

which is in G'. Similarly, $x[a, b][c, d]x^{-1} = (x[a, b]x^{-1})(x[c, d]x^{-1})$ is the composite of two elements of G', hence is in G', and this readily generalizes (induction!) to any composite of commutators, that is (Exercise 3 and Proposition 37.3), to any element of G'.   //

Proposition 5. *Let H be a normal subgroup of G; then G/H is Abelian if and only if H contains G'.*

Proof: For all xH, yH in G/H we have $(xH)(yH)(xH)^{-1}(yH)^{-1} = (xyx^{-1}y^{-1})H$. If $H \supseteq G'$, this reduces to H, and since H is the identity of G/H, this makes G/H Abelian by Exercise 3. Conversely, if G/H is Abelian we must have $(xyx^{-1}y^{-1})H = H$—in other words, $xyx^{-1}y^{-1} \in H$—for all x, y in G, so that H contains every commutator and so contains G'.   //

Corollary. G' *is the smallest normal subgroup of G whose factor group is Abelian.*

Exercise 4. $F(G') \subseteq G'$ *for any homomorphism F of G into itself.*

VIII

FINITENESS CONDITIONS
ON GROUPS

42. FINITENESS CONDITIONS

Let S be a groupoid, $\mathscr{S}_S$ its subgroupoid lattice. We shall consider the following three assumptions about S:

(1) S is finite
(2) $\mathscr{S}_S$ is finite
(3) S is finitely generated (as an element of $\mathscr{S}_S$).

Proposition 1. (1) *implies* (2) *implies* (3).

Proof: If S is finite, so is $\mathscr{S}_S \subseteq \mathscr{P}_S$. If $\mathscr{S}_S$ is finite, it satisfies the maximum condition, so that every element of $\mathscr{S}_S$—in particular, S—is finitely generated. //

If (2) holds, we call S **lattice-finite**.

Our goal in this and the first part of the next chapter is to characterize groupoids (in particular, semigroups and groups) which satisfy (1), (2), or (3). As we shall see, all three cases can be completely described for Abelian groups, and partial descriptions can be given in more general cases.

It will be useful, in studying the "finiteness properties" (1–3), to also consider corresponding "triviality properties":

(a) S is trivial
(b) Any element of $\mathscr{S}_S$ is $\varnothing$, S, or trivial
(c) S is monogenic (as an element of $\mathscr{S}_S$).

If (b) holds, we call S **prime**.

Note that (a) and (c) are obtained from (1) and (3) by replacing a finite set (S itself, or a set of generators of S) by a one-element set. We cannot do this in the case of (2), since any nonempty groupoid has both $\varnothing$ and itself as subgroupoids, and any nontrivial group has both $\{e\}$ and itself as subgroups.

Proposition 2. (a) *implies* (b); (b) *implies* (c) *unless every element of S is idempotent.*

Proof: If S is trivial, $\mathscr{S}_S = \mathscr{P}_S = \{\varnothing, S\}$ satisfies (b). If (b) holds, and $x \in S$ is not idempotent, the subgroupoid (x) generated by x is nonempty and nontrivial, hence must be all of S, proving (c). //

Corollary. *If S is a cancellation semigroup,* (b) *implies* (c).

Proof: Corollary to Proposition 34.1. //

We also immediately have

Proposition 3. (a) *implies* (1); (b) *implies* (2) *unless infinitely many elements of S are idempotent;* (c) *implies* (3).

Corollary. *If S is a cancellation semigroup,* (b) *implies* (2).

Theorem 1. (1–3) *and* (a–c) *all pass to homomorphic images.*

Proof: For (1), use the fact that any image set of a finite set is finite. For (2) and (b), use the fact that $\mathscr{S}_{F(S)}$ is order isomorphic to a sublattice of $\mathscr{S}_S$ (Theorem 26.5). For (3) and (c), use the fact that a homomorphism takes sets of generators into sets of generators (Proposition 24.4). //

Corollary. *They all pass to quotient groupoids.*

Theorem 2. (1–2) *and* (b) *pass to subgroupoids.*

Proof: Any subset of a finite set is finite; while if A is a subgroupoid of S, then $\mathscr{S}_A$ is a sublattice of $\mathscr{S}_S$, since a subgroupoid of a subgroupoid is a subgroupoid. //

> Clearly (a) passes to nonempty subgroupoids. We shall see below (Corollary 2 to Proposition 43.1) that (c) does not necessarily pass to nonempty subgroupoids even if S is a semigroup, but it does if S is a semigroup with identity (Corollaries to Theorem 43.4 and Proposition 43.3; Proposition 45.5). As for (3), it does not even pass to subgroups of a group, but it does in the case of an Abelian group (Theorem 50.3).

If G is a group, we can consider four additional properties analogous to (2–3) and (b–c), but defined in terms of the subgroup lattice $\mathscr{S}_G^*$ rather than the subgroupoid lattice $\mathscr{S}_G$:

(2*) $\mathscr{S}_G^*$ is finite

(3*) G is finitely generated as an element of $\mathscr{S}_G^*$

(b*) $\mathscr{S}_G^* = \{\{e\}, G\}$
(c*) G is monogenic as an element of $\mathscr{S}_G^*$.
In analogy with Propositions 1–3 we immediately have

Proposition 4. (b*) *implies* (c*) *and* (2*), *and either of these implies* (3*).

Since $\mathscr{S}_G^* \subset \mathscr{S}_G$, we also have

Proposition 5. (2) *implies* (2*); (3) *implies* (3*); (b) *implies* (b*); (c) *implies* (c*).

> We shall see in Sections 44–45 that the reverse implications (2*) implies (2), (3*) implies (3), and (b*) implies (b) also hold for any group (see the Corollary to Proposition 45.3; Proposition 45.1; and Theorem 44.2). We can thus use the terms "lattice-finite," "finitely generated," and "prime" in speaking about groups, without having to specify whether we mean the starred or unstarred property. It also follows as in Theorems 1–2 that properties (2*), (3*), and (b*) pass to quotient groups, and that (2*) and (b*) pass to subgroups. Clearly (c*) also passes to quotient groups; in Section 43 (Corollary 2 to Theorem 3 and the corollary to Proposition 3) we shall see that it also passes to subgroups. A group with property (c*) is called **cyclic**.

43. MONOGENIC SEMIGROUPS AND CYCLIC GROUPS

In this section we give a partial description of the monogenic semigroups, and a complete description of the cyclic (and in particular, the monogenic) groups.

Theorem 1. *A semigroup is monogenic if and only if it is a homomorphic image of* **N** (*under addition*).

Proof: In any semigroup we have $(x) = \{x^k \mid k \in \mathbf{N}\}$; hence

$$F = \{(k, x^k) \mid k \in \mathbf{N}\}$$

is a homomorphism of **N** onto (x). Conversely, $\mathbf{N} = (1)$ is monogenic, hence (Theorem 42.1) so are all its homomorphic images.   //

Corollary 1. *A semigroup is monogenic if and only if it is isomorphic to a quotient semigroup of* **N** (*under addition*).

Corollary 2. *A monogenic semigroup is commutative.*

The description of the monogenic semigroups provided by Theorem 1 is not very explicit, since we have no catalog of the congruences on **N**. Some additional information is provided by

Proposition 1. *A monogenic semigroup is either finite or isomorphic to* **N**.

Proof: If no two x^k's are equal, F in the proof of Theorem 1 is an isomorphism. Conversely, if $x^r = x^s$, where $r < s$, then the powers of x beyond x^s are just repetitions of those between x^r and x^{s-1}, so that (x) is finite.   //

Corollary 1. *An infinite monogenic semigroup has infinitely many subsemigroups.*

Proof: For example, $(x) \supset (x^2) \supset (x^4) \supset \cdots$.   //

Corollary 2. *A subsemigroup of an infinite monogenic semigroup need not be monogenic.*

Proof: For example, (x^2, x^3).   //

Proposition 2. *A monogenic semigroup with identity is a finite group.*

Proof: Let $x^r = e$ be the identity of (x); then readily

$$(x) = \{x, x^2, \ldots, x^{r-1}, e\},$$

and $x^i x^{r-i} = e \ (1 \leq i < r)$, so that every x^i has an e-inverse.   //

Corollary. *A monogenic group is finite.*

We next consider cyclic groups. Here we have

Theorem 2. *A group is cyclic if and only if it is a homomorphic image of* **I** *under addition.*

Proof: Analogous to the proof of Theorem 1.

Corollary 1. *A group is cyclic if and only if it is isomorphic to a factor group of* **I** *under addition.*

Corollary 2. *A cyclic group is Abelian.*

Since we know (Proposition 38.7) that any factor group of **I** is isomorphic to **I** or to $\mathbf{I}_n$ for some $n \in \mathbf{N}$, we can restate Theorem 2 as

Theorem 3. *A group is cyclic if and only if it is isomorphic to* **I** *or to* $\mathbf{I}_n$ *for some* $n \in N$.

This gives us a complete, explicit description of the cyclic groups as isomorphic to "known" groups.

Corollary 1. *A cyclic group is either finite or isomorphic to* **I**.

Corollary 2. *Any nontrivial subgroup of an infinite cyclic group is infinite and cyclic.*

Corollary 3. *Any proper factor group of an infinite cyclic group is finite and cyclic.* [Here "proper" means "by a congruence other than the equality relation."]

Corollary 4. *An infinite cyclic group has infinitely many subgroups.*

Clearly I is not monogenic, but $I_n = (1)$ is monogenic for every $n \in N$. Since a monogenic group is cyclic, we thus have

Theorem 4. *A group is monogenic if and only if it is finite and cyclic.*

Corollary. *A semigroup with identity is monogenic if and only if it is a finite cyclic group.*

We have already described the subgroups and factor groups of the infinite cyclic group I. We conclude this section with a description of the subgroups and factor groups of the finite cyclic groups.

Proposition 3. *For any $n \in N$ and each $d \in N$ dividing n, the finite cyclic group $(x) \cong I_n$ has exactly one subgroup $(x^{n/d})$ and one factor group $(x)/(x^d)$ which are isomorphic to I_d; these are its only subgroups and factor groups.*

Proof: Evidently $(x^{n/d}) = \{x^{n/d}, x^{2n/d}, \ldots, x^{(d-1)n/d}, e\}$ is a subgroup of (x), and $\{(k, x^{kn/d}) \mid k \in I_d\}$ is an isomorphism of I_d with $(x^{n/d})$. Conversely, if H is any subgroup of $I_n \cong I/nI$, let mI be the corresponding L_{nI}-invariant subgroup of I; then $mI \supseteq nI$ (Proposition 38.6), so that m divides n, while $mI = (m)$ in $\mathscr{S}_I^*$, so that $H = (m)$ in $\mathscr{S}_{I_n}^*$ [that is, (x^m) in $\mathscr{S}_{(x)}^*$]. As regards factor groups, since the cosets of (x^d) are just $x^i(x^d)$, $0 \le i < d$, we have $(x)/(x^d) \cong (x^{n/d})$. Conversely, if H is any factor group of I_n, it is isomorphic to the factor group of I by some normal subgroup containing nI—that is, to some I/mI with m dividing n. $\quad \parallel$

Corollary. *Any subgroup of a finite cyclic group is cyclic.*

Exercise 1. *If (x) is infinite, the only elements of it which generate it are x and x^{-1}. If $(x) \cong I_n$, x^m generates it if and only if m is relatively prime to n.*

44. PRIME SEMIGROUPS AND GROUPS

Theorem 1. *A semigroup which is not a group is prime if and only if it has at most two elements.*

Proof: A semigroup with at most two elements must be prime, since its only subsets are itself, $\varnothing$, and trivial sets. To see the converse, let S be a prime semigroup but not a group; we consider several cases:

(a) If S has both left and right absorbent elements, by Proposition 31.1 it has a unique two-sided absorbent element a which is its only left or right absorbent element. Thus by Exercise 31.2, $\{a\}$ is the only trivial left or right ideal of S. Since a left or right ideal is a subsemigroup, we must thus have $xS = \{a\}$ or S, and $Sx = \{a\}$ or S, for all $x \in S$.

(a') If $xS = Sx = \{a\}$ for all $x \in S$, the composition on S is defined by $xy = a$ for all x, y in S; but for this composition, any subset containing a is a subsemigroup, so that S can have at most two elements.

(a'') Otherwise, there exists $b \in S$, evidently $\neq a$, such that (say) $Sb = S$. (The proof if there exists $b \in S$ such that $bS = S$ is exactly analogous.) In particular, there exists $e \in S$, $\neq a$, such that $eb = b$. Now $\{x \mid x \in S; ex = x\}$ is a right ideal and contains b, so cannot be trivial; hence it must be all of S, making e a left identity. Moreover, for all $y \in S$, $\neq a$, Sy is a left ideal and contains $ey = y$, so cannot be trivial and must be all of S; thus there exists $y' \in S$ such that $y'y = e$. It follows from Exercise 37.2 that $S - \{a\}$ is a subgroup of S, and since this subgroup must be trivial, S has just two elements.

(b) Suppose now that S has no right absorbent elements (the proof if it has no left absorbent elements is exactly analogous). Then S has no trivial left ideals, so that we have $Sx = S$ for all $x \in S$; in particular, for any $x \in S$ there exists $e_x \in S$ such that $e_x x = x$.

(b') If S has an element z which is not left absorbent, $\{z\}$ cannot be a right ideal; hence the right ideal $\{w \mid w \in S; e_z w = w\}$, which contains z, must be all of S, making e_z a left identity. Since for all $x \in S$ we have $Sx = S$, there exists $x' \in S$ such that $x'x = e_z$; thus S is a group, contradiction.

(b'') Hence every element of S is left absorbent, so that the composition on S is defined by $xy = x$ for all x, y in S; but for this composition, any subset is a subsemigroup, so that S can have at most two elements.   //

Corollary. *A semigroup has no subsemigroups other than itself and $\varnothing$ if and only if it is trivial.*

Proof: If S is nontrivial, cases (a') and (a'') cannot hold, since if $a \in S$ were absorbent, $\{a\}$ would be a subsemigroup; case (b') cannot hold, since if S were a group, $\{e\}$ would be a subsemigroup; while in case (b''), $\{x\}$ would be a subsemigroup for any $x \in S$.   //

From the proof of Theorem 1 we also have

Proposition 1. *The semigroup S has no nontrivial left or right ideals other than itself and $\varnothing$ if and only if one of the following is true:*

(1) *S is a group*
(2) *$S - \{a\}$ is a group, where a is absorbent*
(3) *S has at most two elements.*

Proof: By the proof of Theorem 1, one of the following must be the case:

(1) S is a group (Case b'); $\varnothing$ and S are the only ideals.

(2) $S - \{a\}$ is a group, where a is absorbent (Case a''); here the ideals are $\varnothing$, $\{a\}$, and S.

(3a) $xy = a$ for all x, y in S, where a is absorbent (Case a'). In this case any subset containing a is a two-sided ideal, so that S can have at most two elements.

(3b) $xy = x$ for all x, y in S, or $xy = y$ for all x, y in S (Cases b''). In the former case any subset is a right ideal, in the latter case a left ideal, so that here also S can have at most two elements.   //

Corollary. *A semigroup has no left or right ideals other than itself and $\varnothing$ if and only if it is a group or empty.*

It remains only to describe the prime groups, which we do in

Theorem 2. *The following statements about the group G are equivalent:*

(1) *G has no proper subgroups*

(2) *G is prime*

(3) *$G \cong \mathbf{I}_p$, where $p = 1$ or is prime.*

Proof: If G has no proper subgroups, and $x \in G$, $\neq e$, then the subgroup (x) must be all of G, so that G is cyclic. Now $\mathbf{I}$ certainly has proper subgroups, while by Proposition 43.3, $\mathbf{I}_n$ has no proper subgroups if and only if n has no proper divisors, so that (1) implies (3). Conversely, if $G \cong \mathbf{I}_p$, the subsemigroup generated by any $x \in G$, $\neq e$, is all of G, so that G is prime, proving that (3) implies (2).   //

By this theorem, as remarked at the end of Section 42, we need only one concept of "prime" for groups.

Exercise 1. *Exhibit all the semigroups which have two elements.*

Exercise 2. *Prove that G is prime if and only if $\mathscr{S}^*_G$ is one-dimensional (that is, $\dim (S:\{e\}) = 1$.*

45. FINITE SEMIGROUPS AND GROUPS

We cannot completely describe the finite, let alone the finitely generated, semigroups or groups (though we will be able to give, in the next chapter, complete descriptions of these cases for Abelian groups); however, we can give some useful partial descriptions. For the finitely generated case we prove here only

Proposition 1. The group G is finitely generated as an element of $\mathscr{S}_G$ if and only if it is finitely generated as an element of $\mathscr{S}^*_G$.

Proof: If $\{x_1, \ldots, x_n\}$ generates G as an element of $\mathscr{S}^*_G$, then $\{x_1, x_1^{-1}, \ldots, x_n, x_n^{-1}\}$ generates it as an element of $\mathscr{S}_G$.   //

By this proposition, as remarked at the end of Section 42, we need only one concept of "finitely generated" for groups.

A subsemigroup of a finitely generated semigroup, or even group, need not be finitely generated. For example, the additive Abelian group $\mathbf{I} \times \mathbf{I}$ is finitely generated—as a group, by $(1, 0)$ and $(0, 1)$; as a semigroup, use also $(-1, 0)$ and $(0, -1)$. However, it is easily seen that its subsemigroup corresponding to $\mathbf{N} \times \mathbf{N}$ is not finitely generated; in fact, any set of generators of this subsemigroup must contain $\{(1, k) \mid k \in \mathbf{N}\}$.

Exercise 1. *Any subsemigroup of a monogenic semigroup is finitely generated.*

Lattice-finiteness for both semigroups and groups is equivalent to finiteness:

Proposition 2. *A semigroup is lattice-finite if and only if it is finite.*

Proof: By Corollary 1 to Proposition 43.1, if S has a finite subsemigroup lattice it cannot have an infinite monogenic subsemigroup. Let it have k monogenic subsemigroups, and let them have $n_1, \ldots, n_k$ elements, respectively. Since any element of S must be in (in fact, must generate) one of them, S is their union, and so can have at most $n_1 + \cdots + n_k$ elements. $\quad //$

Proposition 3. *A group has a finite subgroup lattice if and only if it is finite.*

Proof: Analogous to that of Proposition 2, using Corollary 4 to Theorem 43.3. $\quad //$

Corollary. *The following statements about the group G are equivalent:*

(1) *G is finite*
(2) $\mathscr{S}_G$ *is finite*
(3) $\mathscr{S}_G^*$ *is finite.*

We thus need only one concept of "lattice-finite" for groups.

We now consider finite semigroups and groups, beginning with

Proposition 4. *A nonempty finite semigroup has an idempotent element.*

Proof: If S is trivial, its sole element is idempotent; we proceed by induction on the number of elements in S. Let $x \in S$; if $x = x^2$, x is idempotent, while if $x \notin (x^2)$, this subsemigroup is proper, and so has an idempotent element by induction hypothesis. Otherwise, we have $x \in (x^2)$ but $x \neq x^2$, say $x = x^k$ with $k > 2$, so that $(x^{k-1})^2 = x^{2k-2} = x^k x^{k-2} = xx^{k-2} = x^{k-1}$, proving x^{k-1} idempotent. $\quad //$

Thus the results of Section 39, for example, all hold for finite semigroups.

Proposition 5. *A nonempty finite cancellation semigroup is a group.*

Proof: Let S be such a semigroup. Since any $x \in S$ is left cancellable, the function L_x (Exercise 32.1) is one-to-one, and since S is finite, it follows that

L_x is onto (Corollary to Proposition 5.3), so that $xS = S$ for all $x \in S$. Similarly, $Sx = S$ for all $x \in S$, making S a group by Proposition 34.12.   //

A useful generalization of Proposition 5 is provided by

Proposition 6. *Let S be a semigroup whose set of principal left ideals, ordered by inclusion, satisfies the minimum condition. If S contains a right cancellable element, it has a right identity e, and every right cancellable element has a left e-inverse.*

Proof: Let $x \in S$ be right cancellable, and let $\mathscr{A}$ be the set of principal left ideals $\{Sx^n \mid n \in \mathbf{N}\}$; evidently $Sx^k \supseteq Sx^{k+1}$ for all $k \in \mathbf{N}$. Let Sx^m be a minimal element of $\mathscr{A}$; then we must have $Sx^m = Sx^{m+1}$. In particular, there exists $e \in S$ such that $xx^m = ex^{m+1}$, or (cancelling x^m) $x = ex$, making e a right identity by Proposition 34.4. Finally, since $Sx^m = Sx^{m+1}$, there exists $x' \in S$ such that $ex^m = x'x^{m+1}$, or (cancelling x^m) $e = x'x$, so that x' is a left e-inverse of x.   //

Corollary 1. *If S also contains a left cancellable element, it has an identity.*

Proof: The corollary to Proposition 34.4.

Corollary 2. *If every element of S is right cancellable, and some element is left cancellable, S is a group.*

Proof: By the foregoing, there is an identity e, and every element has a left e-inverse; now use Proposition 34.11.   //

Although there is little that we can say about finite groups in general, we do have some interesting results about subgroups of finite groups, which will be presented in the next section.

46. SUBGROUPS OF FINITE GROUPS

The number of elements in a finite group G is called the **order** of G, and is denoted by $o(G)$. If H is any subgroup of G, both H and the quotient set G/L_H are also finite; the number of elements in G/L_H is called the **index** of H in G, and is denoted by $i_G(H)$.

Proposition 1. *If the group G has a finite subgroup H which is of finite index in G, then G is finite, and $o(G) = o(H)i_G(H)$.*

Proof: By Exercise 38.2, every L_H-class is in one-to-one correspondence with $(L_H)_e = H$, so that each class has $o(H)$ elements, while the number of classes is $i_G(H)$.   //

Corollary 1 (Lagrange's theorem). *The order and index of any subgroup of a finite group divide the order of the group.*

If H is normal, $i_G(H)$ is the same thing as $o(G/H)$; thus

Corollary 2. *The order of any factor group of a finite group divides the order of the group; in fact, $o(G/H) = o(G)/o(H)$.*

Since any homomorphic image is isomorphic to a factor group, we have

Corollary 3. *Let F be a homomorphism of the group G, and let K be its kernel. If K and F(G) are finite, so is G; in fact, $o(G) = o(K)o(F(G))$. Thus the order of any homomorphic image of a finite group divides the order of the group.*

Exercise 1. Let G, F, K be as in Corollary 3, and let H be a *subgroup of G such that F(H) is finite; then KH is also finite—in fact, $o(KH) = o(K)o(F(H))$.* [Hint: $KH = L_K H = E_F H$ is a union of E_F-classes.]

Exercise 2. *Let the group G have a normal series $\{e\} = G_0 \subseteq G_1 \subseteq \cdots \subseteq G_n = G$ with G_i/G_{i-1} finite, $1 \le i \le n$. Then G is finite; in fact, $o(G) = \prod_{i=1}^{n} o(G_i/G_{i-1})$.*

As an immediate application of Lagrange's theorem we have

Proposition 2. *A group is prime if and only if it is trivial or has prime order.*

Proof: A group whose order has no proper divisors cannot have proper subgroups.   //

Lagrange's theorem gives us a partial description of the subgroups (and factor groups) of a finite group G; they are finite groups whose orders divide $o(G)$. Our principal goal in the remainder of this section is a partial answer to the following converse question: For which divisors d of $o(G)$ does G have a subgroup of order d?

Before we can attack this problem, we need some results about the orders of finite *cyclic* groups (x). We denote the order of (x) by $o(x)$, rather than $o((x))$, and call it the order "of x." [If (x) is infinite, we sometimes say that x has infinite order.] Evidently $o(x)$ is the smallest natural number m such that $x^m = e$, and $o(x) = 1$ if and only if $x = e$. Some other useful properties of $o(x)$ are given by

Proposition 3. *$x^k = e$ if and only if $o(x)$ divides k.*

Proof: Let $k = qo(x) + r$, where $0 \le r < o(x)$; then $x^r = x^{k-qo(x)} = x^k((x^{-1})^{o(x)})^q = e$, contradicting the minimality of $o(x)$ unless $r = 0$, so that $k = qo(x)$.   //

Proposition 4. *Let $o(x) = m$, and let the greatest common divisor of m and k be d; then $o(x^k) = m/d$.*

Proof: Let $m = dm'$, $k = dk'$; then $(x^k)^{m/d} = (x^{dk'})^{m'} = (x^{dm'})^{k'} = e$, so that $o(x^k)$ divides m/d (Proposition 3). On the other hand, if $(x^k)^h = e$, then $o(x) = m = dm'$ must divide $kh = dk'h$, so that m' divides $k'h$, and since $m' = m/d$ is relatively prime to k', it must divide h.   //

Corollary 1. $o(x^k) = o(x)$ *if and only if k and* $o(x)$ *are relatively prime.*

Corollary 2. *For any d dividing* $o(x)$ *we have* $o(x^d) = o(x)/d$.

Exercise 3. $o(x) = o(zxz^{-1})$.

Exercise 4. $o(x) \mid o(G)$ *for all* $x \in G$; *if* $o(x) = o(G)$ *for some* $x \in G$, *G is cyclic.*

Exercise 5 (the Euler–Fermat theorem). *Let k, n be natural numbers, k relatively prime to n; let* $\varphi(n)$ *denote the number of elements of* $\mathbf{N}_n$ *which are relatively prime to n. Then there exists* $q \in \mathbf{N}$ *such that* $k^{\varphi(n)} = qn + 1$. [Hint: use Corollary 1 to Exercise 38.8.]

Corollary. *Let* $p \in \mathbf{N}$ *be prime and not divide* $k \in \mathbf{N}$; *then there exists* $q \in \mathbf{N}$ *such that* $k^{p-1} = qp + 1$.

Proposition 5. *In an Abelian group, if* $o(x)$ *and* $o(y)$ *are relatively prime, then* $o(xy) = o(x)o(y)$.

Proof: Let $o(x) = m$, $o(y) = n$; clearly $(xy)^{mn} = e$. On the other hand, if $(xy)^k = e$, we have $e = (xy)^{mk} = y^{mk}$, so that n divides mk, and since n is relatively prime to m, this implies that n divides k. Similarly, $e = (xy)^{nk} = x^{nk}$, so that m also divides k; hence mn divides k.   //

Corollary 1. *In an Abelian group, let* $o(a) = r$, $o(b) = s$; *then there exists an element whose order is the least common multiple of r and s.*

Proof: Let d be the greatest common divisor of r and s, and let $r' = r/d$; then r' and s are relatively prime. By Proposition 4, $o(a^d) = r'$; hence by Proposition 5, $o(a^d b) = r's$, which is readily the least common multiple of r and s.   //

Corollary 2. *In an Abelian group G, let* $o(x) = m$, *and let* $o(y) \le m$ *for all* $y \in G$; *then* $y^m = e$ *for all* $y \in G$.

Proof: If $o(y)$ did not divide m, the least common multiple of $o(y)$ and m would be greater than m, so that by Corollary 1 m could not be maximal.   //

Using Propositions 3–4, we next prove our first converse to Lagrange's theorem:

Theorem 1. *If G is an Abelian group of order n, and p is a prime which divides n, then G has a subgroup of order p.*

Proof: We use induction; the assertion is trivial if $n = 1$ or n is prime. Let $n > 1$ not be prime, and suppose the theorem true for orders $< n$. Since n is not prime, G is not prime, so that it has a proper subgroup H, where $1 < o(H) < n$. Now since G is Abelian, H is normal, and we have $o(H)o(G/H) = n$; thus if $p \mid n$, it divides either $o(H)$ or $o(G/H)$. If $p \mid o(H)$, by induction hypothesis H has a subgroup of order p, hence so has G.

Similarly, if $p \mid o(G/H)$, then G/H has a subgroup K of order p. Since K is a prime group, it is cyclic, say $K = (xH)$. Let $o(x) = m$; then $(xH)^m = x^m H = eH = H$, which is the identity of G/H, so that $p = o(xH)$ must divide m. Thus $x^{m/p}$ has order p, so that G has a subgroup $(x^{m/p})$ of order p. //

As an interesting application of Theorem 1 and Proposition 5 we have

Proposition 6. *An Abelian group of squarefree order is cyclic.*

A natural number is called squarefree if it is not divisible by the square of any prime.

Proof: If $o(G)$ is squarefree, we have $o(G) = \prod_{i=1}^{n} p_i$, where the p's are distinct primes. By the proof of Theorem 1, G has elements of orders $p_1, \ldots, p_n$; hence by Proposition 5 and induction, G has an element of order the least common multiple of $p_1, \ldots, p_n$, which is just $\prod_{i=1}^{n} p_i = o(G)$. Thus this element generates all of G, making G cyclic. //

To extend Theorem 1 to nonabelian groups, we need

Proposition 7. *Let G be a finite group; then for any $x \in G$, the number of conjugates of x is $i_G(C(x))$.*

Proof: Proposition 41.3. //

Corollary. *In a finite group, the number of elements in any conjugate class divides the order of the group.*

Theorem 2 (Cauchy). *If G is a group of order n, and p is a prime which divides n, then G has a subgroup of order p.*

Proof: We again use induction. If G has a proper subgroup H such that p does not divide $i_G(H)$, then p must divide $o(H)$, so that the induction hypothesis gives us a subgroup of H, hence of G, having order p. Otherwise, p must divide the index of every proper subgroup of G. Now G is the union of its conjugate classes $C_1, \ldots, C_k$ (say), so that $n = \sum_{i=1}^{k} n_i$, where n_i is the number of elements in C_i. Let $x_i \in C_i$; then by Proposition 7, $n_i = i_G(C(x_i))$. If $n_i > 1$, this is the index of a proper subgroup of G, and so is divisible by p. On the other hand, we have $n_i = 1$ (that is, $C_i = \{x_i\}$) if and only if x_i is in the center of G; hence the number of n_i which are 1 is just $o(C(G))$. We thus have $n = \sum_{i=1}^{k} n_i = o(C(G)) + \sum_{i=1}^{h} m_i$ (say), where the m's are those of the n's which > 1. Since p divides n and each m_i, it must divide $o(C(G))$; and since $C(G)$ is Abelian, it thus has a subgroup of order p by Theorem 1. //

By a very similar argument, we have finally

Theorem 3 (Sylow). *If G is a group of order n, and p^k divides n, where p is prime, then G has a subgroup of order p^k.*

Proof: Once again we use induction. If G has a proper subgroup H such that p does not divide $i_G(H)$, we have $p^k \mid o(H)$, proving the theorem by the induction hypothesis. Otherwise, as in the proof of Theorem 2, we have $p \mid o(C(G))$, so that $C(G)$ has a subgroup (x) of order p. Now (x) is normal (Exercise 41.1), and $o(G/(x)) < o(G)$; hence, by induction hypothesis, $G/(x)$ has a subgroup of order p^{k-1}, and by Exercise 1, the corresponding subgroup of G has order $o(x)p^{k-1} = p^k$. //

If p^r is the highest power of p which divides $o(G)$, a subgroup of G of order p^r is called a **Sylow p-subgroup**. Note that in Theorems 1–2, G must have an *element* of order p (in fact, this is the same thing as having a subgroup of order p, since such a subgroup is prime, hence cyclic). In Theorem 3, on the other hand, G need not have an element of order p^k if $k > 1$. For example, let $G = \prod_{i=1}^{k} G_i$, where each G_i is $\mathbf{I}_p$; then $o(G) = p^k$, but every element of G has order 1 or p.

The equation $o(G) = o(C(G)) + \sum m_i$ (where the m's are the numbers of elements in the nontrivial conjugate classes of G), which we established in the course of proving Theorem 2, is called the **class equation** of G. We conclude this section by applying it to prove

Proposition 8. *A group whose order is the square of a prime must be Abelian.*

Proof: If $o(G) = p^2$, the order and index of any proper subgroup of G must be p; hence in the class equation of G, every m_i must be p, so that p divides $o(C(G))$. On the other hand, if $x \notin C(G)$ we have $C(x) \supseteq C(G) \cup \{x\} \supset C(G)$, so that $o(C(x)) > o(C(G)) \geq p$; hence $o(C(x)) = p^2$, that is, $C(x) = G$, which means that $x \in C(G)$, contradiction. Thus $C(G)$ must be all of G, making G Abelian. //

Proposition 9. *A group of order pq, where p, q are primes, $p < q$, and p does not divide $q - 1$, must be cyclic.*

Proof: By Theorem 2, G has elements of orders both p and q, but if it is not cyclic, it has no element of order pq. Since distinct cyclic subgroups of prime orders can have no element but e in common, the number of elements of order p must be divisible by $p - 1$, and the number of order q by $q - 1$, so that $o(G) = pq = 1 + r(p - 1) + s(q - 1)$ (say), where the "1" counts e. If G is not Abelian, its center $C(G)$ has order 1, p, or q. If $o(C(G)) = p$, let $x \notin C(G)$; then as in the proof of Proposition 8, $C(x)$ must be all of G, which implies $x \in C(G)$, contradiction. Hence $o(C(G)) \neq p$, and similarly $o(C(G)) \neq q$, so that $o(C(G)) = 1$, that is, $C(G) = \{e\}$, and the class equation of G is $pq = 1 + ap + bq$ (say). Now the centralizer of an element x of order p has order divisible by p (since $(x) \subseteq C(x)$), and this order cannot be pq since $x \notin C(G)$; hence it is exactly p, and similarly if $o(y) = q$ then $o(C(y)) = q$. Thus $i_G(C(x)) = q$, $i_G(C(y)) = p$, so that in the class equation, the p-element classes consist of elements of order q and vice versa. Hence $ap = s(q - 1)$, $bq = r(p - 1)$, and since $q > p$, we must have $q \mid r$, say $r = tq$. Thus $pq = 1 + tq(p - 1) + s(q - 1)$, so that $(t - 1)pq + sq + 1 = tq + s$, where $sq > s$ and $(t - 1)p \geq 2(t - 1) \geq t$ unless $t = 1$. To avoid a contradiction we must have $t = 1$, so that $sq + 1 = q + s$, that is, $s(q - 1) = q - 1$; hence $s = 1$, and we have $ap = q - 1$, that is, p divides $q - 1$, contradiction. //

47. SIMPLE AND INDECOMPOSABLE GROUPS

One can define additional "finiteness properties" of a groupoid S by using subsets of $\mathscr{S}_S$ in Section 42 in place of $\mathscr{S}_S$ itself. In this section we consider two of the simplest such properties, both of them analogs of primeness:

(b′) S has no proper normal subgroupoids
(b″) S has no proper supplemented subgroupoids

—where by "proper" we mean "other than $\varnothing$ and S, and nontrivial." Note that conversely, an improper subgroupoid must be normal ($\varnothing$ is normal by definition, S is an $S \times S$-class, any trivial subgroupoid is an I_S-class), and a nonempty improper subgroupoid must be supplemented (I_S and $S \times S$ are supplemented congruences). Clearly (b) implies (b′) implies (b″).

If $S = G$ is a group, properties (b′) and (b″) can be characterized in a number of alternative ways:

Proposition 1. *The following statements about the group G are all equivalent:*

(1) $\mathscr{C}_G = \{I_G, G \times G\}$—*in other words, there are no proper congruences on G*
(2) G *has no proper normal subsets*
(3) G *has no proper normal subgroupoids*
(4) G *has no proper normal subgroups.*

Proof: Clearly (1) implies (2) implies (3) implies (4). Conversely, any congruence on G is an L_H, where H is a normal subgroup; thus if (4) holds, the only congruences on G are $L_G = G \times G$ and $L_{\{e\}} = I_G$, proving (1). //

A group with these properties is called **simple**.

Exercise 1. *A homomorphism defined on a simple group is either a constant function or an isomorphism.*

Proposition 2. *The following statements about the group G are equivalent:*

(1) *There are no proper supplemented congruences on G*
(2) G *has no proper supplemented subgroupoids*
(3) G *has no proper supplemented subgroups.*

Proof: Like that of Proposition 1, using the fact that the kernel of a proper supplemented congruence is a proper supplemented subgroup.   //

By Proposition 29.6, a group has these properties if and only if it is **indecomposable.**

Since the lattice of normal subgroupoids of a homomorphic image of S is order isomorphic to a sublattice of that of S, it is clear that any homomorphic image (or quotient groupoid) of a groupoid with property (b') also has property (b'). In particular, a homomorphic image or factor group of a simple group is simple. We shall show below that a factor group of an indecomposable group need not be indecomposable, and that neither simplicity nor indecomposability need pass to subgroups. To this end, we study two special cases—the cyclic groups and the groups of permutations.

An Abelian group is simple if and only if it is prime, since all of its subgroups are normal. However, there exist nonprime Abelian, and even cyclic, groups which are indecomposable; in fact, we have

Proposition 3. I *is indecomposable;* I_n *is indecomposable if and only if* $n = p^k$, *where $p \in \mathbf{N}$ is prime and $k \in \mathbf{N}°$.*

Proof: By Proposition 40.3, I cannot have a proper supplemented subgroup, since any two nontrivial subgroups of I have a nontrivial intersection (in fact, $m\mathbf{I} \cap n\mathbf{I} \supseteq mn\mathbf{I}$). The same argument applies to I_{p^k}, since readily its nontrivial subgroups all contain (p^{k-1}).

To prove the converse, let $n \neq p^k$; then by Exercise 35.9, there exist r, s in $\mathbf{N}$, relatively prime and neither $= 1$, such that $n = rs$. Now by Exercise 38.9, for any $m \in \mathbf{I}_r, n \in \mathbf{I}_s$ there exists $k \in I$ such that $r \mid k - m, s \mid k - n$. Thus for any (m, n) in $\mathbf{I}_r \times \mathbf{I}_s$ we have $(m, n) = k(1, 1)$, so that $(1, 1)$ generates $\mathbf{I}_r \times \mathbf{I}_s$. Hence $\mathbf{I}_r \times \mathbf{I}_s$ is cyclic, and since it has order $rs = n$, it must be isomorphic to $\mathbf{I}_n$, so that $\mathbf{I}_n$ is decomposable.   //

Corollary 1. *A factor group of an indecomposable group need not be indecomposable.* [Example: $\mathbf{I}_6 \cong \mathbf{I}/6\mathbf{I}$.]

Corollary 2. *A normal subgroup which is a direct factor need not be supplemented.*

Proof: $\mathbf{I} \cong 2\mathbf{I} \cong 2\mathbf{I} \times \{0\}$, so that the proper normal subgroup $2\mathbf{I}$ is a direct factor of $\mathbf{I}$; but $\mathbf{I}$ has no proper supplemented subgroups.   //

GROUPS OF PERMUTATIONS

We next consider groups of permutations. The group (under $\circ$) of all permutations of $\mathbf{N}_n$ is called the **symmetric group** on n elements, and is denoted by S_n; we recall (Exercise 5.9) that $o(S_n) = n!$. An element of S_n which leaves all but two elements of N_n fixed is called a **transposition**; it is understood that the two elements are *not* left fixed—in other words, the identity function I_n on N_n is not a transposition. If two elements are r and s, we denote the transposition by f_{rs}; thus $f_{rs}(r) = s$, $f_{rs}(s) = r$, and $f_{rs}(k) = k$ for all $k \in N_n$ other than r, s. Note that $f_{rs} \circ f_{rs} = I_n$, so that $f_{rs}^{-1} = f_{rs}$.

Proposition 4. S_n *is generated by the transpositions.*

Proof: This is trivial for $n = 1$ or 2. If it is true through $n - 1$, let $f \in S_n$, and let $f(n) = k$; then $f \circ f_{kn}$ leaves n fixed, and so is in S_{n-1}. Thus by induction hypothesis $f \circ f_{kn}$ is a composite of transpositions; hence so is $f \circ f_{kn} \circ f_{kn}^{-1} = f$. //

Let A_n be the subset of S_n consisting of those permutations which are composites of an even number of transpositions. Evidently A_n is a subgroup; it is called the **alternating group** on n elements. We show that A_n cannot be all of S_n—in particular, that no transposition is in A_n. Indeed, if f_{rs} were in A_n, then $I_n = f_{rs}^{-1} \circ f_{rs}$ would be the composite of an odd number of transpositions. Let $f_{rs} \circ \cdots$ be such a composite with the smallest possible number k of factors; let $\mathscr{F}_r$ be the set of such k-factor composites which begin with f_{rx} for some $x \in N_n$; and let $f_{rt} \circ \cdots \in \mathscr{F}_r$ have the fewest factors of the form f_{ry}. Now this composite must contain at least one factor f_{ry} besides its first factor f_{rt}, since otherwise it would take t into r and so could not be equal to I_n. Let f_{rw} be the leftmost such factor. Since if a, b, r, w are all different we have $f_{ab} \circ f_{rw} = f_{rw} \circ f_{ab}$, while if r, w, z are all different we have $f_{zw} \circ f_{rw} = f_{rz} \circ f_{zw}$, we can thus (induction!) move f_{rw} to the left until it becomes the second factor, so that I_n is also equal to a k-factor composite of the form $f_{rt} \circ f_{rw} \cdots$. If $t = w$, the first two factors cancel, making I_n a composite of $k - 2$ transpositions, contrary to the minimality of k. But if $t \neq w$, we have $f_{rt} \circ f_{rw} = f_{rw} \circ f_{tw}$ since r, t, w are all different; hence there is a composite in $\mathscr{F}_r$ having fewer factors of the form f_{ry}, contradiction.† It follows immediately that no permutation can be a composite of both an odd and an even number of transpositions, since (transposing all but one of the odd number of factors) we would then have a transposition in A_n. A permutation is called **even** if it is in A_n, **odd** otherwise.

Proposition 5. $A_n = (\{ f_{ij} \circ f_{ik} \mid i, j, k \text{ distinct elements of } N_n \})$.

Proof: If a, b, c, d are all different, we have $f_{ab} \circ f_{cd} = (f_{ab} \circ f_{ac}) \circ (f_{ad} \circ f_{ac})$; hence any composite of an even number of transpositions is generated by the $f_{ij} \circ f_{ik}$'s. //

Proposition 6. $o(A_n) = n!/2$.

---

† This proof is taken from E. L. Spitznagel, Jr., "Note on the alternating group," *Amer. Math. Monthly* **75**, January 1968, 68–69.

Proof: If f and g are odd, $f \circ g^{-1}$ is even, so that A_n and $S_n - A_n$ are the only cosets of A_n. $\parallel$

Corollary. A_n *is normal in* S_n.

Proof: Corollary 3 to Proposition 38.3. $\parallel$

Evidently $S_1 = A_1 = \{I_1\}$ is the trivial group; S_2 has two elements, so that $S_2 \cong I_2$ and $A_2 = \{I_2\}$ is the trivial group; and S_3 has six elements, so that $A_3 \cong I_3$ since it has three elements. It can be verified (Exercise: do so) that A_3 is the only proper normal subgroup of S_3, and that A_4 and

$$\{I_4, f_{12} \circ f_{34}, f_{13} \circ f_{24}, f_{14} \circ f_{23}\}$$

are the only proper normal subgroups of S_4. In particular, A_1, A_2, and A_3 are simple, but A_4 is not.

Theorem 1. A_n *is simple for all* $n > 4$.

Proof: We show first that any nontrivial normal subgroup H of A_n must contain $f_{ij} \circ f_{ik}$ for some i, j, k in $\mathbf{N}_n$, all distinct. To this end, let $g \neq I_n$ be an element of H which leaves the greatest number of elements of $\mathbf{N}_n$ fixed. Since g is even, it is the composite of an even number of transpositions. If no two of these transpositions have subscripts in common, we have $g = f_{ij} \circ f_{rs} \circ g'$ (say), where i, j, r, s are distinct and g' leaves them fixed. Let k not be i, j, r, or s, and let $f = f_{kr} \circ f_{ks}$. Thus $f \in A_n$, and since H is normal in A_n we have $g^* = (f^{-1} \circ g \circ f) \circ g^{-1}$ in H. Now $g^* \neq I_n$, since $g^*(s) = g'(k) \neq s$. On the other hand, we have $g^*(i) = i$, $g^*(j) = j$, while if $g(m) = m$, where $m \neq k$, then $g^*(m) = m$; thus g^* leaves more elements of $\mathbf{N}_n$ fixed than does g, contradiction.

We have shown that g cannot be a composite of transpositions no two of which have a common subscript. It follows that there exists an $i \in \mathbf{N}_n$ such that $g(g(i)) \neq i$. Let $g(i) = j$, $g(j) = k$; then i, j, k are distinct, and $g(k) \neq k$. Let $g = f_{ij} \circ f_{ik} \circ g'$ (say); then g' leaves j and k fixed. If $g' \neq I_n$, since it must be even there are at least three elements of $\mathbf{N}_n$ which it does not leave fixed. Hence there are at least two such elements r, s different from i (and evidently from j and k) which it, whence g, does not leave fixed. Define f and g^* as in the first paragraph of the proof; then here too $g^* \neq I_n$, since $g^*(j) \neq j$. Moreover, anything left fixed by g is not k, r, or s, so is also left fixed by g^*, while i is left fixed by g^* but not by g. Thus g^* leaves more elements of $\mathbf{N}_n$ fixed than g, contradiction, unless $g' = I_n$, that is, $g = f_{ij} \circ f_{ik}$, as desired.

To complete the proof, note that for all i, j, k, x, y, z in $\mathbf{N}_n$, i, j, k distinct, x, y, z distinct, there exists an f^* in A_n such that $f^*(i) = x$, $f^*(j) = y$, $f^*(k) = z$. [In fact, define f^* arbitrarily on $\mathbf{N}_n - \{i, j, k\}$; if the result is odd, use its composite with any f_{uv}, where u, v are different from i, j, k.] Thus if $f_{ij} \circ f_{ik}$ is in H, so is $f^{*-1} \circ f_{ij} \circ f_{ik} \circ f^*$, which readily $= f_{xy} \circ f_{xz}$. Thus by

Proposition 5, H contains a set of permutations which generates A_n, so must be all of A_n. $/\!/$

Corollary. *A subgroup of a simple group need not be simple.*

Proof: A_5 is simple, but its subset consisting of those permutations which leave 5 fixed is a subgroup isomorphic to A_4, which is not simple. $/\!/$

Proposition 7. *For all $n > 4$, A_n is the only proper normal subgroup of S_n.*

Proof: Note first that a subgroup of S_n of order 2 cannot be normal. Indeed, if $\{I_n, f\}$ is such a subgroup, let $f(i) \neq i$, and let j be different from both i and $f(i)$; then $f_{f(i)j} \circ f \circ f_{f(i)j}^{-1}$ takes i into j, so that it is neither I_n nor f.

Let H be any normal subgroup of S_n; then $H \cap A_n$ is normal in A_n, and since A_n is simple, we must have $H \cap A_n = \{I_n\}$ or A_n. If $H \cap A_n = A_n$, that is, $H \supseteq A_n$, then since A_n has index 2 we have $H = A_n$ or $H = S_n$. Otherwise, $H \cap A_n = \{I_n\}$; if $H = \{I_n\}$, we are done. But if not, by the first paragraph of the proof, H has order at least 3, and so has at least two elements f, g different from I_n. Since $H \cap A_n = \{I_n\}$, f and g must be odd; but then $f \circ f$ and $f \circ g$ are even, and so are both in $H \cap A_n$ and must both be I_n, which is impossible. $/\!/$

Corollary 1. *S_n is indecomposable for all $n \in \mathbf{N}$.*

Proof: It cannot have two proper normal subgroups whose intersection is $\{I_n\}$. $/\!/$

Corollary 2. *A subgroup of an indecomposable group need not be indecomposable.*

Proof: $\{I_n, f_{12} \circ f_{34}, f_{13} \circ f_{24}, f_{14} \circ f_{23}\}$, which is isomorphic to

$$\{I_n, f_{12} \circ f_{34}\} \times \{I_n, f_{13} \circ f_{24}\},$$

is a subgroup of S_n for any $n \geq 4$. [The case $n = 4$ shows that even a normal subgroup of an indecomposable group need not be indecomposable.] $/\!/$

Corollary 3. *A supplemented subgroup of a normal subgroup of G need not be normal in G.*

Proof: Take $G = S_4$ and use the proof of Corollary 2. $/\!/$

48. SOME STRUCTURE THEOREMS, I: DIRECT PRODUCTS

The descriptions of the cyclic and prime groups given in Sections 43–44 illustrate one method of characterizing a given type of group—namely, proving that it must be isomorphic to a group which is already known. Another method of describing a group G in terms of known groups G_i is to show that G is isomorphic to a direct product of G_i's, since this completely determines the composition on G in terms of those on the G_i's.

For certain types of G_i's, direct products yield nothing new. For example, we have

Proposition 1. *A groupoid with identity is isomorphic to a direct product of finitely many finitely generated groupoids if and only if it is finitely generated.*

Proof: Corollary 2 to Proposition 39.5 and Exercise 16.3.   //

The analog of Proposition 1 with "finite" in place of "finitely generated" is immediate, and does not require an identity. Similarly, the analogous proposition with "commutative" is immediate, and requires neither an identity nor finiteness of the number of direct factors.

In the remainder of this section we prove three nontrivial "structure theorems" about groups which are isomorphic to direct products of "known" groups. The first of these gives a sufficient condition for a group to be isomorphic to a finite direct product of (short for: direct product of finitely many) indecomposable groups. The second and third give necessary and sufficient conditions for a group to be isomorphic to a weak direct product of simple or prime groups. [In Section 50 we shall give necessary and sufficient conditions for a group to be isomorphic to a finite direct product of cyclic or monogenic groups.]

Theorem 1. *Let G be a group whose set of supplemented subgroups, ordered by inclusion, satisfies the minimum condition; then G is isomorphic to a finite direct product of indecomposable groups.*

Proof: If G is indecomposable, there is nothing to prove. If not, the set of its proper supplemented subgroups is nonempty, so has a minimal element G_1. If G_1 were not indecomposable, we would have $G_1 \cong A \times B$, where A and B are proper supplemented subgroups of G_1. By Proposition 40.5, A and B would then be proper supplemented subgroups of G, and since they are properly contained in G_1, this contradicts its minimality.

Let G' be a supplement of G_1 in G. If G' is indecomposable, we have $G \cong G_1 \times G'$ and we are done. If not, in any case G' is a proper supplemented subgroup of G, so that by Proposition 40.5 its supplemented subgroups also satisfy the minimum condition; hence by the first paragraph of the proof, it too has a proper indecomposable supplemented subgroup G_2. Let G'' be a supplement of G_2 in G'. If G'' is indecomposable, we have $G \cong G_1 \times G' \cong G_1 \times (G_2 \times G'')$, and we are done. If not, in any case G'' is a proper supplemented subgroup of G', hence of G, and we can repeat the argument. If none of the $G^{(k)}$ obtained in this way were indecomposable, they would constitute a descending chain $G \supset G' \supset G'' \supset \cdots$ of supplemented subgroups of G, which is impossible. Hence some $G^{(n)}$ is indecomposable, and we have

$$G \cong G_1 \times G' \cong G_1 \times G_2 \times G'' \cong \cdots \cong G_1 \times G_2 \times \cdots \times G_n \times G^{(n)},$$

where every direct factor in the right member is indecomposable.   //

If $\mathcal{N}_G^*$ is finite dimensional, G certainly satisfies the hypothesis of the theorem, and in this case the direct "factorization" whose existence is guaranteed by the theorem is also "unique" by the Krull–Schmidt theorem.

Theorem 2. *The following statements about the group G are equivalent:*

(1) *G is isomorphic to a weak direct product of simple groups*
(2) *G is the sup (in $\mathcal{N}_G^*$) of a set of simple normal subgroups of G*
(3) *Every normal subgroup of G is supplemented.*

Proof: (1) implies (2) by Exercises 39.2. If (2) holds, let $G = \sup \mathcal{K}$, where each $K \in \mathcal{K}$ is a simple normal subgroup of G. Let H be a proper normal subgroup of G; we must show that H is supplemented. Let $\mathcal{S} = \{\mathcal{L} \mid \mathcal{L} \subseteq \mathcal{K}; H \cap \sup \mathcal{L} = L \cap \sup (\mathcal{L} - \{L\} \cup \{H\}) = \{e\}$ for all $L \in \mathcal{L}\}$. We first prove that $\mathcal{S} \neq \varnothing$. In fact, since $H \cap K$ is normal in K, and K is simple, we must have $H \cap K = K$ or $\{e\}$ for each $K \in \mathcal{K}$. But if $H \cap K = K$ for every $K \in \mathcal{K}$, we would have $H \supseteq \sup \mathcal{K} = G$, contradicting the properness of H. Hence there exists an $L \in \mathcal{K}$ such that $H \cap L = \{e\}$, so that $\{L\} \in \mathcal{S}$. It is easily verified that the union of any inclusion-ordered chain of elements of $\mathcal{S}$ is in $\mathcal{S}$—in other words, $\mathcal{S}$ ordered by inclusion is inductive, so that by Zorn's lemma, $\mathcal{S}$ has an inclusion-maximal element $\mathcal{L}^*$.

Let $L^* = \sup (\mathcal{L}^* \cup \{H\})$; by definition of $\mathcal{S}$, H is a supplemented subgroup of L^*. Now for any $K \in \mathcal{K}$, $L^* \cap K$ is normal in K, hence must be K or $\{e\}$. But if $L^* \cap K = \{e\}$, it follows by Exercise 40.3 that $\mathcal{L}^* \cup \{K\}$ is in $\mathcal{S}$, and since $\mathcal{L}^*$ is maximal, this means that K must be in $\mathcal{L}^*$. Thus for all K *not* in $\mathcal{L}^*$ we must have $L^* \cap K = K$, that is, $L^* \supseteq K$; and L^* certainly contains every K which *is* in $\mathcal{L}^*$. Hence L^* contains every $K \in \mathcal{K}$, so that $L^* \supseteq \sup \mathcal{K} = G$, making H supplemented in G and proving (3).

Finally, let (3) hold, and note first that by Proposition 40.4 and the remark following Proposition 40.5, if K is normal in H and H normal in G, then H and K are supplemented in G, so that K is supplemented in H. We next prove that any proper normal subgroup H of G contains a proper simple normal subgroup of G. In fact, if H is simple, there is nothing to prove; if not, it has a proper normal subgroup K. Let x be in H but not in K; then the set of proper normal subgroups of H which contain K but not x is nonempty (K is in it), and is clearly inductive under the inclusion ordering, so that by Zorn's lemma it has a maximal element M. By the remarks at the beginning of this paragraph, M is supplemented in H, say $MM^* = H$, $M \cap M^* = \{e\}$; we show that M^* is simple. If not, it too has a proper supplemented subgroup, say $NN^* = M^*$, $N \cap N^* = \{e\}$. Thus NM and N^*M both properly contain M, so that by the maximality of M each of them must contain x. We thus have $x \notin M$ but $x \in NM \cap N^*M$, say $x = uv = yz$, where $u \in N$, $y \in N^*$—so that u and y are both in M^*—and v, z are in M. By Proposition 40.1 we thus have $u = y$; hence u is in $N \cap N^* = \{e\}$, that is, $u = e$, so that $x = v$ is in M, contradiction.

It follows from what we have just proved that if G itself is not simple, it has a proper simple normal subgroup H. Since by (3) H is supplemented, we have $H \cap K = \{e\}$ for some proper normal subgroup K of G, so that there exists a proper simple normal subgroup L of G contained in K, where clearly $H \cap L = \{e\}$. Let $\mathscr{I}$ be the set of all independent sets of proper simple normal subgroups of G; $\mathscr{I}$ is nonempty, since $\{H, K\} \in \mathscr{I}$. As in the first paragraph of the proof, $\mathscr{I}$ ordered by inclusion is inductive, so has a maximal element $\mathscr{J}$. Let $J = \sup \mathscr{J}$; this is a normal subgroup of G, hence is supplemented, say $J \cap J^* = \{e\}$. If J^* is nontrivial, it contains a proper simple normal subgroup I of G, and we have $J \cap I = \{e\} \subset I$, so that $I \notin \mathscr{J}$. By Exercise 40.3 this implies that $\mathscr{J} \subset \mathscr{J} \cup \{I\} \in \mathscr{I}$, contradicting the maximality of $\mathscr{J}$. Hence J^* must be trivial, so that $G = J$, which is isomorphic to the weak direct product of the simple normal subgroups in $\mathscr{J}$, proving (1).   //

Using Theorem 2 we can also prove

Theorem 3. The following statements about the group G are equivalent:

(1) G is isomorphic to a weak direct product of prime groups
(2) Every subgroup of G is supplemented
(3) G is Abelian and every element of G has finite, squarefree order.

Proof: If (1) holds, G is Abelian since the direct factors are, and by Theorem 2, every normal subgroup of G is supplemented; but since G is Abelian, every subgroup of G is normal, proving (2). Moreover, if (1) holds, any $x \in G$ corresponds to an I-tuple $(x_i)_I$ in which only finitely many x_i's are not the identity; the set of orders of these x_i's is thus a finite set of primes $\{p_1, \ldots, p_n\}$ (say). Let $r = \prod_{i=1}^n p_i$; then evidently $x^r = e$, so that the order of x divides a product of distinct primes and is thus squarefree, proving (3).

If (2) holds, since any $(x) \subseteq G$ is supplemented we have $G = (x)H$ (say), where x commutes with every $h \in H$. Hence for any $y \in G$ we have $y = x^k h$ for some $x^k \in (x)$, $h \in H$, so that $yx = x^k hx = x^{k+1} h = xy$, proving G Abelian. By Theorem 2, G is isomorphic to a weak direct product of simple groups, and since G is Abelian so are they, making them prime and proving (1).

Finally, if (3) holds, let G_p be the subgroup of G consisting of the elements whose orders are powers of p, where p is prime; since these orders must be squarefree, they must all be 1 or p. Thus every element of G_p is in a prime subgroup, making G_p the sup (in its subgroup lattice) of a set of prime subgroups, which are normal since G is Abelian. Hence by the proof of Theorem 2, G_p is isomorphic to the weak direct product of some of these prime groups; while by Proposition 51.6 below, G is isomorphic to the weak direct product of the G_p's, which proves (1).   //

[These characterizations of groups whose (normal) subgroups are all supplemented suggest that it would also be of interest to characterize groups whose subgroups are all normal; we shall do so in Section 55.]

49. SOME STRUCTURE THEOREMS, II: NORMAL SERIES

Let S be a groupoid with idempotent element e, and let $S \cong \prod_{i=1}^{n} S_i$. Let E_i be the congruence on S corresponding to that on $\prod_{i=1}^{n} S_i$ defined by its projection on S_i, $1 \leq i \leq n$, and let $S_{(k)} = (\bigcap_{i=1}^{k} E_i)_e$, where $k \in \mathbf{N}_n$. Then $S_{(k)} \cong \prod_{i=k+1}^{n} S_i$, so that the restriction E'_{k+1} of E_{k+1} to $S_{(k)}$ is a supplemented congruence (it has the restriction of $\bigcap_{i=k+2}^{n} E_i$ to $S_{(k)}$ as a supplement), and $(E'_{k+1})_e = S_{(k+1)}$. Moreover, $S_{(k)}/E'_{k+1}$ is isomorphic to the quotient of $\prod_{i=k+1}^{n} S_i$ by the corresponding congruence on it, and this quotient is in turn isomorphic to S_{k+1}. A chain $S = S_{(0)} \supseteq S_{(1)} \supseteq \cdots \supseteq S_{(n)} = \{e\}$ is thus defined such that $S_{(i)}$ is a supplemented subgroupoid of $S_{(i-1)}$, $1 \leq i \leq n$. In particular, this chain is a normal series, and the step $[S_{(i)}, S_{(i-1)}]$ has a quotient isomorphic to S_i, $1 \leq i \leq n$. In short: if $S \cong \prod_{i=1}^{n} S_i$, there exists a special type of normal series (which we can call a "supplemented series") from $\{e\}$ to S which has quotients isomorphic to the S_i's.

In the "structure theorems" of Section 48 we considered group(oid)s which are isomorphic to direct products of "known" group(oid)s. By the preceding paragraph, if there is an idempotent element and the number of direct factors is finite, these groupoids have supplemented series with known quotients. This suggests that one might also consider weaker types of "structure theorems" involving groupoids S which have weaker types of series (for example, chains of normal subgroupoids, or normal series) from a trivial subgroupoid to S with known quotients. Such groupoids are, of course, not completely determined in terms of the known ones, as they were in the supplemented series case.

In this section we consider groups having normal series whose factors are finitely generated, finite, simple, prime, monogenic, cyclic, or Abelian.

Proposition 1. *The group G has a normal series from $\{e\}$ to G with finitely generated factors if and only if G is finitely generated.*

Proof: Exercise 38.5 and induction.   //

The analogous proposition with "finite" in place of "finitely generated" is also evidently true (see Exercise 46.2).

Proposition 2. *A normal series in a group has simple factors if and only if it is unrefinable (in other words, is a composition series).*

Proof: Theorems 26.2 and 38.1.   ‖

Exercise 1. *If a normal series in a groupoid is unrefinable, it has quotients which have no proper normal subgroupoids.* [Hint: Use Theorem 27.1. Is the converse true?]

In what follows, "G has a composition series" means "there exists a composition series from $\{e\}$ to G."

Proposition 3. *The group G has a composition series if and only if*

(1) *The normal subgroups of any subnormal subgroup of G satisfy the ascending chain condition; and*

(2) *There exists no descending chain $G = G_0 \supset G_1 \supset \cdots$ of subgroups of G such that G_i is normal in G_{i-1} for all $i \in \mathbf{N}$.*

Proof: If (1–2) hold, apply (1) to G itself to show that it has a maximal normal subgroup $G_1 \subset G$; then to G_1, to obtain a maximal normal subgroup $G_2 \subset G_1$; and so on. By (2), this process must terminate, say at G_n, which can only happen if $G_n = \{e\}$, so that G has the composition series $G \supset G_1 \supset \cdots \supset G_n$. Conversely, if G has a composition series, by the Schreier refinement theorem (28.1), no normal series from $\{e\}$ to G can have more terms than it, which readily implies (1–2).   ‖

Corollary 1. *If G has a composition series, so has any subnormal subgroup of G.*

Corollary 2. *If G has a composition series, so has any factor group of G.*

Proof: Apply the Schreier refinement theorem to the given composition series and the normal series $\{e\} \subseteq H \subseteq G$ to obtain a composition series refining $H \subseteq G$; this readily corresponds to a composition series for G/H.   ‖

Exercise 2. *Generalize these results and those in the rest of this section, as far as possible, to groupoids.*

SOLVABLE GROUPS

The group G is called **solvable** if there exists a normal series from $\{e\}$ to G which has Abelian factors.

Exercise 3. *Any refinement of a normal series with Abelian factors also has Abelian factors.* [Hint: Use Proposition 41.5.]

Proposition 4. *Any subgroup of a solvable group is solvable.*

Proof: Let $\{e\} = G_0 \subseteq G_1 \subseteq \cdots \subseteq G_n = G$ be a normal series with Abelian factors; then for any subgroup H of G,

$$\{e\} = G_0 \cap H \subseteq G_1 \cap H \subseteq \cdots \subseteq G_n \cap H = H$$

is a normal series, and its factors are Abelian since, by Corollary 3 to Theorem 26.1, they are isomorphic to subgroups of the factors of the original normal series. //

Proposition 5. *Any factor group of a solvable group is solvable.*

Proof: Analogous to that of Corollary 2 to Proposition 3. //

Exercise 4. *The group G is solvable if and only if there exists a normal series from $\{e\}$ to G which has solvable factors.*

Exercise 5. *Let G be a group, G' the derived group of G (Section 41), G'' the derived group of G', and so on. Prove that every $G^{(k)}$ is normal in G, and that G is solvable if and only if $G^{(n)} = \{e\}$ for some $n \in \mathbf{N}$.*

Corollary. *The group G is solvable if and only if there is a finite chain from $\{e\}$ to G in $\mathcal{N}_G^*$ which has Abelian factors.*

An Abelian group is evidently solvable; examples of nonsolvable groups are provided by

Proposition 6. *S_n is solvable if and only if $n \le 4$.*

Proof: For $n = 1, 2$, S_n is prime. For $n = 3$, A_n is normal and prime, so that $\{I_3\} \subset A_3 \subset S_3$ is a normal series with prime factors. For $n = 4$, readily $\{I_4\} \subset \{I_4, f_{12} \circ f_{34}\} \subset \{I_4, f_{12} \circ f_{34}, f_{13} \circ f_{24}, f_{14} \circ f_{23}\} \subset A_4 \subset S_4$ is such a normal series. For $n > 4$, A_n is the only proper normal subgroup of S_n, and is simple; hence the only normal series from $\{I_n\}$ to S_n are $\{I_n\} \subset S_n$ and $\{I_n\} \subset A_n \subset S_n$, neither of which has Abelian factors. //

A group which has a normal series (from $\{e\}$ to G) with prime, monogenic (= finite cyclic), or cyclic factors is evidently solvable, and in the cases of prime and monogenic factors, it is also finite. In fact, we have

Proposition 7. *The following statements about the group G which has a composition series are all equivalent:*

(1) *G is solvable*
(2) *There exists a normal series from $\{e\}$ to G with cyclic factors*
(3) *There exists a normal series from $\{e\}$ to G with monogenic factors*
(4) *There exists a normal series from $\{e\}$ to G with prime factors.*

Moreover, if (1–4) hold, G is finite.

Proof: Clearly (4) implies (3) implies (2) implies (1) for any group. Conversely, if G is solvable and has a composition series, by the Schreier refinement theorem a normal series with Abelian factors can be refined to a composition series, the factors of which are Abelian and simple, hence prime. //

IX

ABELIAN GROUPS

It is customary to denote the composition on an Abelian group *additively*. In particular, we denote the identity element by 0, and we write $\sum_{i=1}^{n} k_i a_i$ instead of $\prod_{i=1}^{n} a_i^{k_i}$. We also speak of *direct sums* rather than direct products, denoting the direct sum of A and B by $A \oplus B$, and the direct sum of $(A_i)_I$ by $\sum_I A_i$.

50. FINITELY GENERATED ABELIAN GROUPS

In this section we give a complete description of the finitely generated, and in particular the finite, Abelian groups. Thus for Abelian groups we have complete characterizations of all the cases considered in Section 42. [In fact, trivial, prime, monogenic, and cyclic groups are automatically Abelian, and have already been completely described, so that there is nothing more to do.] The main result of this section, known as the "fundamental theorem on Abelian groups," is that any finitely generated Abelian group is isomorphic to a finite direct sum of cyclic groups.

Let G be an Abelian group, A a subset of G. We call A **independent** if $\{(a) \mid a \in A\}$ is an independent subset of $\mathscr{S}_G^*$—in other words, if A is independent with respect to the I-lattice $\mathscr{S}_G^*$ (Section 16, end). Note that $\{a\}$ is independent if and only if $a \neq 0$, so that any nontrivial G has independent subsets. By Proposition 40.1 and Theorem 40.1 we have immediately

178

Proposition 1. *Let G be an Abelian group, and A a subset of G not containing 0; then the following statements are all equivalent:*

(1) *A is independent*

(2) *For any $a \in A$ we have $ka \in (A - \{a\})$ if and only if $ka = 0$*

(3) $\sum_{j=1}^{m} k_j a_j = 0$ *implies that each $k_j a_j = 0$, for all $m \in \mathbf{N}$, all k_j's in $\mathbf{I}$, and all distinct a_j's in A.*

Moreover, if (1–3) hold, (A) is isomorphic to the weak direct sum of the cyclic groups generated by the elements of A (in brief: $(A) \cong \sum_A^* (a)$).

> Note that if G were a vector space, this would be the familiar definition of independence; in fact, in a vector space $k_j a_j$ can be 0 only if $k_j = 0$, since $a_j \neq 0$. We will study the vector space case in Chapter XI.

Exercise 1. *An isomorphism takes independent sets into independent sets.*

Theorem 1. *Let G be an Abelian group which is generated by n of its elements; then G is isomorphic to a direct sum of at most n cyclic groups.*

Proof: If $n = 1$, G itself is cyclic; we proceed by induction. If $\{a_1, \ldots, a_n\}$ generates G, then (Corollary 3 to Proposition 37.4, rewritten in additive notation) G is the set of all "linear combinations" $\sum_{i=1}^{n} k_i a_i$, where the k_i's are in $\mathbf{I}$. We can assume that $\{a_1, \ldots, a_n\}$ is not independent, since if it were, G would be isomorphic to $(a_1) \oplus \cdots \oplus (a_n)$. Hence there exist integers $k_1, \ldots, k_n$, not all zero, such that $\sum_{i=1}^{n} k_i a_i = 0$; and since $\sum_{i=1}^{n} -k_i a_i = 0$ too, we can assume that some k_i is positive. Thus the set of positive "coefficients" which occur in linear combinations of sets of n generators of G which are equal to 0 is nonempty.

Let m_1 be the smallest element of this set, and let $\sum_{i=1}^{n} m_i b_i = 0$, where $\{b_1, \ldots, b_n\}$ generates G, be a linear combination of a set of n generators of G in which m_1 occurs as a coefficient. Let $m_i = q_i m_1 + r_i$ $(2 \leq i \leq n)$, where $0 \leq r_i < m_1$, and let $b_1^* = b_1 + \sum_{i=2}^{n} q_i b_i$. Clearly $\{b_1^*, b_2, \ldots, b_n\}$ still generates G, and $m_1 b_1^* + \sum_{i=2}^{n} r_i b_i = \sum_{i=1}^{n} m_i b_i = 0$. Thus each r_i is a coefficient of a linear combination of n generators of G which $= 0$; but this is impossible by definition of m_1 unless each $r_i = 0$, so that $m_1 b_1^* = 0$.

Suppose that $k_1 b_1^* + \sum_{i=2}^{n} k_i b_i = 0$, and let $k_1 = q_1 m_1 + r_1$, where $0 \leq r_1 < m_1$. Then $r_1 b_1^* + \sum_{i=2}^{n} k_i b_i = (k_1 b_1^* + \sum_{i=2}^{n} k_i b_i) - q_1 m_1 b_1^* = 0 - 0 = 0$, contradicting the definition of m_1 unless $r_1 = 0$; hence $k_1 b_1^* = q_1 m_1 b_1^* = 0$, so that $\sum_{i=2}^{n} k_i b_i = 0$ also. We have thus shown that if $k_1 b_1^*$ is any element of (b_1^*), and $b = \sum_{i=2}^{n} k_i b_i$ is any element of $G_1 = (b_2, \ldots, b_n)$, then $k_1 b_1^* + b = 0$ implies $k_1 b_1^* = b = 0$. It follows by Proposition 1 that $G = \sup \{(b_1^*), G_1\} \cong (b_1^*) \oplus G_1$. Since G_1 is generated by $n - 1$ elements, by induction hypothesis it is isomorphic to a direct sum of at most $n - 1$

cyclic groups; hence G is isomorphic to a direct sum of at most n cyclic groups. ∥

Conversely, let $G \cong (a_1) \oplus \cdots \oplus (a_n)$, and let $a_i' \in G$ correspond to $(0, \ldots, 0, a_i, 0, \ldots, 0)$ under the isomorphism; then evidently the a_i' $(1 \leq i \leq n)$ generate G. Moreover, since the (a_i) are Abelian, so is G. We have thus proved

Theorem 2. *A group is Abelian and finitely generated if and only if it is isomorphic to a finite direct sum of cyclic groups.*

Clearly $(a_1) \oplus \cdots \oplus (a_n)$ is finite if and only if each (a_i) is finite, so that we also have

Corollary. *A group is abelian and finite if and only if it is isomorphic to a finite direct sum of finite cyclic groups.*

For Abelian groups, the property of being finitely generated passes to subgroups. In fact, we have

Theorem 3. *Let the Abelian group G be generated by n elements; then any subgroup of G is generated by n elements.*

Proof: Let $\{a_1, \ldots, a_n\}$ generate G, and let H be any subgroup of G; then H consists of, and so is generated by some set of, linear combinations of the a_i's. Suppose, more generally, that H is generated by $b_1, \ldots, b_k$ (elements of H) together with a set of linear combinations of $c_{k+1}, \ldots, c_n$ (elements of G). We show by induction on $n - k + 1$ that H must be generated by n elements of H.

If $n - k + 1 = 1$, there are no c's, and the b's generate H. Suppose the assertion true when there are $n - k - 1$ c's, and let m_1 be the smallest positive coefficient of c_{k+1} in all linear combinations of the c's which lie in H. [If no such linear combination lies in H, then H contains only linear combinations of the $n - k - 1$ elements $c_{k+2}, \ldots, c_n$, and the induction hypothesis applies.] Let $b_{k+1} = \sum_{i=1}^{n-k} m_i c_{k+i}$ be such a linear combination. By the argument used in proving Theorem 1, m_1 must divide the coefficient of c_{k+1} in any linear combination of the c's which lies in H. Hence b_{k+1}, together with the linear combinations of $c_{k+2}, \ldots, c_n$ which lie in H, generate all of the linear combinations of $c_{k+1}, \ldots, c_n$ which lie in H. Thus H is generated by $b_1, \ldots, b_{k+1}$ and linear combinations of $c_{k+2}, \ldots, c_n$, and the induction hypothesis applies. ∥

Corollary. *An Abelian group is finitely generated if and only if its subgroup lattice satisfies the maximum condition.*

Proof: "If" is a special case of Proposition 16.2. Conversely, since the subgroup lattice is "closed under union of chains," and since by the theorem every subgroup is finitely generated, "only if" follows immediately from Proposition 16.3.   //

Exercise 2. *Every subgroupoid of the groupoid S is finitely generated if and only if $\mathscr{S}_S$ satisfies the maximum condition.*

As a consequence of Theorem 1 we also have

Proposition 2. *An Abelian group is finite if and only if its subgroup lattice satisfies the maximum and minimum conditions.*

Proof: "Only if" is trivial. For "if," note that by the maximum condition the group is finitely generated (Proposition 16.2), hence by Theorem 1 it is a finite direct sum of cyclic groups. If any of these were infinite, the minimum condition would be violated (Section 43); hence they are all finite, making the group finite.   //

Corollary. *An Abelian group is finite if and only if its subgroup lattice is finite dimensional.*

Proof: "Only if" is trivial; conversely, if the lattice is finite dimensional, since it has greatest and least elements it must satisfy the maximum and minimum conditions.   //

We can also prove

Proposition 3. *The Abelian group G is finite if and only if there is a finite unrefinable chain from $\{e\}$ to G in $\mathscr{S}_G^*$.*

Proof: Since G is Abelian, the subgroups in the chain are all normal, so that the chain is a composition series; thus its factors are all simple, and since they are Abelian, this makes them prime, hence finite, making G finite.   //

We conclude this section by establishing a refinement of Theorem 2. Let $G \cong (a_1) \oplus \cdots \oplus (a_n)$. By the proof of Proposition 47.3, if any of the (a_i)'s has finite order which is not a power of a prime, it can be further decomposed as a direct sum of cyclic groups of lower orders. It follows (induction) that each finite (a_i) is a finite direct sum of cyclic groups of prime power orders, so that we have

Proposition 4. *A finitely generated Abelian group is isomorphic to a finite direct sum of indecomposable cyclic groups—in other words, cyclic groups which are either infinite or of prime power order.*

Corollary. *A finite Abelian group is isomorphic to a finite direct sum of cyclic groups of prime power orders.*

In Section 52 we shall show that these indecomposable cyclic groups are uniquely determined. First, however, we need some general results about direct sums of cyclic subgroups of an Abelian group, which we establish in Section 51.

51. RANK

Let G be a nontrivial Abelian group. It is easily verified (use (3) of Proposition 50.1) that the set of independent subsets of G, ordered by inclusion, is "closed under union of chains," hence inductive, so that by Zorn's lemma we have

Proposition 1. *Any independent subset of an Abelian group is contained in a maximal independent subset.*

> In the case of a vector space, a maximal independent subset generates the space; but this need not be so in an Abelian group. In fact, let A be a maximal independent subset of G; then for any $x \in G$, $\notin A$, the set $A \cup \{x\}$ cannot be independent. Hence there exist integers m, k, $k_1, \ldots, k_m$ and distinct $a_1, \ldots, a_m$ in A such that $kx + \sum_{i=1}^{m} k_i a_i = 0$, but no term is 0. Thus any $x \in G$, $\notin A$ has a nonzero multiple in (A)—but x itself need not be in (A). We do, however, have

Proposition 2. *An independent subset of G which generates G is maximal.*

Proof: If A is independent and $(A) = G$, then for any $x \in G$ we have $x - \sum_{i=1}^{m} k_i a_i = 0$ for some $m \in \mathbf{N}$, $k_1, \ldots, k_m$ in $\mathbf{I}$, and distinct $a_1, \ldots, a_m$ in A, where not every term is $= 0$ (unless $x = 0$), so that $A \cup \{x\}$ is not independent. //

> Note that by Proposition 16.4, such an A is a minimal set of generators of G. In a vector space, conversely, a minimal set of generators is independent, but this is not necessarily true in an Abelian group.

Exercise 1. *Let A be an independent subset of G, and for each $a \in A$, let $k_a \in I$ be such that $k_a a \neq 0$; then $\{k_a a \mid a \in A\}$ is independent.* [Hint: Proposition 12.3.]

> In a vector space, all maximal independent subsets have the same cardinality. Our goal in this section is to prove that, in an Abelian group, all maximal *unrefinable* independent sets have the same cardinality. [In a vector space, unrefinability is automatic, since any monogenic subspace is indecomposable, as we shall see in Chapter XI.]

The independent subset A of G is called **unrefinable** if $\{(a) \mid a \in A\}$ is unrefinable. By Propositions 40.6–7, A is unrefinable if and only if each (a) is indecomposable, that is, infinite or of prime power order. Analogously to Proposition 1 we have

Proposition 3. *Any unrefinable independent subset of an Abelian group is contained in a maximal unrefinable independent subset.*

We also have

Proposition 4. *Any independent subset of an Abelian group has an unrefinable refinement.*

Proof: Each finite (a) which is not of prime power order is the sup of a finite independent set of (b)'s (where each b is a multiple of a) which do have prime power orders. //

Let A be an unrefinable independent subset of G; let $A_0 = \{x \mid x \in A;$ (x) infinite$\}$, and for each prime $p \in N$, let $A_p = \{x \mid x \in A; o(x)$ a power of $p\}$. Let r be the cardinality of A, r_0 that of A_0, and r_p that of A_p. We shall prove that all maximal unrefinable independent subsets of a given Abelian group G have the same r_0 and r_p's. Since A_0 and the A_p's are all disjoint, and their union is A, it follows that all such subsets have the same r. This r is called the **rank** of G; r_0 is called the **0-rank**, and r_p the **p-rank** [Notation: $r(G)$, $r_0(G)$, $r_p(G)$].

> This definition of rank is equivalent to the one in Section 12 (generalized to allow the rank to be any cardinal number, not necessarily finite). In fact, if G has rank r, there exists an independent subset of $\mathscr{S}_G^*$—namely, any maximal unrefinable independent set—with cardinality r, and each element $\subseteq G$; and there cannot exist an independent subset of $\mathscr{S}_G^*$ of cardinality $> r$, since there would then (Propositions 3–4) exist a maximal unrefinable independent set of cardinality $> r$, contradicting the uniqueness of r. Thus $G \in \mathscr{S}_G^*$ has rank r in the sense of Section 12. Conversely, if G has rank r in that sense, and $\mathscr{B}$ is an independent subset of $\mathscr{S}_G^*$ of cardinality r, let F be a choice function on G, and let $A = \{F(B) \mid B \in \mathscr{B}\}$; then A is an independent subset of G of cardinality r, and by the maximality of r, a maximal unrefinable independent subset of G which contains an unrefinable refinement of A still has cardinality r, so that G has rank r as defined in this section.

The uniqueness of 0-rank and p-rank will be established by proving a series of propositions which reduce the general case to a set of special cases.

A group is called **periodic** if every element of it has finite order; **aperiodic** if no element but the identity has finite order. [An aperiodic group is sometimes called "torsion-free," while a periodic group is called a "torsion" group.]

Proposition 5. *Let G be an Abelian group, and let G_P be the set of elements of G which have finite order; then G_P is a periodic subgroup of G, and G/G_P is aperiodic.*

Proof: If $o(a) = m$ and $o(b) = n$, then $o(a + b)$ divides mn, so that G_P is a subgroup. If $o(x + G_P) = r$, we have $rx \in G_P$, so that rx has finite order, say s. Hence $srx = 0$, so that x has finite order and is thus in G_P, that is, $x + G_P = G_P$. Thus the only element of G/G_P which has finite order is G_P itself, proving G/G_P aperiodic.   //

Proposition 6. *Let G, G_P be as in Proposition 5, and let G_p be the set of elements of G_P whose orders are powers of p, where $p \in \mathbf{N}$ is prime. Then G_p is a subgroup of G_P, and G_P is isomorphic to the weak direct sum of the G_p's.*

Proof: Readily each G_p is a subgroup, and the set of nontrivial G_p's is independent in the subgroup lattice [to see this, let $\sum_{i=1}^{n} k_i a_i = 0$, where a_i has order $p_i^{n_i}$ with the p's all different, and "multiply through" by the product of the $p_i^{n_i}$'s other than $p_j^{n_j}$ to prove that $k_j a_j = 0$ (see Exercise 43.1)], so that their sup is isomorphic to their weak direct sum. To see that their sup is G_P, let $x \in G_P$ have order $\prod_{i=1}^{n} p_i^{k_i}$, where the p's are primes in $\mathbf{N}$ and the k's are in $\mathbf{N}$, and let $q_j = (\prod_{i=1}^{j-1} p_i^{k_i})(\prod_{i=j+1}^{n} p_i^{k_i})$. By Exercise 36.5, there exist $r_1, \ldots, r_n$ in $\mathbf{I}$ such that $\sum_{i=1}^{n} r_i q_i = 1$; hence $x = (\sum_{i=1}^{n} r_i q_i)x = \sum_{i=1}^{n} r_i(q_i x)$, where $q_i x \in G_{p_i}$ since $o(q_i x) = p_i^{k_i}$.   //

We shall denote the weak direct sum of the G_p's by $\sum_p^* G_p$. A group in which the order of every element is a power of p is called a **p-group**.

Exercise 2. *Let G be an Abelian group, and let H_n be the set of elements of G whose orders divide n, where $n \in \mathbf{N}$; then H_n is a subgroup of G.*

Exercise 3. *Let G be an Abelian group; prove that there exists a subgroup H of G such that H is isomorphic to a weak direct sum of cyclic groups and G/H is periodic.*

Exercise 4. *Let $x = \sum_{i=1}^{n} k_i x_i$, where the x_i's are distinct elements of an unrefinable independent set; then*

    (a) *x has finite order if and only if each x_i has finite order*
    (b) *x has order a power of p if and only if each x_i has order a power of p.*

Corollary. *Let G be a weak direct sum of indecomposable cyclic groups (x_i);*

then G_P is the weak direct sum of those (x_i) which have finite order, and G_p is the weak direct sum of those (x_i) whose orders are powers of p.

We next prove the uniqueness of r_p in three steps:

Proposition 7. *If every element of G has order dividing p, then $r_p(G)$ is uniquely defined.*

Proof: Let A be a maximal independent subset of G ("unrefinable" is automatic, since the (a)'s are of order p, hence indecomposable). We must show that any such A has the same cardinality. Now as pointed out at the beginning of the section, any nonzero $x \in G$ has a nonzero multiple in (A), say $kx = \sum_{i=1}^{n} k_i a_i$, where we can assume that no $k_i a_i$ is 0. Let $k = qp + r$, where $0 \le r < p$; since $qpx = 0$, but $kx \ne 0$, we have $r \ne 0$ and $rx = kx$. Since r and p are relatively prime, there exist integers r', h such that $r'r = hp + 1$; hence $x = (hp + 1)x = r'(rx) = r'(kx) = \sum_{i=1}^{n} (r'k_i)a_i$ is in (A). Moreover, let $r'k_i = q_i p + r_i$, $1 \le i \le n$; then $x = \sum_{i=1}^{n} r_i a_i$, where $0 < r_i < p$ for each $i \in \mathbf{N}_n$. Suppose that we also had $x = \sum_{i=1}^{m} s_i b_i$, where $0 < s_i < p$ for each $i \in \mathbf{N}_m$, and the b's are in A. Then evidently $m = n$ and the b's (in some order) are the same as the a's, since otherwise $\sum_{i=1}^{n} r_i a_i - \sum_{i=1}^{m} s_i b_i = 0$ would yield a contradiction to the independence of A. Furthermore, since $0 < r_i < p$ and $0 < s_j < p$, we cannot have $(r_i - s_j)a_i = 0$ unless $r_i = s_j$. Thus for a given $x \ne 0$, the a_i's and r_i's are uniquely determined, so that the set of nonzero x's (that is, $G - \{0\}$) is in one-to-one correspondence with the set of linear combinations $\sum r_i a_i$, where the a_i's are distinct elements of A, and $0 < r_i < p$ for each i.

If $A = \{a_1, \ldots, a_t\}$ is finite, this set of linear combinations is in one-to-one correspondence with the set of $\sum_{i=1}^{t} r_i a_i$ where $0 \le r_i < p$ for each $i \in \mathbf{N}_t$ and not all the r_i's are 0; thus G is in one-to-one correspondence with $\{\sum_{i=1}^{t} r_i a_i \mid 0 \le r_i < p \text{ for each } i \in \mathbf{N}_t\}$, so that $o(G) = p^t$. Hence if A is finite, so is G, and the number of elements in A is uniquely determined by $o(G)$.

On the other hand, if A is infinite, let A_n be the set of n-element subsets of A, and let $A_n^* = \{\sum_{i=1}^{n} r_i a_i \mid \{a_1, \ldots, a_n\} \in A_n; \ 0 < r_i < p \text{ for each } i \in \mathbf{N}_n\}$. Then $A_n^* \sim \mathbf{N}_p{}^n \times A_n \sim A_n \sim A$ (Proposition 21.7 and the corollary to Theorem 21.1), and $G \sim G - \{0\} \sim \bigcup_\mathbf{N} A_n^* \sim \bigcup_\mathbf{N} A_n \sim A$ by Proposition 21.8. Thus $K(A) = K(G)$ is also uniquely determined in this case.   //

Proposition 8. *r_p is uniquely defined for any Abelian p-group.*

Proof: Let G be such a group; let H be the subgroup of G consisting of the elements whose orders divide p (Exercise 2); and let A be a maximal independent subset of G (here, too, "unrefinable" is superfluous). We must show that all such A's have the same cardinality. Let $a \in A$ have order p^{k_a}, and let $A' = \{p^{k_a - 1}a \mid a \in A\}$. Thus $A' \subseteq H$, and by Exercise 1, A' is still independent.

Moreover, if a, b in A are distinct we cannot have $p^{k_a-1}a = p^{k_b-1}b$, since $(a) \cap (b) = \{0\}$; hence $A' \sim A$. Thus it suffices to show that A' is a maximal independent subset of H, which will imply by Proposition 7 that its cardinality, whence that of A, is uniquely determined.

Let $x \in H$, $\notin A'$; since A is maximal, there exists a linear combination $hx + \sum_{i=1}^{n} h_i a_i = 0$ with no term zero. If one of these $h_i a_i$ has order $> p$, let p^k be the greatest of their orders, so that $k > 1$; then $0 = p^{k-1}(hx + \sum_{i=1}^{n} h_i a_i) = \sum_{i=1}^{n} p^{k-1} h_i a_i$ with not all terms zero, contrary to the independence of A. Hence every $h_i a_i$ has order p, in other words, is a multiple of $p^{k_i-1}a_i$ (where a^{k_i} is the order of a_i), say $= h_i' p^{k_i-1}a_i$. Thus for any $x \in H$, $\notin A'$ there exists p linear combination $hx + \sum_{i=1}^{n} h_i'(p^{k_i-1}a_i) = 0$ with no term $= 0$, which proves that A' is a maximal independent subset of H.   //

Proposition 9. r_p *is uniquely defined for any Abelian group.*

Proof: Let A be a maximal unrefinable independent subset of the Abelian group G; we must show that A_p has the same cardinality for all such A. Let G_p be as in Proposition 6; then $A_p = A \cap G_p$ is evidently an unrefinable independent subset of G_p. Let $x \in G_p$, $\notin A_p$; since A is maximal, there exists a linear combination $hx + \sum_{i=1}^{n} h_i a_i = 0$ with no term zero. If any of these a_i had infinite order, then $0 = o(x)(hx + \sum_{i=1}^{n} h_i a_i) = \sum_{i=1}^{n} o(x)h_i a_i$ would contradict the independence of A. Similarly, if any of them had order a power of $q \neq p$, and we multiply through by the product of $o(x)$ and the $o(a_i)$'s which are powers of primes other than q, we get the same contradiction. Hence every a_i has order a power of p, that is, a_i is in A_p. We have thus shown, as in the proof of Proposition 8, that A_p is a maximal independent subset of G_p; and by Proposition 8, all such A_p have the same cardinality.   //

We now turn to the proof that r_0 is unique; here we begin by·treating the case of an aperiodic Abelian group. Note first that in this case the criterion for independence can be recast in the following form: A is independent if and only if $\sum_{i=1}^{n} k_i a_i = 0$ implies that each $k_i = 0$, for all $n \in \mathbf{N}$, all $k_i \in \mathbf{I}$ ($1 \leq i \leq n$), and all distinct $a_1, \ldots, a_n$ in A. (Equivalently: A is independent if and only if $a \in A$ and $ka \in (A - \{a\})$ imply $k = 0$.)

Lemma. *Let $\{a_1, \ldots, a_m\}$ be an independent subset of the aperiodic Abelian group G, and let $B \subseteq G$ be such that each a_i has a nonzero multiple in (B). Then $m \leq K(B)$, and there exists $\{b_1, \ldots, b_m\} \subseteq B$ such that every element of B has a nonzero multiple in $(B - \{b_1, \ldots, b_m\} \cup \{a_1, \ldots, a_m\})$.*

Proof: This is trivial for $m = 0$; suppose it true for $m - 1$. Then $m - 1 \leq K(B)$, and there exist $b_1, \ldots, b_{m-1}$ in B such that every element of B has a nonzero multiple in $(B') = (B - \{b_1, \ldots, b_{m-1}\} \cup \{a_1, \ldots, a_{m-1}\})$. By hypothesis, a_m has a nonzero multiple in (B), say $ra_m = \sum_{i=1}^{n} r_i x_i$ with the x_i's in B. But every x_i has a nonzero multiple in (B'), say $s_i x_i \in (B')$, $1 \leq i \leq n$, so that $(\prod_{i=1}^{n} s_i)ra_m$ is in (B') and $\neq 0$, say $= \sum_{i=1}^{t} t_i y_i$ with the y_i's distinct elements of B'. Since the a_i's are independent, not every y_i can be an a_i; hence some y_j is in $B - \{b_1, \ldots, b_{m-1}\}$, and in particular this set is nonempty, so that $K(B) \geq m$. Moreover, denoting this y_j by b_m, we have $0 \neq t_j b_m = (\prod_{i=1}^{n} s_i)ra_m - \sum_{i=1}^{j-1} t_i y_i - \sum_{i=j+1}^{t} t_i y_i \in (B' - \{b_m\} \cup \{a_m\})$. $\quad\parallel$

Corollary 1. *No finite independent set can have cardinality greater than that of any maximal independent set.*

Proof: Take B maximal independent in the lemma. $\quad\parallel$

Corollary 2. *Any two finite maximal independent sets have the same cardinality.*

Proof: By Corollary 1, neither can have greater cardinality than the other. $\quad\parallel$

Corollary 3. *If there is a finite maximal independent set, there cannot be an infinite independent set.*

Proof: If such existed, it would have finite independent subsets of arbitrarily high cardinality, which would lead to a contradiction of Corollary 1. $\quad\parallel$

We can now prove

Proposition 10. r_0 *is uniquely defined for any aperiodic Abelian group.*

Proof: Let G be such a group, and A a maximal independent subset of G ("unrefinable" is superfluous since every element of A has infinite order); we must show that all such A have the same cardinality. Now any nonzero $x \in G$ has a nonzero multiple in (A), say $kx = \sum_{i=1}^{n} k_i a_i$. Moreover, specifying $a_1, \ldots, a_n$ and $k_1/k, \ldots, k_n/k$ uniquely determines x. In fact, suppose that we had $hy = \sum_{i=1}^{n} h_i a_i$, where $h_i/h = k_i/k$, $1 \leq i \leq n$. Then

$$hkx = \sum_{i=1}^{n} (hk_i)a_i = \sum_{i=1}^{n} (kh_i)a_i = khy,$$

so that $hk(x - y) = 0$, and since G is aperiodic, this implies $x = y$. Thus the cardinality of $G - \{0\}$ is no greater than the cardinality of the set of finite subsets of A times the cardinality of the set of finite sets of rational numbers. If A is infinite, we have thus proved (using Proposition 21.8 and Exercise 36.10) that $K(A) \leq K(G - \{0\}) \leq K(A)\aleph_0 = K(A)$, so that any infinite maximal independent set has cardinality $K(G)$. This result, together with Corollaries 2–3 to the lemma, proves the proposition. $\quad\parallel$

We finally complete the proof of the uniqueness of rank with

Proposition 11. r_0 *is uniquely defined for any Abelian group.*

Proof: Let A be a maximal unrefinable independent subset of the Abelian group G; we must show that A_0 has the same cardinality for all such A. Let G_P be as in Proposition 5, and let $A_0^* = \{a + G_P \mid a \in A_0\}$. If $a + G_P = b + G_P$, where a, b are distinct elements of A, we have $a - b$ in G_P, say

$k(a - b) = 0$, so that $ka = kb$ is in $(a) \cap (b)$, contradicting independence. Thus $A_0 \sim A_0^*$, and it suffices by Proposition 10 to show that A_0^* is a maximal unrefinable independent subset of the aperiodic Abelian group G/G_P.

We first show that A_0^* is independent (unrefinability is then automatic, since G/G_P is aperiodic). In fact, if $\sum_{i=1}^n k_i(a_i + G_P) \subseteq G_P$, then $\sum_{i=1}^n k_i a_i \in G_P$, and so has finite order, say k. Hence $\sum_{i=1}^n k k_i a_i = 0$, and since the a_i's are independent and have infinite order, this requires $k k_i = 0$, so that $k_i = 0$, $1 \leq i \leq n$, proving the $(a_i + G_P)$'s independent. Next, let $x + G_P \in G/G_P$, $\neq G_P$, so that x has infinite order; then since A is maximal, there exists a linear combination $hx + \sum_{i=1}^m h_i a_i = 0$ with no term zero. If any of these a_i have finite order, they can be eliminated by multiplying through by the product of their orders; hence we can assume that each a_i has infinite order. Thus for any such $x + G_P$ there exist $a_i + G_P$'s in A_0^* such that $h(x + G_P) + \sum_{i=1}^m h_i(a_i + G_P) = 0$ with no term zero, which proves that A_0^* is maximal. //

Exercise 5. *The rank (0-rank, p-rank) of any subgroup or factor group of G cannot exceed that of G.*

52. SUBGROUPS OF FINITELY GENERATED ABELIAN GROUPS

In this section we apply the results of Section 51 to prove that the indecomposable cyclic groups of which a given finitely generated Abelian group is the direct sum are uniquely determined. At the same time, we can describe the cyclic direct summands of the subgroups of such a group in terms of those of the group.

Let $G = (a_1) \oplus \cdots \oplus (a_n)$ be a finite direct sum of indecomposable cyclic groups. Let n_0 of the (a_i)'s be infinite, and for each prime $p \in \mathbf{N}$, let n_p of the (a_i)'s have orders which are powers of p; thus n is the sum of n_0 and the n_p's. Moreover, let the powers of p which are orders of (a_i)'s be $k_{p1} \geq \cdots \geq k_{pn_p}$. The $(n - n_0 + 1)$-tuple

$$(n_0; k_{21}, \ldots, k_{2n_2}; k_{31}, \ldots, k_{3n_3}; k_{51}, \ldots, k_{5n_5}; \ldots)$$

is called the **type** of G.

Let $H = (b_1) \oplus \cdots \oplus (b_m)$ be another finite direct sum of indecomposable cyclic groups of type $(m_0; h_{21}, \ldots, h_{2m_2}; \ldots)$. We say that the type of H is *lower* than the type of G if $m_0 \leq n_0$; $m_p \leq n_p$ for each prime $p \in \mathbf{N}$; and $h_{pi} \leq k_{pi}$ for each prime $p \in \mathbf{N}$ and each $i \in \mathbf{N}_{m_p}$.

Proposition 1. *Let G and H be finite direct sums of indecomposable cyclic groups such that H has lower type than G; then G has a subgroup isomorphic to H.*

Proof: Let $G = (a_1) \oplus \cdots \oplus (a_n)$, $H = (b_1) \oplus \cdots \oplus (b_m)$. By definition of "lower type," we can set up a one-to-one correspondence of the (b_i)'s with some of the (a_j)'s such that each (b_i) is isomorphic to a subgroup of the corresponding (a_j); hence the direct sum of the (b_i)'s is isomorphic to a subgroup of the direct sum of the (a_i)'s.   //

This proposition shows that G has subgroups of all types lower than its own. We shall now show that the converse is also true: Let $G = (a_1) \oplus \cdots \oplus (a_n)$, and let $H = (b_1) \oplus \cdots \oplus (b_m)$ be any subgroup of G, where the (a_i)'s and (b_i)'s are indecomposable. Let the types of G and H be $(n_0; k_{21}, \ldots, k_{2n_2}; \ldots)$ and $(m_0; h_{21}, \ldots, h_{2m_2}; \ldots)$, respectively; we must show that the type of H is lower than that of G.

Let $a_j' = (0, \ldots, 0, a_j, 0, \ldots, 0)$, $b_i' = (0, \ldots, 0, b_i, 0, \ldots, 0)$; then $\{a_1', \ldots, a_n'\}$ and $\{b_1', \ldots, b_m'\}$ are maximal independent subsets of G and H, respectively, and since $(a_j') \cong (a_j)$, $(b_i') \cong (b_i)$, $0 \le j \le n$, $0 \le i \le m$, these sets are unrefinable. Hence n_0 and n_p are respectively the 0-rank and p-rank of G, and m_0, m_p are the same for H. Since the 0-rank or p-rank of a subgroup cannot exceed that of the group (Exercise 51.5), we immediately have $m_0 \le n_0$ and $m_p \le n_p$ for each p.

Let (a_{pi}) be the direct summand of G of order $p^{k_{pi}}$, $1 \le i \le n_p$, and (b_{pi}) the direct summand of H of order $p^{h_{pi}}$, $1 \le i \le m_p$. Then (Exercise 51.4) $G_p = (a_{p1}) \oplus \cdots \oplus (a_{pn_p})$ and $H_p = (b_{p1}) \oplus \cdots \oplus (b_{pm_p})$. Suppose that $h_{pi} \le k_{pi}$ for $i = 1, \ldots, j-1$, but $h_{pj} > k_{pj}$. Then $p^{k_{pj}}G_p = (p^{k_{pj}}a_{p1}) \oplus \cdots \oplus (p^{k_{pj}}a_{p,j-1})$ with at most $j-1$ nontrivial summands, so that $r_p(p^{k_{pj}}G_p) \le j-1$. On the other hand, $p^{k_{pj}}H_p = (p^{k_{pj}}b_{p1}) \oplus \cdots \oplus (p^{k_{pj}}b_{pm_p})$ in which at least the first j summands are nontrivial, so that $r_p(p^{k_{pj}}H_p) \ge j$, which is impossible since $p^{k_{pj}}H_p$ is a subgroup of $p^{k_{pj}}G_p$. Hence $h_{pi} \le k_{pi}$ for all $i \in N_{m_p}$, completing the proof that H has lower type than G.

The uniqueness of the type of a given group now follows immediately by taking $G = H$. In fact, if $G \cong (a_1) \oplus \cdots \oplus (a_n) \cong (b_1) \oplus \cdots \oplus (b_m)$, then each of these decompositions must have type lower than the other, which clearly implies that their types must be equal. We summarize these results as

Theorem 1. *Any two decompositions of a given group G as finite direct sums of indecomposable cyclic groups have the same type, which we can thus call the type of G.*

Theorem 2. *If G is a finitely generated Abelian group, and H is any subgroup of G, then the type of H is lower than the type of G.*

53. DIVISIBLE GROUPS

By the fundamental theorem on Abelian groups, if a finitely generated Abelian group is indecomposable, it

must be cyclic. On the other hand, there exist indecomposable Abelian groups which are not finitely
generated. An example is the group $\mathbf{R}$ of rational numbers under addition. [In fact, let A, B be nontrivial subgroups of $\mathbf{R}$, and let $x/y \in A$, $u/v \in B$; then $xu = uy(x/y)$
$= xv(u/v)$ is in both A and B, so that they have a nontrivial intersection.] In this and the next section we study
Abelian groups which have certain properties in common
with $\mathbf{R}$.

The factor group $\mathbf{R/I}$ (where $\mathbf{I}$ is the group of integers under addition,
regarded as a subgroup of $\mathbf{R}$) is called the group of **rational numbers modulo 1**.
Let $\mathbf{R}_{p^n} = \{x + \mathbf{I} \mid x \in \mathbf{R}; x = a/p^i$ for some $a \in \mathbf{I}$ and some $i \in \mathbf{N}_n\}$, where
$p \in \mathbf{N}$ is prime. Readily, this is a subgroup of $\mathbf{R/I}$ and is isomorphic to $\mathbf{I}_{p^n}$,
being generated by, for example, $1/p^n$. Let $\mathbf{R}_{p^\infty} = \{x + \mathbf{I} \mid x \in \mathbf{R}; x = a/p^i$
for some $a \in \mathbf{I}$ and some $i \in \mathbf{N}\} = \bigcup_{\mathbf{N}} R_{p^n}$; this too is a subgroup of $\mathbf{R/I}$.
We say that the group G is a **group of type p^∞** if it is isomorphic to $\mathbf{R}_{p^\infty}$.
Note that a group of type p^∞ is an Abelian p-group.

Proposition 1. $\mathscr{S}^*_{\mathbf{R}_{p^\infty}}$ *is a chain; there is exactly one cyclic subgroup of order*
p^n *for each $n \in \mathbf{N}$, and these are all of the proper subgroups.*

Proof: If $H \in \mathscr{S}_{\mathbf{R}_{p^\infty}}$ contains a rational number (modulo 1) whose lowest
terms fraction has denominator p^m, but not one with denominator p^n for any
$n > m$, then readily $H = \mathbf{R}_{p^m}$; while if there exists no such m, then readily
H is all of $\mathbf{R}_{p^\infty}$. $/\!/$

Corollary. $\mathbf{R}_{p^\infty}$ *is indecomposable.*

Proposition 2. $\mathbf{R/I}$ *is isomorphic to the weak direct sum of the $\mathbf{R}_{p^\infty}$ ($p \in \mathbf{N}$*
prime).

Proof: Readily $\mathbf{R}_{p^\infty}$ is just the "G_p" of $G = \mathbf{R/I}$. $/\!/$

The group G is called **divisible** (or sometimes **complete**) if $\{nx \mid x \in G\} = G$
for each $n \in \mathbf{N}$. Evidently $\mathbf{R}$, $\mathbf{R/I}$ and every $\mathbf{R}_{p^\infty}$ are divisible, but $\mathbf{I}$ is not;
and a nontrivial finite group can never be divisible, since $\{o(G)x \mid x \in G\} = \{0\}$.
It follows that a subgroup of a divisible group need not be divisible.

Proposition 3. *A homomorphic image of a divisible group is divisible.*

Proof: If G is divisible, for any $n \in \mathbf{N}$ and any $x \in G$ there exists $y \in G$
such that $ny = x$; hence $nF(y) = F(ny) = F(x)$. $/\!/$

Proposition 4. *Let $\mathscr{A}$ be a set of divisible normal subgroups of the group G;*
then $\sup \mathscr{A}$ *(in $\mathscr{N}^*_G$) is divisible.*

Proof: Let $a \in \sup \mathscr{A}$, say $a = \sum_{i=1}^k a_i$, where $a_i \in A_i \in \mathscr{A}$, $1 \le i \le k$, and
let $a_i = nb_i$, where $b_i \in A_i$; then $a = n \sum_{i=1}^k b_i$. $/\!/$

Proposition 5. *A direct sum of groups is divisible if and only if each summand is divisible.*

Proof: $(x_i)_I = n(y_i)_I$ if and only if $x_i = ny_i$ for each $i \in I$. ‖

Corollary. *A direct sum of cyclic groups cannot be divisible.*

Theorem 1. *A divisible subgroup of an Abelian group is supplemented.*

Proof: Let D be a divisible subgroup of the Abelian group G. The set of subgroups D' such that $D \cap D' = \{0\}$ is nonempty (it contains $\{0\}$) and readily inductive, so that by Zorn's lemma it has a maximal element D^*. By definition, D^* is a supplement of D in $D + D^*$; it thus remains only to show that $D + D^* = G$.

If not, let $x \notin D + D^*$, so that $D^* + (x) \supset D^*$; then by the maximality of D^* we must have $(D^* + (x)) \cap D \supset \{0\}$. Let $d \neq 0$ be in this intersection, say $d = d^* + mx$, where $m \neq 0$ since $d \neq 0$; then $mx = d - d^* \in D + D^*$. We can assume without loss of generality that m is the smallest positive integer (evidently > 1 by choice of x) such that $mx \in D + D^*$. Let p be a prime dividing m, and let $y = (m/p)x$; thus $y \notin D + D^*$ by the minimality of m, but $py \in D + D^*$.

Since D is divisible and $d \in D$, there exists $d' \in D$ such that $d = pd'$. Let $z = y - d'$; since $y \notin D + D^*$, we must have $z \notin D + D^*$. On the other hand, $pz = py - pd' = mx - d = -d^* \in D^*$. Now $(D^* + (z)) \cap D \supset \{0\}$; let $0 \neq c = c^* + nz$ be in this intersection. Here p cannot divide n, since we would then have $nz \in D^*$, whence $c \in D^* \cap D$; thus n and p are relatively prime, so that there exist integers r, s such that $rn + sp = 1$. Then $z = rnz + spz = r(c - c^*) - sd^* \in D + D^*$, contradiction. ‖

Exercise 1. *Any Abelian group has a greatest divisible subgroup, and any supplement of this subgroup has no nontrivial divisible subgroups.* [Hint: Use Proposition 4.]

Proposition 6. *An aperiodic Abelian group is divisible if and only if it is isomorphic to a direct sum of* **R**'s.

Proof: "If" follows from Proposition 5. Conversely, if G is aperiodic and divisible, note first that if $n \neq 0$, $ny = nz$ implies $n(y - z) = 0$, so that $y = z$; thus for any $x \in G$ and any $i \in \mathbf{N}$ there is a unique $x_i \in G$ such that $x = ix_i$. Moreover, let i' divide i, say $i = ti'$; then $i'x_{i'} = x = ix_i = i'(tx_i)$, so that $x_{i'} = tx_i$.

Let $x \neq 0$, and let $[x]$ be the subgroup generated by $\{x_i \mid i \in \mathbf{N}\}$. We shall show that this subgroup is isomorphic to **R**. Note first that if $\sum_{j=1}^n h_j x_{i_j}$ is any element of $[x]$, where the h's are in **I**, let m be a common multiple of the i_j's, say $m = m_j i_j$, $1 \leq j \leq n$; then $\sum_{j=1}^n h_j x_{i_j} = (\sum_{j=1}^n h_j m_j)x_m$, so that

$[x] = \{kx_m \mid k \in \mathbf{I}, m \in \mathbf{N}\}$. Let F be the relation $\{(kx_m, k/m) \mid kx_m \in [x]\}$ between $[x]$ and $\mathbf{R}$. Now if $kx_m = rx_s$, then ("multiplying through" by ms) $ksx = rmx$, so that $ks = rm$, that is, $k/m = r/s$. Conversely, if $ks = rm$, then $ms(kx_m) = ms(rx_s)$, so that $kx_m = rx_s$; hence F is a one-to-one correspondence. Finally, $kx_m + rx_s = (ks + rm)x_{ms}$, so that F is a homomorphism.

Let A be an independent subset of G; then the set of subgroups $\{[a] \mid a \in A\}$ is readily independent in $\mathscr{S}_G^*$, so that its sup, call it $[A]$, is isomorphic to a direct sum of $[a]$'s, that is, of $\mathbf{R}$'s. Let A be maximal; then for any $y \in G$ we have $ky \in (A) \subseteq [A]$ for some $k \in \mathbf{N}$. Since $[A]$ is divisible, there exists $z \in [A]$ such that $ky = kz$; but as at the beginning of the proof, this implies that $y = z$, that is, $y \in [A]$, making $[A]$ all of G.   //

Proposition 7. *An Abelian p-group is divisible if and only if it is isomorphic to a direct sum of* $\mathbf{R}_{p^\infty}$*'s.*

Proof: Let G' be the subgroup of the given group G consisting of the elements whose orders divide p. Let $x \in G'$, $x \neq 0$, and let H be a choice function on G. Since G is divisible, the set $X_2 = \{y \mid y \in G; py = x\}$ is nonempty; let $x_2 = H(X_2)$. Similarly, the set $X_3 = \{y \mid y \in G; py = x_2\}$ is nonempty; let $x_3 = H(X_3)$. This procedure defines a sequence $(x_n)_\mathbf{N}$ of elements of G (where x_1 means x) such that x_n has order p^n, and evidently $p^m x_n = x_{n-m}$ for all m, n in $\mathbf{N}$ such that $m \leq n$.

Let $[x]$ be the subgroup generated by $\{x_i \mid i \in \mathbf{N}\}$; we shall show that $[x] \cong \mathbf{R}_{p^\infty}$. Note first that if $\sum_{j=1}^n h_j x_{i_j}$ is any element of $[x]$, where the h's are in $\mathbf{I}$, let m be the greatest of the i_j's; then $\sum_{j=1}^n h_j x_{i_j} = \sum_{j=1}^n h_j p^{m-i_j} x_m$, so that $[x] = \{kx_m \mid k \in \mathbf{I}, m \in \mathbf{N}\}$. Let F be the relation

$$\{(kx_m, k/p^m + \mathbf{I}) \mid k \in \mathbf{I}, m \in \mathbf{N}\}$$

between $[x]$ and $\mathbf{R}_{p^\infty}$. Now if $kx_m = rx_s$, where (say) $m \leq s$, then we have $kp^{s-m}x_s = rx_s$, that is, $(kp^{s-m} - r)x_s = 0$, and since x_s has order p^s, this implies that p^s divides $kp^{s-m} - r$, so that $(kp^{s-m} - r)/p^s = k/p^m - r/p^s$ is an integer, and conversely, proving that F is a one-to-one correspondence. Moreover, $kx_m + rx_s = (kp^{s-m} + r)x_s$ is taken by F into $(kp^{s-m} + r)/p^s + \mathbf{I} = k/p^m + \mathbf{I} + r/p^s + \mathbf{I}$, so that F is a homomorphism.

Let A be a maximal independent subset of G', so that by the proof of Proposition 51.7, $(A) = G'$. Then the set of subgroups $\{[a] \mid a \in A\}$ is readily independent in $\mathscr{S}_G^*$, so that its sup, call it $[A]$, is isomorphic to a direct sum of $\mathbf{R}_{p^\infty}$'s. Since $[A]$ is divisible, it is supplemented, say $[A] \cap H = \{0\}$, $[A] + H = G$. If $H \neq \{0\}$, it contains an element of order p, contrary to the maximality of A; hence $H = \{0\}$ and $[A] = G$.   //

Propositions 6–7 combine to give us

Theorem 2. *An Abelian group is divisible if and only if it is isomorphic to a weak direct sum of* $\mathbf{R}$*'s and* $\mathbf{R}_{p^\infty}$*'s.*

Proof: Let G be a divisible Abelian group, and let G_P, G_p be as in Propositions 51.5–6. Evidently, if x has finite order and $x = ny$, then y must have finite order; hence G_P is divisible, whence supplemented, say $G \cong G_P \oplus Q$, where Q is evidently aperiodic. Thus $G \cong Q \oplus \sum_p^* G_p$, and since G is divisible, so are these summands, so that Propositions 6–7 apply.   //

In Section 50 we characterized the Abelian groups whose subgroup lattices satisfy the maximum condition—namely, they are isomorphic to finite direct sums of cyclic groups. Since the cyclic groups are just the factor groups of **I**, this can be restated as follows: $\mathscr{S}_G^*$ (where G is Abelian) satisfies the maximum condition if and only if G is isomorphic to a finite direct sum of factor groups of **I**. We conclude this section by proving a "dual" result about Abelian groups whose subgroup lattices satisfy the minimum condition:

Theorem 3. *The subgroup lattice of an Abelian group satisfies the minimum condition if and only if the group is isomorphic to a finite direct sum of subgroups of* $\mathbf{R}_{p^\infty}$*'s—in other words, to a finite direct sum of cyclic groups of prime power orders and groups of type* p^∞.

Proof: If $\mathscr{S}_G^*$ satisfies the minimum condition, G must be periodic, since an infinite cyclic group has descending chains of subgroups. Hence $G \cong \sum_p^* G_p$, and by the minimum condition, there can only be finitely many nontrivial G_p's. Moreover, each G_p has finite (p-)rank, since it cannot contain an infinite direct sum of cyclic groups.

The descending chain $\{\{p^k x \mid x \in G_p\} \mid k \in \mathbf{N}\}$ must terminate, say at $\{p^m x \mid x \in G_p\}$, call it $G_p^{(m)}$. It follows readily that $G_p^{(m)}$ is divisible, whence supplemented; let $G_p \cong G_p^{(m)} \oplus H_p$, where evidently $\{p^m x \mid x \in H_p\} = \{0\}$. We shall show that H_p is finite. Since H_p has finite rank, it follows by the proof of Proposition 51.7 that if $m = 1$, H_p is a finite direct sum of cyclic groups of order p, and so is finite; we proceed by induction on m. Let H_p' be the subgroup of H_p consisting of the elements whose orders divide p; thus by the case $m = 1$, H_p' is finite. On the other hand, H_p/H_p' still satisfies the minimum condition, hence still has finite rank, while $\{p^{m-1} x \mid x \in H_p/H_p'\} = \{0\}$, so that H_p/H_p' is finite by induction hypothesis, making H_p finite. Thus G_p is isomorphic to the direct sum of a divisible p-group of finite rank, namely $G_p^{(m)}$, and a finite p-group, H_p. By Proposition 6, $G_p^{(m)}$ is isomorphic to a finite direct sum of $\mathbf{R}_{p^\infty}$'s; while H_p, as a finite Abelian p-group, is isomorphic to a finite direct sum of cyclic groups whose orders are powers of p.

To prove the converse, we use induction on the number of direct summands. If this is 1, G is a subgroup of a group of type p^∞, and evidently does satisfy the minimum condition. Otherwise, let $G \cong H \oplus K$, where K is a subgroup of a group of type p^∞, and H has fewer direct summands than G, so that both H and K satisfy the minimum condition; we can regard H as a subgroup of G. Let $G \supset G_1 \supset G_2 \supset \cdots$ be a descending chain of subgroups of G, and let $H_i = H \cap G_i$; then $H \supseteq H_1 \supseteq \cdots$ terminates, say at H_m, and all the G_i's must contain H_m. Now for $i \geq m$ we have $G_i/H_m = G_i/H_i = G_i/(H \cap G_i) \cong (H + G_i)/H$ by Theorem 26.4, where the right member can be regarded as a subgroup of G/H, hence of its isomorphic image K. Since K satisfies the minimum condition, its descending chain of subgroups corresponding to G_m/H_m, G_{m+1}/H_m, ... must terminate; hence the chain of subgroups $G_m \supset G_{m+1} \cdots$ must also terminate.   //

54. LOCALLY CYCLIC GROUPS

In this section we derive some interesting characterizations of the additive groups **R** and **R/I**.

The group G is called **locally cyclic** if every finitely generated subgroup of G is cyclic. Evidently such a group must be Abelian, since any two of its elements x, y are in its cyclic subgroup (x, y). A cyclic group is locally cyclic, since all of its subgroups are cyclic. On the other hand, a finitely generated group can be locally cyclic only if it is cyclic; in particular, a direct sum of locally cyclic (or even cyclic) groups need not be locally cyclic.

Exercise 1. *Any subgroup or homomorphic image of a locally cyclic group is locally cyclic.*

Proposition 1. **R** *is locally cyclic.*

Proof: Given $m_1/n_1, \ldots, m_k/n_k$ in **R**, let n be the least common multiple of $n_1, \ldots, n_k$, and let $m_i/n_i = r_i/n$, $1 \leq i \leq k$. Let d be the greatest common divisor of $r_1, \ldots, r_k$, and let $r_i = ds_i$, $1 \leq i \leq k$. Then there exist integers $a_1, \ldots, a_k$ such that $\sum_{i=1}^{k} a_i r_i = d$, so that $d/n \in (r_1/n, \ldots, r_k/n) = (m_1/n_1, \ldots, m_k/n_k)$, while $m_i/n_i = r_i/n = s_i(d/n) \in (d/n)$, $1 \leq i \leq k$, proving that $(m_1/n_1, \ldots, m_k/n_k) = (d/n)$.   //

Corollary. **R/I** *is locally cyclic.*

The main result of this section is

Theorem 1. *A group is locally cyclic if and only if it is isomorphic to a subgroup of* **R** *or of* **R/I**.

This will follow immediately from Propositions 2, 3, and 6.

Proposition 2. *A locally cyclic group is either periodic or aperiodic.*

Proof: Let G be locally cyclic, and let x, y be in G, where $x \neq 0$ has finite order and y has infinite order. Let $(x, y) = (z)$, say $x = mz$, $y = nz$. Then $o(z)$ cannot be finite, since nz has infinite order; nor can $o(z)$ be infinite, since $mz \neq 0$ has finite order.   //

Proposition 3. *Any aperiodic locally cyclic group is isomorphic to a subgroup of* **R**.

Proof: Let G be such a group; let $x \neq 0$ be any element of G; and for any $y \in G$, let $(x, y) = (z_y)$, say $x = n_y z_y$, $y = m_y z_y$, where $z_y \neq 0$ and $n_y \neq 0$ since $x \neq 0$. Let $F_x = \{(y, m_y/n_y) \mid y \in G\}$. By Exercise 43.1, specifying x and y determines z_y "up to inverse," hence determines m_y and n_y except for sign; thus m_y/n_y is determined, and F_x is a function. We show that F_x is an isomorphism of G into **R**. In fact, given a, b in G, we have $(x, a + b) = (z_{a+b}) \subseteq (x, a, b) = (z_a, z_b) = (z)$, say; let $z_a = rz$, $z_b = sz$, $z_{a+b} = tz$. Then $a + b = m_a z_a + m_b z_b = (m_a r + m_b s)z$, and also $a + b = m_{a+b} z_{a+b} = (m_{a+b} t)z$. Since $z \neq 0$, it has infinite order, so that we must have $m_{a+b} t = m_a r + m_b s$. Moreover, $x = n_a z_a = n_b z_b = n_{a+b} z_{a+b}$, so that $n_a r = n_b s = n_{a+b} t \neq 0$. Hence

$$\begin{aligned} F_x(a + b) &= m_{a+b}/n_{a+b} = (m_{a+b} t)/(n_{a+b} t) = (m_a r + m_b s)/(n_{a+b} t) \\ &= (m_a r)/(n_{a+b} t) + (m_b s)/(n_{a+b} t) \\ &= (m_a r)/(n_a r) + (m_b s)/(n_b s) = m_a/n_a + m_b/n_b \\ &= F_x(a) + F_x(b), \end{aligned}$$

proving that F_x is a homomorphism. Finally, $F_x(y) = 0$ only if $m_y = 0$, that is, only if $y = 0$, so that F_x is one-to-one. //

Turning to the periodic case, we first prove

Proposition 4. *A periodic locally cyclic group has at most one cyclic subgroup of any order* n.

Proof: Any two cyclic subgroups (x), (y) are both subgroups of the cyclic subgroup $(z) = (x, y)$; and by Proposition 43.3, (z) has exactly one subgroup of any given order. //

Proposition 5. *Any locally cyclic p-group is isomorphic to a subgroup of* $\mathbf{R}_{p^\infty}$.

Proof: If the group (call it G) has an element x of maximal order p^m, then for any $y \in G$ we have $(x, y) = (z)$, so that $o(x) \leq o(z)$, but since $o(x)$ is maximal, this implies $o(x) = o(z)$. Thus x generates (z), so that any $y \in G$ is in (x), that is, $G = (x)$ is a cyclic group of prime power order p^m.

Otherwise, the orders of the elements of G are unbounded, so that G has elements of order p^n for every $n \in \mathbf{N}^\circ$. Let $\mathscr{F}$ be the set of isomorphisms of subgroups of G with subgroups of $\mathbf{R}_{p^\infty}$; clearly $\mathscr{F}$ is nonempty, for example, $\{0\} \cong \{0\}$. We define an order relation R on $\mathscr{F}$ as follows: Let A, B be subgroups of G, and F_A, F_B isomorphisms of A, B, respectively, with subgroups of $\mathbf{R}_{p^\infty}$; we say that $(F_A, F_B) \in R$ if $A \subseteq B$ and the restriction of F_B to A is F_A. It is easily verified that $\mathscr{F}$, ordered by R, is inductive, so that by Zorn's lemma, it has a maximal element F. Let F be an isomorphism of the subgroup H of G

with a subgroup of $\mathbf{R}_{p^\infty}$; we shall show that H must be all of G, which will prove the proposition.

Note first that if the orders of the elements of H are unbounded, it has elements of order p^n for every n, and by Proposition 4, this makes it all of G. Thus if H were a proper subgroup of G, its elements would have bounded orders, so that by the first paragraph of the proof it would be a cyclic group (x), say of order p^r, and $F(H)$ would be the unique cyclic subgroup of $\mathbf{R}_{p^\infty}$ of order p^r, namely $\mathbf{R}_{p^r}$. Let $y \in G$ have order p^{r+1}; then (y) has a cyclic subgroup of order p^r, so that by Proposition 4, $H \subset (y)$. Let x' be the element of H such that $F(x') = 1/p^r + \mathbf{I}$; thus x' has order p^r and so generates H. Let $y' \in (y)$ be such that $py' = x'$; thus y' has order p^{r+1} and generates (y). Define the function F^* from (y) into $\mathbf{R}_{p^\infty}$ by $F^*(ky') = k/p^{r+1} + \mathbf{I}$, $0 \le k < p^{r+1}$; readily F^* is an isomorphism of $(y') = (y)$ with $\mathbf{R}_{p^{r+1}} \subset \mathbf{R}_{p^\infty}$. Moreover, $F^*(hx') = hF^*(x') = hF^*(py') = h/p^r + \mathbf{I} = F(hx'), 0 \le h < p^r$, so that the restriction of F^* to H coincides with F. We have thus shown that if H were a proper subgroup of G, F could not be maximal; hence H must be all of G.   ∥

Proposition 6. *Any periodic locally cyclic group is isomorphic to a subgroup of* $\mathbf{R}/\mathbf{I}$.

Proof: Any such group G is isomorphic to the weak direct sum of the G_p, which are p-subgroups of G, hence locally cyclic. By Proposition 5, each G_p is isomorphic to a subgroup of $\mathbf{R}_{p^\infty}$; hence G is isomorphic to a subgroup of the weak direct sum of the $\mathbf{R}_{p^\infty}$, which is $\mathbf{R}/\mathbf{I}$.   ∥

We conclude this section with a remarkable characterization of the locally cyclic groups in terms of their subgroup lattices:

Theorem 2. *A group is locally cyclic if and only if its subgroup lattice is distributive.*

Proof: Let G be locally cyclic and let A, B, C be subgroups of G; we must show that $A \cap (B + C) \subseteq (A \cap B) + (A \cap C)$. Let $a = b + c$ be in $A \cap (B + C)$, and let $(b, c) = (d)$, say $b = md$, $c = nd$; moreover, let $d = rb + sc$. Then

$$a = b + c = (m + n)d = (m + n)(rb + sc) = (m + n)(rm + sn)d$$
$$= mr(m + n)d + sn(m + n)d,$$

where the first term $= mra = (m + n)rb$, which is in $A \cap B$, and similarly the second term is in $A \cap C$, so that $a \in (A \cap B) + (A \cap C)$, completing the proof of "only if." The converse will be proved as Proposition 9.   ∥

Proposition 7. *A group with distributive subgroup lattice is Abelian.*

Proof: Let $\mathscr{S}_G^*$ be distributive, and let x, y be in G. By distributivity, we have $(x + y) = (x + y) \cap ((x) + (y)) = ((x) \cap (x + y)) + ((y) \cap (x + y))$.

Let $(x) \cap (x + y) = (u)$, $(y) \cap (x + y) = (v)$ [they are subgroups of cyclic groups, hence cyclic]. Since u and v are both in the cyclic group $(x + y)$, they commute, so that $x + y$ (as an element of $(u) + (v)$) $= ru + sv = sv + ru$ (say). Since $u \in (x)$, it commutes with x, so that every element of (u) commutes with x, and similarly every element of (v) commutes with y. Thus $x + y = ru + sv$ implies $y - sv = -x + ru = ru - x$, so that

$$(x + y) - (y + x) = (sv + ru) - x - y = sv + (ru - x) - y$$
$$= sv + (y - sv) - y = 0,$$

proving that x and y commute. //

Proposition 8. *A group with distributive subgroup lattice is either periodic or aperiodic.*

Proof: Let $x \neq 0$ have finite order, and y infinite order. Then (using commutativity) $x + y$ has infinite order, so that $(x) \cap (x + y) = \{0\}$ and $(x) \cap (y) = \{0\}$. By distributivity, it follows that $(x) \cap [(x + y) + (y)] = \{0\}$; but this contains $(x + y) - y = x \neq 0$, contradiction. //

Proposition 9. *A group with distributive subgroup lattice is locally cyclic.*

Proof: Let x, y in G be such that (x, y) is not cyclic; since (x, y) is a finitely generated Abelian group, in any case it is isomorphic to the direct sum of two of its cyclic subgroups, say (u) and (v).

If G is aperiodic, let z be in $(u + v) \cap (u)$, say $z = mu = n(u + v)$; then $nv = (m - n)u$ is in $(u) \cap (v)$. But (u) and (v) are independent, so that this implies $nv = (m - n)u = 0$, and since u and v have infinite order, this requires $m = n = 0$, so that $z = 0$, that is, $(u + v) \cap (u) = \{0\}$. Similarly, $(u + v) \cap (v) = \{0\}$, so that by distributivity, $(u + v) = (u + v) \cap [(u) + (v)] = \{0\}$, contradiction.

Similarly, if G is periodic, note first that (u) and (v) cannot have relatively prime orders, since if they did, their direct sum would be cyclic (proof of Proposition 47.3). Let p be a prime dividing both their orders, and let $u' \in (u)$ and $v' \in (v)$ each have order p. Since $(u' + v') \cap (u')$ is a subgroup of the prime group (u'), it is either $\{0\}$ or (u'). If it were (u'), then since $u' + v'$ has order dividing p, we would have $(u') = (u' + v')$, and this group would then also contain v', which also has order p, so that $(u') = (v')$. We would thus have $0 \neq u' \in (u') \subseteq (u) \cap (v)$, contradicting the independence of (u) and (v). Hence $(u' + v') \cap (u') = \{0\}$, and similarly $(u' + v') \cap (v') = \{0\}$, so that by distributivity, $(u' + v') = (u' + v') \cap [(u') + (v')] = \{0\}$. But if $u' + v' = 0$, we have $v' = -u'$ in $(u) \cap (v)$, contradicting the independence of (u) and (v).

We have thus shown in either case that for any x, y in G, the subgroup (x, y) is cyclic; it follows by an easy induction that any finitely generated subgroup of G is cyclic, making G locally cyclic. //

Exercise 2. $\mathscr{S}_G^*$ *is a chain if and only if* G *is a subgroup of a group of type* p^∞.

Exercise 3. *The* sup *in* $\mathscr{S}_G^*$ *is the union if and only if* $\mathscr{S}_G^*$ *is a chain.*

55. HAMILTONIAN GROUPS

In Section 48 we characterized groups all of whose (normal) subgroups are supplemented. A related problem is that of describing the groups all of whose subgroups are normal; such a group is called **Hamiltonian**. *In this section we use multiplicative notation.*

An Abelian group is certainly Hamiltonian, but there are also non-Abelian Hamiltonian groups. The simplest example is the **quaternion group** Q, defined by the following composition table:

	e	e'	i	i'	j	j'	k	k'
e	e	e'	i	i'	j	j'	k	k'
e'	e'	e	i'	i	j'	j	k'	k
i	i	i'	e'	e	k	k'	j'	j
i'	i'	i	e	e'	k'	k	j	j'
j	j	j'	k'	k	e'	e	i	i'
j'	j'	j	k	k'	e	e'	i'	i
k	k	k'	j	j'	i'	i	e'	e
k'	k'	k	j'	j	i	i'	e	e'

Exercise 1. *Verify that* Q *is Hamiltonian, and prove also that it is indecomposable.*

Exercise 2. *Any subgroup or homomorphic image of a Hamiltonian group is Hamiltonian.*

A complete description of the non-Abelian Hamiltonian groups in terms of Q and Abelian groups is provided by

Theorem 1. *A non-Abelian group is Hamiltonian if and only if it is isomorphic to* $Q \times A$, *where* A *is a periodic Abelian group with no element of order* 4.

Proof: To prove "if," it suffices to show that any cyclic subgroup of such a $Q \times A$ is normal—in other words, that for all x_1 and x_2 in $Q \times A$ we have $x_1 x_2 x_1^{-1} \in (x_2)$. Let $x_1 = (q_1, a_1)$, $x_2 = (q_2, a_2)$, where q_1, q_2 are in Q and a_1, a_2 in A; then $x_1 x_2 x_1^{-1} = (q_1 q_2 q_1^{-1}, a_1 a_2 a_1^{-1}) = (q_1 q_2 q_1^{-1}, a_2)$ since A is Abelian. We must show that this is equal to a power of (q_2, a_2).

Since Q is Hamiltonian, we have $q_1 q_2 q_1^{-1} \in (q_2)$, say $= q_2^r$, so that $x_1 x_2 x_1^{-1} = (q_2^r, a_2)$. Since q_2 has order 4 at most, we can assume that $r = 1, 2, 3,$ or 4. If $r = 1$, we have $(q_2^r, a_2) = (q_2, a_2)$, as desired. If $r = 4$, we have $q_1 q_2 q_1^{-1} = e$, so that $q_2 = e$, and $(q_2{}^r, a_2) = (e, a_2) = (q_2, a_2)$, as desired. If $r = 2$, then $q_1 q_2 q_1^{-1} = q_2{}^2 = e$ or e', so that $q_2 = e$ or e'; but then q_2 commutes with q_1, so that $q_1 q_2 q_1^{-1} = q_2$, as desired.

Finally, let $r = 3$, and note that since no element of A can have order divisible by 4, we have $A \cong A_2 \times \prod_p^* A_p$ where the p's are odd primes and the elements of A_2 all have order ≤ 2; thus any element of A is the product of an element of order ≤ 2 and an element of odd order. Let $a_2 = a_2' a_2''$, where a_2' has order ≤ 2 and a_2'' has odd order s; let t be such that $4 \mid t - 3$ (so that t is odd) and $s \mid t - 1$ (Exercise 38.9). Then $(q_2{}^3, a_2) = (q_2{}^3, a_2' a_2'') = (q_2{}^t, (a_2' a_2'')^t) = (q_2, a_2)^t$, as desired. "Only if" will be proved at the end of the section. $\;/\!/$

To prove the propositions which will give us "only if," we need some lemmas about commutators in Hamiltonian groups. We recall that the commutator of a and b is defined as $[a, b] = aba^{-1}b^{-1}$.

Lemma 1. *In a Hamiltonian group,* $[a, b] \in (a) \cap (b)$.
Proof: $[a, b] = a(ba^{-1}b^{-1})$, where $ba^{-1}b^{-1} \in (a^{-1}) = (a)$ since (a^{-1}) is normal; hence $[a, b]$ is in (a), and similarly it is in (b). $\;/\!/$

Corollary. *In a Hamiltonian group,* $[a, b]$ *commutes with a and b.*

Lemma 2. *In any group, if $[x, y]$ commutes with x, then* $[x, y]^n = [x^n, y]$ *for all $n \in \mathbf{N}^\circ$.*
Proof: For any a, b, c we have $[ab, c] = abcb^{-1}a^{-1}c^{-1} = a[b, c]a^{-1}[a, c]$. Take $a = x$, $b = x^{n-1}$, $c = y$, and suppose the lemma true for $n - 1$; then $[x^n, y] = x[x^{n-1}, y]x^{-1}[x, y] = x[x, y]^{n-1}x^{-1}[x, y] = [x, y]^n$ since x and $[x, y]$ commute. $\;/\!/$

Corollary. *In a Hamiltonian group,* $[a^m, b^n] = [a, b]^{mn}$ *for all a, b in the group and all m, n in $\mathbf{N}^\circ$.*

Lemma 3. *In any group, if $[x, y]$ commutes with x and y, then* $(xy)^k = x^k y^k [y, x]^{k(k-1)/2}$ *for all $k \in \mathbf{N}$.*
Proof: This is trivial for $k = 1$; suppose that it holds for k. Then

$$x^{k+1} y^{k+1} [y, x]^{k(k+1)/2} = x^{k+1} y^{k+1} [y, x]^k [y, x]^{k(k-1)/2},$$

and since x and y commute with $[y, x] = [x, y]^{-1}$, this is equal to

$$x[y, x]^k x^k y^{k+1} [y, x]^{k(k-1)/2}.$$

By Lemma 2, we have $[y, x]^k = [y, x^k]$, so that this reduces to

$$
\begin{aligned}
x(yx^k y^{-1} x^{-k}) x^k y^{k+1} [y, x]^{k(k-1)/2} &= xy(x^k y^k [y, x]^{k(k-1)/2}) \\
&= xy(xy)^k \qquad \text{(induction hypothesis)} \\
&= (xy)^{k+1}. \qquad /\!/
\end{aligned}
$$

Corollary. *This holds for all* x, y *in a Hamiltonian group.*

Proposition 1. *A non-Abelian Hamiltonian group is periodic.*

Proof: By Lemma 1, $[a, b]$ is a power of a, say a^r, and commutes with b; hence $e = [[a, b], b] = [a^r, b]$. By Lemma 2 this is equal to $[a, b]^r = a^{r^2}$, so that if $r > 0$, a has finite order. Similarly, if $r < 0$ we have $e = [[a, b]^{-1}, b] = [a^{-r}, b] = [a, b]^{-r} = a^{-r^2}$. Thus whenever $r \neq 0$—and, in particular, whenever $[a, b] \neq e$—we have proved that a has finite order. Hence any $a \notin C(G)$ has finite order, since for such an a there must exist b's such that $[a, b] \neq e$. Finally, let $[x, y] \neq e$, so that $x \notin C(G)$ and has finite order (such x, y exist since the group is not Abelian), and let $z \in C(G)$; then $[zx, y] = [x, y] \neq e$, so that zx has finite order, and since x has finite order, so has z. $/\!/$

Exercise 3. *Generalize the last part of the proof of Proposition 1 to show that if G is any non-Abelian group such that any $x \notin C(G)$ has finite order, then G is periodic.*

Proposition 2. *A non-Abelian Hamiltonian group has a subgroup isomorphic to Q.*

Proof: Let a, b be elements of the group such that $[a, b] \neq e$. Thus the set of elements of (a) which do not commute with b is nonempty; let $c \in (a)$ be such an element of lowest order. Similarly, the set of elements of (a, b) which do not commute with c is nonempty; let d be such an element of lowest order.

Let p be any prime dividing $o(c)$. Since $o(c^p) < o(c)$, c^p commutes with b, and since $c \in (a)$, any power of c commutes with a; hence c^p commutes with any element of (a, b)—in particular, with d, and we have by Lemma 2 $[c, d]^p = [c^p, d] = e$. Thus the order of $[c, d]$ divides any such p, and is not 1 since c and d do not commute. Hence there can be at most one such p, and we have $o([c, d]) = p$, while $o(c)$ is a power of p, say p^r. Similarly, let q be any prime dividing $o(d)$; then $[c, d]^q = [c, d^q] = e$ since $o(d^q) < o(d)$, so that $p = o([c, d])$ divides q. Hence $q = p$, and $o(d)$ is also a power of p, say p^s.

By Lemma 1, $[c, d]$ is power of c and of d; since $[c, d]^p = e$, this implies that $[c, d] = c^{up^{r-1}} = d^{vp^{s-1}}$, where $0 < u < p$, $0 < v < p$. Note that if $r = 1$ we would have $[c, d] = c^u$ with u relatively prime to p, so that c would also be a power of $[c, d]$, hence a power of d, and would commute with d, contradiction; hence $r > 1$, and similarly $s > 1$.

Suppose that $s \leq r$ (if $r < s$, interchange r and s in the argument which follows). By Lemma 3,

$$(c^{-up^{r-s}}d^v)^{p^{s-1}} = c^{-up^{r-1}}d^{vp^{s-1}}[d^v, c^{-up^{r-s}}]^{p^{s-1}(p^{s-1}-1)/2},$$

where the first two terms cancel since they are $[c, d]^{-1}$ and $[c, d]$, respectively.

Moreover, by the corollary to Lemma 2 we have $[d^v, c^{-up^{r-s}}] = [c, d]^{uvp^{r-s}}$; hence

$$(c^{-up^{r-s}}d^v)^{p^s-1} = [c, d]^{uvp^{r-s}p^{s-1}(p^{s-1}-1)/2} = [c, d]^{uvp^{r-1}(p^{s-1}-1)/2}.$$

If p is odd, $uvp^{r-1}(p^{s-1} - 1)/2$ is divisible by p since $r > 1$; hence $[c, d]$ to this power is e. Thus $(c^{-up^{r-s}}d^v)^{p^s-1} = e$, so that $o(c^{-up^{r-s}}d^v) < o(d)$, which implies that $c^{-up^{r-s}}d^v$ commutes with c. But the subgroup $(c, c^{-up^{r-s}}d^v)$ contains d^v, and since v is relatively prime to p it also contains d, which does not commute with c, contradiction. Hence $p = 2$, so that $u = v = 1$.

If $r > 2$, the exponent $2^{r-1}(2^{s-1} - 1)/2$ is divisible by 2, and the argument of the last paragraph yields a contradiction; hence $r = 2$, and since $1 < s \leq r$, we also have $s = 2$. Thus $c^2 = d^2 = [c, d]$, and $[c, d]^2 = e$. Letting c correspond to i, d to j, and $[c, d]$ to e', it is readily verified that the subgroup (c, d) is isomorphic to Q.   //

Proposition 3. *A non-Abelian Hamiltonian group is generated by a quaternion group and an abelian group with no element of order 4.*

Proof: Let G be such a group, and let (c, d) be a quaternion subgroup of G as in Proposition 2. Since (c) is normal, xcx^{-1} is a power of c for any $x \in G$, and since $o(c) = 4$, xcx^{-1} is either e, c, c^2, or c^{-1}. Moreover, it cannot be e, since we would then have $c = x^{-1}ex = e$; and it cannot be c^2, since then $c = x^{-1}c^2x$ would have order 2. Hence it is either c or c^{-1}—the former if x commutes with c, the latter if it does not.

Let x and y not commute with c; then $(xy)c(xy)^{-1} = xc^{-1}x^{-1} = c$, so that xy does commute with c. Since c and d do not commute, it follows in particular that if x does not commute with c, then xd does, and similarly if x does not commute with d, then xc does. In particular, if xd does not commute with d, then xdc does.

Let H be the centralizer of (c, d); then for any $x \in G$ we have four possibilities:

(a) x commutes with both c and d, so that $x \in H$
(b) x commutes with c but not with d; then xc commutes with d, and certainly with c, so that $xc \in H$
(c) x commutes with d but not with c; in this case, analogously, $xd \in H$
(d) x commutes with neither c nor d; then xd commutes with c, so that xdc commutes with c, but xd does not commute with d, so that xdc commutes with d, and we have $xdc \in H$.

Thus for any $x \in G$ we have x, xc, xd, or xdc in H, so that (c, d) and H generate G.

To complete the proof, let $y \in H$ be such that $y^4 = e$. Since y and d commute, yd also has order at most 4, and c does not commute with yd; hence by the argument at the beginning of the proof, whether yd has order 2 or 4, we have $c(yd)c^{-1} = (yd)^{-1}$. Since y commutes with c and d, the left member is equal to $(cdc^{-1})y = d^{-1}y$, while the right member is $d^{-1}y^{-1}$; hence $y = y^{-1}$, so that y has order 2. We have thus shown that no element of H has order 4; and in particular, H has no quaternion subgroup, contradicting Proposition 2 unless H is Abelian. $\|$

We can now complete the proof of Theorem 1. Let G, c, d, H be as in the proof of Proposition 3; then readily $(c, d) \cap H = ([c, d]) = (c^2)$. Let K be the set of elements of H which have odd order, and let $\mathscr{A}$ be the set of subgroups of H which contain K but not c^2. Thus $\mathscr{A}$ is nonempty, since it contains K, and clearly $\mathscr{A}$ ordered by inclusion is inductive, so that it has a maximal element A. Now for any $x \in H$, $o(x)$ cannot be divisible by 4; hence $o(x^2)$ is odd, so that $x^2 \in K \subseteq A$. Moreover, if $x \notin A$ we have $c^2 \in (A \cup \{x\})$ by the maximality of A, and since $x^2 \in A$, this means that $c^2 = ax$ for some $a \in A$, so that $x \in c^2 A$. Thus $H = A \cup c^2 A$, so that $G = \sup \{(c, d), H\} = \sup \{(c, d), A\}$. Since (c, d) and A are normal, and $A \cap (c, d) = \{e\}$, we thus have $G \cong (c, d) \times A$.

X

RINGS

56. UNIVERSAL ALGEBRAS

We have seen that a given set can be the underlying set of more than one composition. For example, we have the inf and sup compositions on any lattice; addition, multiplication, and exponentiation on N; addition, subtraction, and multiplication on I; and so on. In studying groupoids, we restricted ourselves to considering only one composition on a given set at a time. However, the results which we obtained in Chapter V are not specific to groupoids; they generalize immediately to situations in which many compositions on a set S are considered simultaneously. In fact, the compositions need not even be binary; they can be unary, ternary, or even n-ary— that is, functions from S^n into S. In this section we sketch the generalization of the Chapter V material to the case of an arbitrary set of compositions.

Let $\mathscr{F}$ be a set of compositions on the set S. We call $(S, \mathscr{F})$ a **universal algebra** with underlying set S, and say that S is a universal algebra under $\mathscr{F}$.

Let F be an n-ary composition on S, and let A be a subset of S. If $F(A^n) \subseteq A$, we say that A is **stable** under F. The restriction of F "to A" (that is, to A^n) is then a composition on A. If S is a universal algebra under $\mathscr{F}$, and $A \subseteq S$ is stable under every $F \in \mathscr{F}$, we say that A is stable under $\mathscr{F}$. Let $S' \subseteq S$ be stable under $\mathscr{F}$, and let $\mathscr{F}'$ be the set of restrictions to S' of the compositions in $\mathscr{F}$; then S' is a universal algebra under $\mathscr{F}'$, and is called a **subalgebra** of S. Evidently a subalgebra of a subalgebra is a subalgebra, and if A, B are subalgebras such that $A \subseteq B$, then A is a subalgebra of B. Clearly any intersection of subalgebras is a subalgebra, so that the subalgebras of S are a complete lattice $\mathscr{S}_S$ under the inclusion ordering.

Let F, G be n-ary compositions on S, T, respectively, and let H be a function from S into T. If $H(F(x_1, \ldots, x_n)) = G(H(x_1), \ldots, H(x_n))$ for all $(x_1, \ldots, x_n) \in S^n$, we call H an (F, G)-**homomorphism**. Let S, T be universal algebras under $\mathscr{F} = \{F_i \mid i \in I\}$ and $\mathscr{G} = \{G_i \mid i \in I\}$, respectively. If H is an (F_i, G_i)-homomorphism for each $i \in I$, we call it a homomorphism of the algebra S into the algebra T. As in the case of groupoids, a one-to-one homomorphism is called an isomorphism, and similarly for the other terminology of Section 24. Evidently the composite of an (F, G)-homomorphism and a (G, H)-homomorphism is an (F, H)-homomorphism; the inverse of an (F, G)-isomorphism is a (G, F)-isomorphism; and a homomorphic image or preimage of a subalgebra is a subalgebra.

If F is an n-ary composition on S, and E is an equivalence on S, we call E a **congruence** for F if $(x_1, y_1) \in E, \ldots, (x_n, y_n) \in E$ imply $(F(x_1, \ldots, x_n), F(y_1, \ldots, y_n)) \in E$ for all $(x_1, \ldots, x_n)$ and $(y_1, \ldots, y_n)$ in S^n. If S is a universal algebra under $\mathscr{F}$, and E is a congruence for every $F \in \mathscr{F}$, we call it a congruence on the algebra. Readily, if E is a congruence on S, the quotients by E of the compositions of $\mathscr{F}$ (defined analogously with Section 25) are compositions on the quotient set S/E. The algebra S/E under these compositions is called a **quotient algebra** of S. Evidently any intersection of congruences is a congruence, so that the set $\mathscr{C}_S$ of congruences on S is a complete lattice under the inclusion ordering. Moreover, a composite of congruences is a congruence provided that it is an equivalence; hence if S is a universal algebra on which all congruences commute, $\mathscr{C}_S$ is modular. It also follows readily from the foregoing definitions that all the theorems about canonical homomorphisms, normal subsets, and normal series (Sections 26–28) hold for universal algebras.

Let $(S_i)_I$ be an I-tuple of sets, let F_i be an n-ary composition on S_i, and define the n-ary composition F on $S = \prod_I S_i$ by $F((x_{i1})_I, \ldots, (x_{in})_I) = (F_i(x_{i1}, \ldots, x_{in}))_I$ for all $((x_{i1})_I, \ldots, (x_{in})_I) \in S^n$. If S_i is a universal algebra under $\mathscr{F}_i = \{F_{ij} \mid j \in J\}$, and F_j denotes the composition on S defined in this way, using the compositions F_{ij} on the S_i, then S is a universal algebra under $\mathscr{F} = \{F_j \mid j \in J\}$, and we call it the **direct product** of the S_i. It is easily verified that results analogous to those of Section 29 hold for direct products of universal algebras.

A universal algebra with only one element is called *trivial*. Evidently, for any $n \in \mathbf{N}$ there is just one n-ary composition on the one-element set $\{e\}$, namely F defined by $F(e, \ldots, e) = e$. Thus two trivial universal algebras are isomorphic provided that they have the same number of n-ary compositions for each $n \in \mathbf{N}$. Readily, results analogous to those of Sections 30 and 39 hold for universal algebras which have a trivial subalgebra.

We could go on to define analogs of identities, absorbent elements, cancellable and invertible elements, associativity and commutativity for n-ary compositions; however, properties of this sort have not been extensively studied. From here on we will once again restrict ourselves to binary compositions, but will now consider two of them on the given underlying set. A universal algebra for which $\mathscr{F}$ consists of two binary compositions might be called a **bigroupoid**. In the remainder of this chapter we study bigroupoids with special properties, paralleling the material in Chapters VI–VII.

57. RINGOIDS

Let S be a bigroupoid under the compositions F and G. We shall denote F additively and G multiplicatively. The groupoid S under F will be called the *additive groupoid* of S, while S under G will be called the *multiplicative groupoid* of S.

In considering bigroupoids with special properties, we can assume, of course, that any of the properties considered in Chapter VI hold for F, for G, or for both; as an example, we might assume that the additive or multiplicative groupoid is a semigroup or a group. However, as long as we make only assumptions of the type considered in Chapter VI, involving only F alone or G alone, our bigroupoid will be nothing more than two unrelated groupoids which happen to have the same underlying set. If we want to go beyond groupoid theory, we must consider assumptions which involve *both* F and G.

The most commonly studied assumption of this type is the familiar **distributivity**. We say that G distributes over F from the left, if $x(y + z) = xy + xz$ for all x, y, z in S; from the right, if $(x + y)z = xz + yz$ for all x, y, z in S.

Examples:

(a) sup and inf on a lattice distribute over each other from both left and right

(b) Multiplication on **N** distributes over addition from both sides, and exponentiation distributes over multiplication from the right.

Exercise 1. *Give a nontrivial example of a composition which distributes over itself.*

Proposition 1 (the general distributive law). *If G distributes over F from the left, then $x \sum_{i=1}^{n} y_i = \sum_{i=1}^{n} xy_i$ for all $n \in \mathbf{N}$ and all $x, y_1, \ldots, y_n$ in S, and analogously for right distributivity.*

Proof: This is trivial for $n = 1$, and if it holds for $n - 1$ we have $x \sum_{i=1}^{n} y_i = x(\sum_{i=1}^{n-1} y_i + y_n) = \sum_{i=1}^{n-1} xy_i + xy_n = \sum_{i=1}^{n} xy_i$, so that it also holds for n. $\parallel$

Corollary. *If G distributes over F from both sides, then $(\sum_{i=1}^{m} x_i)(\sum_{j=1}^{n} y_j) = \sum_{i=1}^{m} (\sum_{j=1}^{n} x_i y_j) = \sum_{j=1}^{n} (\sum_{i=1}^{m} x_i y_j)$ for all m, n in **N** and all $x_1, \ldots, x_m, y_1, \ldots, y_n$ in S.*

Proof: Use Proposition 1 first on the right, then on the left, and vice versa. $\parallel$

A bigroupoid in which G distributes over F from both sides will be called a **ringoid**. Like associativity and commutativity, distributivity passes to subringoids, quotient ringoids, and homomorphic images of ringoids, and the direct product bigroupoid $\prod_I S_i$ is a ringoid if and only if each S_i is a ringoid.

In a ringoid, we can no longer make arbitrary assumptions about special properties of F and G; distributivity forces them to be "compatible" in certain respects. For example, we prove

Proposition 2. *Let F, G be compositions on S such that G distributes over F from the right; then an element of S which is absorbent for G is idempotent for F.*

Proof: If a is absorbent, we have $(a + a)x = ax + ax = a + a$, so that $a + a$ is left absorbent; now use Proposition 31.1.   //

Proposition 3. *Let S be a ringoid such that every element is right cancellable for F; then a left identity for F is absorbent for G.*

Proof: For all $x \in S$ we have $e + xe = xe = x(e + e) = xe + xe$, so that (cancelling xe) $e = xe$, and similarly $e = ex$.   //

Corollary. *The additive and multiplicative groupoids of a nontrivial ringoid cannot both be groups.*

Proposition 4. *Let S, T be ringoids in which there is a left identity, and every element is right cancellable, for the additive composition. Let H be a function from S into T such that $H(xy) = H(x) + H(y)$ for all x, y in S; then $H(S)$ is trivial.*

Proof: Let d, e be left identities for the additive compositions on S, T, respectively; then for all $x \in S$ we have (using Proposition 3) $e + H(d) = H(d) = H(xd) = H(x) + H(d)$, so that $H(x) = e$.   //

By Proposition 4, a nontrivial homomorphism of such ringoids (that is, a homomorphism which is not a constant function) must be an (F, F)- and (G, G)-homomorphism (where we have denoted both additive compositions by F, both multiplicative compositions by G); it cannot be an (F, G)- and (G, F)-homomorphism. From now on, when we speak about ringoid homomorphisms, we shall always mean (F, F)- and (G, G)-homomorphisms.

Proposition 5. *Let S be a ringoid whose additive groupoid is a cancellation semigroup; then all G-composites commute under F.*

Proof: Let $x = ab$, $y = cd$; then

$$ad + cd + ab + cb = (a + c)d + (a + c)b = (a + c)(d + b)$$
$$= a(d + b) + c(d + b) = ad + ab + cd + cb.$$

Cancelling ad on the left, cb on the right thus gives $cd + ab = ab + cd$, that is, $y + x = x + y$.   //

Corollary. *In such a ringoid, if G is onto, F is commutative.*

Proposition 6. *Let S be a ringoid whose additive groupoid is a group; then* $(-x)y = x(-y) = -(xy)$ *for all x, y in S.*

Proof: $xy + (-x)y = (x + (-x))y = 0y = 0$, where 0 is the additive identity. Since inverses in a group are unique, this means that $(-x)y$ is the inverse of xy, that is, $(-x)y = -(xy)$, and similarly for $x(-y)$. $\;/\!/$

Corollary 1. *In such a ringoid,* $(-x)(-y) = xy$ *for all x, y.*

Proof: $(-x)(-y) = -(x(-y)) = -(-(xy)) = xy$. $\;/\!/$

Corollary 2. *In such a ringoid, if x has an inverse for G, so has* $-x$, *namely,* $(-x)^{-1} = -(x^{-1})$.

Proof: $(-(x^{-1}))(-x) = x^{-1}x$. $\;/\!/$

58. SEMIRINGS

A ringoid in which F is associative and commutative, and G is associative, will be called a **semiring**. [Proposition 57.5 provides a rationale for requiring that F be commutative.]

Examples:

(a) S any lattice, $F = \sup$, $G = \inf$ (or vice versa)
(b) $S = N$, $F =$ addition, $G =$ multiplication
(c) S any commutative semigroup under F with idempotent element 0; G defined by $xy = 0$ for all x, y in S. [Such a semiring is called a **zero-semiring**.]

Evidently the trivial bigroupoid is a semiring. A semiring in which G is commutative is called a commutative semiring.

Exercise 1. *Prove the* **binomial theorem** *for a commutative semiring S:* $(a + b)^n = \sum_{i=0}^{n} \binom{n}{i} a^i b^{n-i}$ *for all a, b in S and all* $n \in N^\circ$.

Examples (a–c) are all commutative semirings. In the remainder of this section we introduce three very important examples of semirings which can be defined in terms of a given one—power series, polynomials, and matrices. The third of these will give us a class of examples of noncommutative semirings.

POWER SERIES

Let S be any semiring, and let S^{N° be the set of "sequences with 0th terms" whose terms are in S. Let F^* be the direct power composition of F on S^{N°, that is, $F^*((a_i)_{N^\circ}, (b_i)_{N^\circ}) = (a_i + b_i)_{N^\circ}$. Let G^* be the composition on S^{N° defined by $G^*((a_i)_{N^\circ}, (b_i)_{N^\circ}) = (\sum_{j=0}^{i} a_j b_{i-j})_{N^\circ}$. It is easily verified, using the general distributive law, that G^* is associative and distributes over F^*. Hence S^{N° is a semiring under F^* and G^*; it is called the semiring of **power series** in one indeterminate over S.

POLYNOMIALS

Let $0 \in S$ be absorbent for G (and hence idempotent for F), and let $S[x] = \{(a_i)_{N^\circ} \mid a_i \in S; a_i = 0 \text{ for all but finitely many } i \in N^\circ\}$. It is easily verified that this subset of S^{N° is stable under F^* and G^*, making it a sub-semiring; it is called the semiring of **polynomials** in one indeterminate over S.

Readily, $\bar{S} = \{(a_i)_{N^\circ} \mid a_i \in S; a_i = 0 \text{ for all } i > 0\}$ is a subsemiring of $S[x]$, and $\{((a_i)_{N^\circ}, a_0) \mid (a_i)_{N^\circ} \in \bar{S}\}$ is an isomorphism of $\bar{S}$ with S. The elements of $\bar{S}$ are called *constant polynomials*. We shall denote the constant polynomial $(a_i)_{N^\circ}$ by a_0, relying on context to avoid confusion with the element a_0 of S. From now on we shall also denote F^* and G^* additively and multiplicatively. Note that the constant polynomial 0 is absorbent for G^*.

If $a_i = 0$ for all $i > n$, but $a_n \neq 0$, the polynomial $(a_i)_{N^\circ}$ is said to have (or be of) **degree** n. In particular, the constant polynomial a_0 has degree 0, provided $a_0 \neq 0$; the degree of the polynomial 0 is not defined. The terms of a polynomial are called its **coefficients**; if it has degree n, its nth term is called its *leading coefficient*. The 0th term of any polynomial is called its *constant term*.

Proposition 1. *Let 0 be an identity for F (as well as absorbent for G), and let $1 \neq 0$ be an identity for G. Let x denote the polynomial $(x_i)_{N^\circ}$ in which $x_1 = 1$; $x_i = 0$ for all $i \neq 1$. Then for any polynomial $(a_i)_{N^\circ}$ we have $(a_i)_{N^\circ} = \sum_{i=0}^{n} a_i x^i$, where n is the degree of $(a_i)_{N^\circ}$.*

Proof: Readily, $x^k = (x_{ik})_{N^\circ}$ with $x_{kk} = 1$, $x_{ik} = 0$ for all $i \neq k$; and $a(b_i)_{N^\circ} = (ab_i)_{N^\circ}$ for all $a \in S$ and all $(b_i)_{N^\circ} \in S[x]$. //

Note that if 0, 1 are as in Proposition 1, the constant polynomial 0 is an identity for F^*, and the constant polynomial 1 is an identity for G^*. We assume from now on, whenever we deal with polynomials over S, that S is as in Proposition 1, and we write polynomials in the form $\sum_{i=0}^{n} a_i x^i$, referring to a_i as the coefficient of x^i.

Exercise 2. *Let $a \in S$ commute (under G) with every element of S; then $\{(\sum_{i=0}^{n} c_i x^i, \sum_{i=0}^{n} c_i a^i) \mid \sum_{i=0}^{n} c_i x^i \in S[x]\}$ is a homomorphism of $S[x]$ into S.* [It is called a **substitution** homomorphism.]

Exercise 3. *Let φ, ψ in $S[x]$ have degrees m, n, respectively. Prove that the* *degree of* $\varphi + \psi$ *is* sup $\{m, n\}$ *if* $m \neq n$, *and is* $\leq m$ *if* $m = n$ (*unless* $\varphi + \psi = 0$). *Prove also that* $\varphi\psi$ *has degree* $\leq m + n$ (*unless it is* 0), *and that if*

$$ab = 0 \quad \text{implies } a \text{ or } b = 0 \quad \text{for all } a, b \text{ in } S, \qquad (*)$$

then its degree is exactly $m + n$.

Corollary 1. *If* (*) *holds, any unit of the multiplicative semigroup* $S[x]$ *must have degree* 0.

Corollary 2. *If* (*) *holds and* φ *divides* ψ, *then the degree of* $\varphi \leq$ *that of* ψ.

Let $\varphi = \sum_{i=0}^{n} c_i x^i$ be in $S[x]$; then the function $\{(a, \sum_{i=0}^{n} c_i a^i) \mid a \in S\}$ from S into S is called a **polynomial function** on S. It is customary to denote both a polynomial and the polynomial function which it defines by the same symbol, relying on context to prevent confusion; thus $\varphi(a)$ would denote the image of a under the polynomial function φ. If $\varphi(a) = 0$, a is called a **root** of φ.

Exercise 4. *Generalize all of the foregoing by defining and describing semirings of power series and polynomials in* two *indeterminates.* [Hint: Use $(S^{N^\circ})^{N^\circ}$ and $(S[x])[x]$. We shall denote the semiring of polynomials in two indeterminates over S by $S[x, y]$.] *Generalize further to* n *indeterminates, and to an arbitrary set of indeterminates.*

MATRICES

Let $M_S^{(n)} = (S^n)^n$, the set of n-tuples whose terms are n-tuples of elements of S. The element

$$((a_{11}, \ldots, a_{1n}), (a_{21}, \ldots, a_{2n}), \ldots, (a_{n1}, \ldots, a_{nn}))$$

of $M_S^{(n)}$ will be denoted for brevity by $(a_{ij})^{(n)}$ [omitting the (n) if there is no doubt as to which n is meant], or more fully by

$$\begin{pmatrix} a_{11} & \cdots & a_{1n} \\ \vdots & & \vdots \\ a_{n1} & \cdots & a_{nn} \end{pmatrix},$$

and will be called an n-by-n **matrix** over S.

Let $F_{(n)}$ be the direct power composition of F on $M_S^{(n)}$; in other words, let $F_{(n)}((a_{ij}), (b_{ij})) = (a_{ij} + b_{ij})$. Let $G_{(n)}$ be the composition on $M_S^{(n)}$ defined by $G_{(n)}((a_{ij}), (b_{ij})) = (\sum_{k=1}^{n} a_{ik}b_{kj})$. It is easily verified that $M_S^{(n)}$ is a semiring under these compositions; it is called the semiring of n-by-n **matrices** over S. Clearly $M_S^{(1)} \cong S$. Moreover, if $0 \in S$ is absorbent for G, let $S_{(n)} = \{(a_{ij}) \mid a_{ij} = 0 \text{ if } i \neq j; a_{ii} = a, 1 \leq i \leq n, \text{ where } a \in S\}$; then readily the function which takes $a \in S$ into the element of $S_{(n)}$ just described is an isomorphism of S with $S_{(n)}$. The elements of $S_{(n)}$ are called n-by-n *scalar matrices* over S.

Exercise 5. *If S is commutative, so are the semirings S^{N° and $S[x]$, but not necessarily $M_S^{(n)}$ if $n > 1$.*

Exercise 6. *Let $M_S^{(n)*}$ be the semiring of n-by-n matrices over S under the compositions $F_{(n)}$ and $G_{(n)}^*$ (see Exercise 34.12); then $M_S^{(n)*} \cong M_S^{(n)}$.* [Hint: Use $\{((a_{ij}), (a_{ji})) \mid (a_{ij}) \in M_S^{(n)}\}$.]

59. RINGS, DOMAINS, AND FIELDS

A semiring R whose additive semigroup is an Abelian group is called a **ring**. If the multiplicative semigroup of R is commutative, we call R commutative; if there is an identity for multiplication, we say that R has (or is with) identity.

Examples:
(a) $\mathbf{I}$ under addition and multiplication is a commutative ring with identity.
(b) $\mathbf{I}_n$ under addition and multiplication modulo n is a commutative ring with identity.
(c) If R is a ring, so are R^{N°, $R[x]$, and $M_R^{(n)}$ (for any $n \in \mathbf{N}$); if R has identity, so have they.
(d) Let R be any Abelian group under F, and define G by $xy = 0$ for all x, y in R. [Such a ring is called a **zero-ring**; this example shows that any Abelian group is the additive group of a ring.]
(e) Let A be any Abelian group under $+$, and let $E(A)$ be the set of all endomorphisms of A. Define the composition $+$ on $E(A)$ by $(f + g)(x) = f(x) + g(x)$ for all f, g in $E(A)$ and all $x \in A$. Then $E(A)$ under $+$ and $\circ$ is a ring with identity.

By Proposition 57.3, the additive identity 0 of a ring is absorbent for multiplication, and so cannot be cancellable for multiplication unless the ring is trivial. If every element of R except 0 is cancellable for multiplication, we call R a **domain** (or sometimes more fully, an *integral domain* or *domain of integrity*).

Examples:
(a) $\mathbf{I}$ is a domain
(b) $\mathbf{I}_n$ is a domain if and only if $n = 1$ or is prime
(c) If R is a domain, so are R^{N° and $R[x]$, but not necessarily $M_R^{(n)}$ if $n > 1$.

Proposition 1. *The element a of the ring R is left cancellable if and only if it is not a left **divisor of zero**, that is, if and only if $ab = 0$ implies $b = 0$ for all $b \in R$.*

Proof: If $ab = 0$ and a is left cancellable, we have $ab = a0 = 0$, so that (cancelling a) $b = 0$. Conversely, if a is not a left zero-divisor and $ab = ac$, we have $a(b - c) = 0$, so that $b - c = 0$, that is, $b = c$, proving a left cancellable. //

Corollary. *The following statements about the ring R are equivalent:*
 (1) *R is a domain*
 (2) *R has no left or right divisors of zero other than 0*
 (3) *$R - \{0\}$ is a multiplicative subsemigroup of R.*

Again by Proposition 57.3, 0 cannot be invertible for multiplication except in a trivial ring. If R has a multiplicative identity $1 \neq 0$, and every element of R but 0 is invertible for multiplication, we call R a **division ring**. Note that since $1 \neq 0$, a division ring cannot be trivial; and conversely, by Exercise 31.6, nontriviality insures that $1 \neq 0$. A commutative division ring is called a **field**. [A division ring is sometimes called a *skew field*.]

Examples:
 (a) **R** is a field under addition and multiplication.
 (b) I_p is a field if p is prime.

Let S be a semiring with additive identity 0 and multiplicative identity $1 \neq 0$. If there is no $n \in \mathbf{N}$ such that $n1 = 0$ (where $n1$ denotes the sum of n 1's), we say that S has **characteristic** 0. If such n's do exist, let m be the smallest one; in this case we say that S has characteristic m.

Exercise 1. *Let S have characteristic m; then $n1 = 0$ if and only if m divides n.*

Exercise 2. *If 0 is absorbent for multiplication, then $n1 = 0$ if and only if n "annihilates" S, that is, $nx = 0$ for all $x \in S$.*

Corollary. *Let S have characteristic $\neq 0$; then 0 is absorbent for multiplication if and only if S is a ring.* [Note in particular that the characteristic of a ring is 2 if and only if $-x = x$ for all x.]

Proposition 2. *The characteristic of a domain is either 0, 1, or prime.*

Proof: Let the characteristic be $m \neq 0$, and let $m = rs$. Since $(rs)1 = (r1)(s1)$, by Proposition 1 we must have $r1 = 0$ or $s1 = 0$, so that by Exercise 1, m divides r or s. //

Exercise 3. *Let S be a commutative semiring of prime characteristic p; then for all $k \in \mathbf{N}$ and all a, b in S we have $(a + b)^{p^k} = a^{p^k} + b^{p^k}$.* [Hint: Prove that if p is prime and $0 < i < p^k$, then p divides $\binom{p^k}{i}$.]

Corollary 1. *$\{(a, a^{p^k}) \mid a \in S\}$ is a homomorphism.*

Corollary 2. *If S is also a ring and has no nilpotent elements (Exercise 34.7)* *except* 0, *then this homomorphism is an isomorphism. In particular, it is an isomorphism if S is a commutative domain.*

Let x, y be elements of the ring R; then $xy - yx$ is called the **commutator** of x and y, and is denoted by $[x, y]$. [Since R can never be a multiplicative group, and since its additive group is commutative, one need never consider "group commutators" of ring elements; thus there is no danger of confusion if we use the same notation and terminology for the "ring commutator" as just defined.]

Exercise 4. *Verify, for all x, y, z in R, that*

  (a) $[x, x] = 0$
  (b) $[x, y] + [y, x] = 0$
  (c) $[[x, y], z] + [[y, z], x] + [[z, x], y] = 0.$

Exercise 5. *Let g_a denote the function $\{(x, [x, a]) \mid x \in R\}$. Verify, using induction, that $g_a^n(x) = \sum_{i=0}^{n} (-1)^i \binom{n}{i} a^i x a^{n-i}$ for all $x \in R$ and all $n \in \mathbf{N}$.*

Corollary. *If R has prime characteristic p, then $g_a^{p^n}(x) = x a^{p^n} - a^{p^n} x$ for all $x \in R$ and all $n \in \mathbf{N}$.*

60. SUBRINGS

Since associativity and commutativity pass to restrictions of compositions, a subringoid of a semiring is a subsemiring.

Examples:
  (a) The subsemirings of a lattice are just its sublattices.
  (b) In a zero-semiring, any subsemigroup of the additive semigroup which contains 0 is a subsemiring.
  (c) S is isomorphic to a subsemiring of $S[x]$, which is in turn a subsemiring of $S^{\mathbf{N}^\circ}$; S is also isomorphic to a subsemiring of $M_S^{(n)}$ for any $n \in \mathbf{N}$.
  (d) If A is a subsemiring of S, then $A^{\mathbf{N}^\circ}$, $A[x]$ and $M_A^{(n)}$ are isomorphic to subsemirings of $S^{\mathbf{N}^\circ}$, $S[x]$, and $M_S^{(n)}$, respectively.

Let $\mathscr{S}_S$ be the complete lattice of subsemirings of S, and for any $A \subseteq S$, let (A) denote the subsemiring of S generated by A.

Proposition 1. $(A) = \{\sum_{i=1}^{m} (\prod_{j=1}^{n_i} a_{ij}) \mid m \in \mathbf{N}; \ n_i \in \mathbf{N}, \ 1 \le i \le m; \ each \ a_{ij} \in A\}.$

Proof: This set is readily stable under addition and multiplication (use the general associative and distributive laws), and contains A (take $m = n_1 = 1$), whereas any stable subset containing A must contain it.   //

Corollary 1. $(x) = \{\sum_{i=1}^{k} n_i x^i \mid k \in \mathbf{N};\, n_i \in \mathbf{N}^\circ,\, 1 \leq i \leq k;\, \text{not every } n_i = 0\}$, where "$0x^i$" means that there are no x^i's in the sum.

> Thus (x) can be described, informally, as the set of non-zero polynomials in x with nonnegative integer coefficients and without constant term. Note that Corollary 1 makes use of the commutativity of addition on S, but Proposition 1 does not.

Corollary 2. (x) is commutative.

Proposition 2. In a commutative semiring, $(A) = \{\sum_{i=1}^{m}(\prod_{j=1}^{n_i} a_{ij}^{k_{ij}}) \mid m$ and each n_i and k_{ij} in $\mathbf{N}$; each a_{ij} in A; $a_{i1}, \ldots, a_{in_i}$ distinct for any given $i\}$.

Corollary. If S has additive and multiplicative identities 0 and 1; A is a commutative subsemiring of S which contains 0 and 1; and $x \in S$ commutes with every element of A; then $(A \cup \{x\}) = \{\sum_{i=0}^{k} a_i x^i \mid k \in \mathbf{N}^\circ$; each $a_i \in A\}$, where x^0 denotes 1.

> Informally: $(A \cup \{x\})$ is the set of polynomials in x with coefficients in A.

SUBRINGS

Evidently a subsemiring of a ring is a ring if and only if it is a subgroup of the ring's additive group. [If not, it need not be a ring; for example, $\mathbf{N} \subset \mathbf{I}$.] A subsemiring which is a ring is called a **subring**. It follows from the corresponding facts about subgroups that the set of subrings of a ring R is a complete lattice $\mathscr{S}_R^*$ under the inclusion ordering, with least element $\{0\}$ and greatest element R. Clearly the subrings of a domain are domains ("subdomains"), and a subring of a division ring is a domain (but need not be a division ring; for example, $\mathbf{I} \subset \mathbf{R}$).

Exercise 1. Verify that the subrings of $\mathbf{I}$ are the same as the subgroups of its additive group, and similarly for $\mathbf{I}_n$. [Hint: Multiplication is repeated addition.]

Proposition 3. In a ring, the subring $(A) = \{\sum_{i=1}^{m}(\prod_{j=1}^{n_i} a_{ij}) \mid m \in \mathbf{N};\, n_i \in \mathbf{N},\, 1 \leq i \leq m;\, a_{ij} = 0$ or $a_{ij} \in A$ or $-a_{ij} \in A,\, 1 \leq i \leq m,\, 1 \leq j \leq n_i\}$.

Corollary 1. $(x) = \{\sum_{i=1}^{k} n_i x^i \mid k \in \mathbf{N};\, n_i \in \mathbf{I},\, 1 \leq i \leq k\}$.

Corollary 2. (x) is commutative.

Exercise 2. A ring whose additive group is cyclic is commutative. In fact, if the additive groupoid of a ringoid is monogenic, its multiplicative groupoid is commutative.

Proposition 4. In a commutative ring, $(A) = \{\sum_{i=1}^{m}(\prod_{j=1}^{n_i} a_{ij}^{k_{ij}}) \mid m$ and each n_i in $\mathbf{N}$; each k_{ij} in $\mathbf{N}^\circ$; a_{ij} or $-a_{ij}$ in A for each (i, j); $a_{i1}, \ldots, a_{in_i}$ distinct, and none of them the negative of any other, for any given $i\}$.

Corollary. *In a ring with identity, if A is a commutative subring containing* 1, *and x commutes with every element of A, then* $(A \cup \{x\})$ *is the same as the subsemiring* $(A \cup \{x\})$. *In fact, in a ring with identity, if A is any subset containing* -1, *then the subring* (A) *is the same as the subsemiring* (A).

A subring A of a division ring D is a division ring if and only if $A - \{0\}$ is a subgroup of the multiplicative group $D - \{0\}$. [Note that this requires $A - \{0\}$ to be nonempty, so that A is nontrivial.] Since the division subrings of D all contain 0 and 1, the set of them is closed under intersection and so is a complete lattice under the inclusion ordering. This lattice has greatest element D; we shall defer describing its least element, which is the division subring generated by 0 and 1, until Chapter XII, when we discuss prime rings.

Exercise 3. *State and prove analogs of Propositions 3–4 and their corollaries about the division subring (subfield) of a division ring (field) generated by a given subset.*

Exercise 4. *Let x be an element of the semiring S, and let $C(x)$ be the set of elements of S which commute with x; this set is called the* **centralizer** *of x. [In short: $C(x)$ is the same as the centralizer of x in the multiplicative semigroup of S.] Prove that $C(x)$ is a subsemiring, and that if S is a ring or division ring, so is $C(x)$. State and verify semiring and ring analogs of the other observations made in Section 41 about centralizers in semigroups and groups.*

IDEALS

A subset of the ring R is called a (left, right) **ideal** if it is a subgroup of the additive group of R and a (left, right) ideal of the multiplicative semigroup of R. Evidently a left or right ideal is a subring.

Exercise 5. *Let L be a left ideal of the multiplicative semigroup of R, and let $\bar{L} = \{\sum_{i=1}^{k} x_i \mid k \in \mathbf{N}, \text{ the x's in } L\}$; then $\bar{L}$ is a left ideal of R (and evidently is the smallest one containing L), and similarly for right and two-sided ideals.*

Corollary. *A principal left (right) ideal of the multiplicative semigroup of R is a left (right) ideal of R.*

Exercise 6. *If R is a commutative ring with identity, A is an ideal of the multiplicative semigroup of R if and only if it is empty or a union of ideals of R.*

Exercise 7. *Ideals, subrings, and subgroups of the additive group are all the same for a zero-ring, for $\mathbf{I}$, or for $\mathbf{I}_n$.*

Exercise 8. *R is a domain if and only if the ideal $\{0\}$ is prime.*

Since any intersection of ideals is evidently an ideal, the set of ideals of R is a complete lattice $\mathscr{J}_R$ under the inclusion ordering, with least element $\{0\}$ and greatest element R.

Exercise 9. $\mathscr{J}_R$ *is a sublattice of* $\mathscr{S}_R^*$, *and similarly for the complete lattices of left and right ideals of R.* [Hint: The sup of the (left, right) ideals A and B is just $A + B$.]

Exercise 10. *If R is commutative, (x) in $\mathscr{J}_R$ is $\{ax + nx \mid a \in R, n \in \mathbf{I}\}$.*

Corollary 1. *If R also has identity, $(x) = Rx$.*

Corollary 2. *In a commutative ring R with identity, (S) in $\mathscr{J}_R$ is*

$$\left\{ \sum_{i=1}^{k} a_i s_i \mid k \in \mathbf{N}, \text{ the } a_i\text{'s in } R, \text{ the } s_i\text{'s in } S \right\}.$$

Proposition 5. *The only left or right ideals in a division ring R are $\{0\}$ and R.*

Proof: If I is an ideal of R, then $I - \{0\}$ is an ideal of the multiplicative group $R - \{0\}$. Thus by Exercise 37.1, $I - \{0\}$ is $\varnothing$ or $R - \{0\}$, so that I is $\{0\}$ or R. //

An element or subset of a ring is called nilpotent if it is nilpotent in the multiplicative semigroup (see Exercises 34.7–8).

Exercise 11. *In a domain, $\{0\}$ is the only nilpotent subset. In a commutative ring, the set of nilpotent elements is an ideal.* [Hint: If $a^m = 0$ and $b^n = 0$, then $(a + b)^{m+n} = 0$ by the binomial theorem.]

Proposition 6. *If I and J are nilpotent left ideals in a ring, so is $I + J$.*

Proof: Let $I^m = J^n = \{0\}$. Every term z of an element of $(I + J)^{m+n}$ contains either at least m factors in I or at least n factors in J, say the former: $z = y_1 x_1 y_2 x_2 \cdots y_m x_m z'$, where the x's are in I, the y's in J, and some of the y's may be missing. Since I is a left ideal, we have $y_i x_i \in I$, $1 \le i \le m$; hence $z \in I^m z' = \{0\}$. //

Corollary 1. *If $I_1, \ldots, I_n$ are nilpotent left ideals, so is $I_1 + \cdots + I_n$.*

Corollary 2. *If $\mathscr{A}$ is a set of nilpotent left ideals, every element of the left ideal generated by $\bigcup_{\mathscr{A}} A$ is nilpotent.*

Proposition 7. *If L is a nilpotent left ideal of the multiplicative semigroup of R, and $\bar{L}$ is the left ideal of R generated by L (Exercise 5), then $\bar{L}$ is also nilpotent.*

FIELDS OF QUOTIENTS

Theorem 1. *Let R be a nontrivial commutative domain; then there exists a field K, and an isomorphism F of R into K, such that every element of K is a quotient of elements of $F(R)$.* [K is called the **field of quotients** of R.]

216 X: RINGS

Proof: $R - \{0\}$ is a nonempty commutative cancellation semigroup under multiplication; hence we can apply Theorem 36.1 to "embed" it, via the isomorphism F' (say), into its group of quotients G. Let $K = G \cup \{0\}$, where we define $0x = x0 = 00 = 0$ for all $x \in G$, and let $F = F' \cup \{(0, 0)\}$; thus F is an isomorphism of the multiplicative semigroup R into the multiplicative semigroup K, and $0 = 0/F'(a) = F(0)/F(a)$ is a quotient of elements of $F(R)$, where a is any element of $R - \{0\}$. Moreover, if we "extend" addition to K as in Exercise 36.7, then readily K is a field under addition and multiplication, and F is also a homomorphism of the additive group of R into that of K. //

Exercise 12. *The field of quotients of* **I** *is isomorphic to* **R**.

The field of quotients of $K[x]$, where K is a field, is called the field of **rational functions** in one indeterminate over K, and is denoted by $K(x)$.

Exercise 13. *Let D be a division ring, and R a nontrivial commutative subring of D; then D has a subfield isomorphic to the field of quotients of R.*

Exercise 14. *Isomorphic domains have isomorphic fields of quotients.*

Exercise 15. *A field is isomorphic to its own field of quotients.*

61. RESIDUE RINGS AND DIRECT SUMS OF RINGS

A homomorphic image or quotient ringoid of a ring is evidently a ring. [We shall call a "quotient ring" a **residue ring** to avoid confusion with "field of quotients"; it is sometimes called a *factor ring* or *difference ring*.] As in the case of groups, we can give a very explicit description of the congruences on a ring. Let E be a congruence on the ring R; then, in particular, E is a congruence on the additive group of R, so that we have $E = L_{E_0} = R_{E_0}$, where E_0 is a subgroup of the additive group (it is automatically normal since this group is Abelian). [Note that in additive notation, $L_A = \{(x, y) \mid y \in x + A\}$, that is, $(x, y) \in L_A$ if and only if $y - x \in A$.] Since E is also a congruence on the multiplicative semigroup of R, we must also in particular have $(ax, 0y)$ and $(xa, y0)$ in E whenever $(a, 0)$ and (x, y) are in E. Since $0y = y0 = 0$, this means that $a \in E_0$ implies $ax \in E_0$ and $xa \in E_0$ for all $x \in R$—in other words, E_0 must be an ideal. Conversely, if A is any ideal of R, then $L_A = R_A$ is an additive congruence since A is a (normal) additive subgroup; moreover, if $a - b \in A$ and $c - d \in A$, we have $(a - b)d$ and $a(c - d)$ in A, so that $(a - b)d + a(c - d) = ac - bd$ is in A, making L_A a multiplicative congruence. We have thus proved

Theorem 1. *If E is any congruence on the ring R, then $E = L_{E_0} = R_{E_0}$, where E_0 is an ideal of R. Conversely, if A is any ideal of R, then $L_A = R_A$ is a congruence on R, and A is its kernel.*

[Note that the proof made no use of the associativity of multiplication.] It follows that analogs of all the results of Section 38 hold for rings (Exercise: State and verify them). In particular, the lattice of congruences $\mathscr{C}_R$ is order isomorphic to the lattice of ideals $\mathscr{J}_R$. As in the case of groups, we denote the residue ring R/L_A by R/A.

Corollary 1. *The only congruences on a division ring D are $D \times D$ and I_D.*

Corollary 2. *Any homomorphism of a division ring is either a constant function or an isomorphism.*

Corollary 3. *Any congruence on the ring $\mathbf{I}$ is congruence modulo m for some $m \in \mathbf{N}°$; any homomophic image of $\mathbf{I}$ is isomorphic to $\mathbf{I}$ itself or to $\mathbf{I}_m$ for some $m \in \mathbf{N}$.*

Exercise 1. *The residue ring R/A is a domain if and only if the ideal A is prime.* [Hint: See Exercise 60.8.]

Since $\mathscr{J}_R$ is a sublattice of $\mathscr{S}_R^*$, it follows that $\mathscr{C}_R$ is a sublattice of the lattice of congruences on the additive group of R. In particular, all congruences on R commute, and $\mathscr{C}_R$ and $\mathscr{J}_R$ are modular. Hence analogs of the results of Section 28 hold for rings.

Finally, we consider direct sums of rings, for which we use additive notation. Let $R \cong \sum_I R_i$; since R has the trivial subring $\{0\}$, there exist ideals of R isomorphic to the R_i, and the set of these (discarding trivial ones) is independent in $\mathscr{J}_R$ and (if finite) has R as its sup. Conversely, using Exercise 60.9 we immediately have the analog of Proposition 40.1 for $\mathscr{J}_R$, while the analog of Proposition 40.2 is trivial since the additive group is commutative. This gives us

Proposition 1. *Let $\mathscr{A}$ be a set of ideals of the ring R such that $A \cap \sup\{\mathscr{A} - \{A\}\} = \{0\}$ for all $A \in \mathscr{A}$; then $\sup \mathscr{A}$ is isomorphic to the weak direct sum of $\mathscr{A}$.*

We can also prove analogs of the remaining results of Section 40 (and 39) for rings.

Exercise 2. *A left ideal of a supplemented ideal of the ring R is a left ideal of R.*

Direct sums are useless in the study of division rings, or even domains, by virtue of

Proposition 2. *A direct sum of rings is a domain if and only if every summand but one is trivial, and that one is a domain.*

Proof: In $\sum_I R_i$, if R_j and R_k are nontrivial, say R_j contains $x_j \neq 0$ and R_k contains $y_k \neq 0$, let $x_i = 0$ for all $i \in I - \{j\}$ and $y_i = 0$ for all $i \in I - \{k\}$; then $(x_i)_I \neq 0$ and $(y_i)_I \neq 0$, but $(x_i)_I(y_i)_I = 0$, so that $\sum_I R_i$ has zero-divisors and cannot be a domain. If only one R_j is nontrivial, we have $\sum_I R_i \cong R_j$, so that $\sum_I R_i$ is a domain if and only if R_j is. //

Corollary. *A domain is indecomposable.*

62. DIVISION IN RINGS

The commutative ring R will be called **Euclidean** if there exists a function F from R into $\mathbf{N}^\circ$ such that

(*) For all $b \neq 0$ in R, and all $a \in R$, $\notin bR$, there exist q, r in R such that $a = qb + r$ and $F(r) < F(b)$.

Examples:

(a) $\mathbf{I}$ is Euclidean—indeed, we can take $F(n) = |n|$ (that is, $= n$ if $n \geq 0$, and $= -n$ if $n < 0$) and apply Exercise 36.4.

(b) If K is a field, $K[x]$ is Euclidean. [Proof: Take $F(\varphi) = $ the degree of φ (0, if $\varphi = 0$). Then for any $\varphi = \sum_{i=0}^m a_i x^i$ and $\psi = \sum_{i=1}^n b_i x^i \neq 0$, if $m < n$, take $q = 0, r = \varphi$. If $m \geq n$, let $\varphi_1 = \varphi - a_m b_n^{-1} x^{m-n} \psi$; thus φ_1 has degree $< m$. If this degree is $< n$, take $q = a_m b_n^{-1} x^{m-n}, r = \varphi_1$. If not, we can repeat the process, subtracting a further multiple of ψ from φ_1 to obtain φ_2 of still lower degree; and so on. Since a descending chain of degrees is impossible, we must eventually obtain an $r = \varphi_k = \varphi_{k-1} - q_{k-1}\psi = \cdots = \varphi - q\psi$ (say), where r has degree $< n$, as required.]

It is easily verified that in a Euclidean ring one can "construct" a greatest common divisor of any two nonzero elements by a procedure analogous to that used in the proof of Proposition 11.1. [This procedure is called the **Euclidean algorithm**.] It follows that in such a ring there exists a greatest common divisor d of a and b which is in the ideal generated by a and b—i.e., such that $d = ra + sb$, where r, s are in R (compare Proposition 36.2). We apply this to prove

Proposition 1. *Let R be a commutative ring, and A a Euclidean subdomain of R. Let a, b be elements of A, and let $d \in A$ be a greatest common divisor of a and b; then d is still a greatest common divisor of a and b when they are regarded as elements of R.*

Proof: Let $d^* \in A$ be the greatest common divisor of a and b constructed by the Euclidean algorithm. In R, d^* is still a common divisor of a and b, and by the proof of Proposition 36.2, it must be a greatest common divisor. Since A is a domain, by Proposition 35.3 we have $d = ud^*$, where u is a unit; thus $dR = d^*R$, so that d is also a greatest common divisor of a and b in R. //

In short, if A is Euclidean, passage to a bigger ring cannot
yield "better" greatest common divisors for elements of
A than those already in A itself.

In particular, if a and b have a nonunit greatest common divisor in R, they
must already have one in A.

The commutative ring R is called **principal** if every ideal of R is a principal
ideal.

Proposition 2. *A Euclidean ring is principal.*

Proof: Let I be any ideal of R, and let $F(b)$ be the smallest nonnegative
integer in $F(I - \{0\})$. If any $a \in I$ is not in bR, by (*) we have $a = qb + r$
with $F(r) < F(b)$. Since $r = a - qb$ is in I, this contradicts the minimality
of $F(b)$ unless $r = 0$; but then $a = qb$ is in bR, contradiction, which proves
that $I = bR$ is principal. $/\!/$

Exercise 1. *A subring of a Euclidean ring need not be Euclidean.*

Exercise 2. *A principal ring has identity.* [Hint: Proposition 34.7.]

If R is a domain, $R' = R - \{0\}$ is a multiplicative semigroup; we call R
Gaussian if R' is Gaussian.

Proposition 3. *A principal domain is Gaussian.*

Proof: The ideals of any ring are closed under intersection and (readily)
union of chains. Hence if R is principal, the same is true for the principal
ideals of R', so that R' is a PL-semigroup; now use the corollary to Proposition
35.15. $/\!/$

Corollary. I *and* $K[x]$ *are Gaussian, where* K *is any field.*

The following exercises relate to division in $K[x]$:

Exercise 3. φ *is a unit of* $K[x]$ *if and only if it has degree* 0 (*that is, is a nonzero
constant polynomial*).

Exercise 4. *If* φ, ψ *are in* $K[x]$ *and* $\{0\} \subset \psi K[x] \subset \varphi K[x]$, *then the degree of*
φ *is strictly less than that of* ψ.

Exercise 5. *If* $\varphi \in K[x]$, *and* $a \in K$ *is a root of* φ, *then* $x - a$ *divides* φ. [Hint:
Let $\varphi = q(x - a) + r$ and substitute a for x (Exercise 58.2).]

Corollary. *If* $\varphi \neq 0$ *has n roots, then* φ *has degree* $\geq n$.

Exercise 6. *If* $(x - a)^2$ *divides* $\varphi = \sum_{i=0}^{n} a_i x^i$, *then* $x - a$ *divides*

$$\varphi' = \sum_{i=0}^{n} i a_i x^{i-1}.$$

Exercise 7. *Let L be a field, K a subfield of L; let ψ, φ, θ, where $\varphi \neq 0$, be in $L[x]$ and $\psi = \varphi\theta$; and let the coefficients of ψ and φ be in K. Then the coefficients of θ are also in K.* [Hint: Let x^j be the highest power of x whose coefficient in θ is not in K; let m be the degree of φ; and consider the coefficient of x^{m+j} in $\theta\varphi$.]

In the remainder of this section we show that if R is a Gaussian domain, so is the polynomial domain $R[x]$. It follows in particular that if K is a field, the domain $K[x, y]$ of polynomials in two indeterminates over K is Gaussian, since $K[x]$ is. Since $K[x, y]$ is certainly not principal (for example, consider the ideal generated by x and y), this shows that there exist Gaussian domains which are not principal.

Let R be a Gaussian domain, and let $\varphi = \sum_{i=0}^{n} a_i x^i$ be a nonzero polynomial in $R[x]$. Let d be a greatest common divisor of $a_0, \ldots, a_n$; the principal ideal dR will be called the **content** of φ [notation: $c(\varphi)$]. If $c(\varphi) = R$, we call φ **primitive**.

Exercise 8. *If $\varphi = a$ is a constant polynomial, then $c(\varphi) = aR$.*

Exercise 9. *$c(\varphi\psi) \subseteq c(\varphi)c(\psi)$ for all φ, ψ in $R[x]$.*

Exercise 10. *$c(\varphi) = dR$ if and only if $\varphi = d\varphi_0$, where φ_0 is primitive.*

Proposition 4 (Gauss' lemma). *$\varphi\psi$ is primitive if and only if φ and ψ are primitive.*

Proof: If $\varphi\psi$ is primitive we have $R = c(\varphi\psi) \subseteq c(\varphi)c(\psi) \subseteq c(\varphi) \cap c(\psi)$, so that $c(\varphi) = c(\psi) = R$, proving "only if." Conversely, let φ and ψ be primitive, and suppose that $\varphi\psi$ is not, so that some irreducible nonunit $p \in R$ divides every coefficient of $\varphi\psi$. Since φ and ψ are primitive, p fails to divide some nonzero coefficient of each of them. Let x^r, x^s be the highest powers of x in φ, ψ, respectively, whose coefficients $\neq 0$ and are not divisible by p. Then the coefficient of x^{r+s} in $\varphi\psi$ readily cannot be divisible by p, contradiction.   //

Corollary 1. *$\varphi_1 \cdots \varphi_n$ is primitive if and only if each φ_i is.*

Corollary 2. *$c(\varphi\psi) = c(\varphi)c(\psi)$ for all φ, ψ in $R[x]$.*

Proof: Let $c(\varphi) = aR$, $c(\psi) = bR$, and let $\varphi = a\varphi_0$, $\psi = b\psi_0$, so that φ_0 and ψ_0 are primitive by Exercise 10. Then $\varphi\psi = ab\varphi_0\psi_0$, where $\varphi_0\psi_0$ is primitive by Gauss' lemma, so that by Exercise 10,

$$c(\varphi\psi) = abR = aRbR = c(\varphi)c(\psi). \quad //$$

Corollary 3. *$c(\varphi_1 \cdots \varphi_n) = c(\varphi_1) \cdots c(\varphi_n)$.*

Proposition 5. *Let R be a Gaussian domain, K its field of quotients; we regard $R[x]$ as a subdomain of $K[x]$. Let φ be a nonzero polynomial in $R[x]$; then*

φ *has degree* > 0 *and is irreducible in* $R[x]$ *if and only if it is primitive and an irreducible nonunit in* $K[x]$.

Proof: If φ is a nonunit in $K[x]$, it has degree > 0 (Exercise 3). Let φ be primitive and irreducible in $K[x]$, and suppose that $\varphi = \varphi_1\varphi_2$, where φ_1 and φ_2 are in $R[x]$. By the irreducibility of φ in $K[x]$, φ_1 or φ_2 (say the former) must be a unit in $K[x]$, that is, must have degree 0, say $\varphi_1 = a_1 \in R$. Hence $\varphi = a_1\varphi_2$, so that $c(\varphi) \subseteq a_1R$; but since φ is primitive, this implies $a_1R = R$, so that $\varphi_1 = a_1$ is a unit.

Conversely, if φ has degree > 0 and is irreducible in $R[x]$, let $\varphi = d\varphi_0$, where φ_0 is primitive. Since φ_0 has the same degree as φ, it cannot be a unit; hence d is a unit, so that $c(\varphi) = dR = R$, proving φ primitive. Suppose that φ were reducible in $K[x]$, say $\varphi = \varphi_1\varphi_2$, where neither factor is a unit, so that they each have degree > 0. Since every coefficient of φ_1 is a quotient of elements of R, there exists $a_1 \in R$ (for example, the product of the denominators of the coefficients of φ_1) such that $a_1\varphi_1 \in R[x]$, and similarly there exists $a_2 \in R$ such that $a_2\varphi_2 \in R[x]$. Let $a_1\varphi_1 = c_1\varphi_{10}, a_2\varphi_2 = c_2\varphi_{20}$, where φ_{10} and φ_{20} are in $R[x]$ and primitive, evidently with the same positive degrees as φ_1 and φ_2, respectively; thus we have $a_1a_2\varphi = c_1c_2\varphi_{10}\varphi_{20} = \psi$ (say). Since by Gauss' lemma $\varphi_{10}\varphi_{20}$ is primitive, the content of ψ is c_1c_2R; but since φ is primitive, this content is a_1a_2R. Hence there exists a unit $u \in R$ such that $c_1c_2 = ua_1a_2$, that is, $a_1a_2\varphi = ua_1a_2\varphi_{10}\varphi_{20}$. Cancelling a_1a_2, we have $\varphi = u\varphi_{10}\varphi_{20}$, where $u\varphi_{10}$ and φ_{20} are polynomials in $R[x]$ of degrees > 0, so that neither of them is a unit, and φ is reducible in $R[x]$, contradiction. //

We can now prove

Theorem 1. *If the domain R is Gaussian, so is $R[x]$.*

Proof: Let $\varphi_0 \in R[x]$ be primitive; then any nonunit divisor of φ_0 must have degree > 0, so that (using induction on the degree of φ_0) φ_0 is a finite product of irreducible polynomials $\varphi_{01}\cdots\varphi_{0m}$ of degrees > 0. By Proposition 5, the φ_{0i} are irreducible nonunits in $K[x]$, and since $K[x]$ is Gaussian, it follows that if $\varphi_0 = \psi_{01}\cdots\psi_{0n}$ is another such factorization, then $m = n$ and (permuting the ψ's as necessary) $\psi_{0i} = (a_i/b_i)\varphi_{0i}$, $1 \le i \le n$, where a_i, b_i are in R. Since φ_{0i} and ψ_{0i}, as divisors of φ_0, are both primitive, this implies that $b_iR = c(b_i\psi_{0i}) = c(a_i\varphi_{0i}) = a_iR$, so that $a_i = u_ib_i$ for some unit $u_i \in R$. Hence $\psi_{0i} = u_i\varphi_{0i}$, that is, the φ_{0i}'s are uniquely determined "up to units in $R[x]$."

To complete the proof, note that clearly the Gaussian property holds for polynomials in $R[x]$ of degree 0, since they can be regarded as elements of R, and any divisor of a polynomial of degree 0 also has degree 0. Hence for any $\varphi \in R[x]$ we have $\varphi = d\varphi_0$, where d has unique factorization in $R[x]$ since it has degree 0, and φ_0 has unique factorization in $R[x]$ by the first paragraph of the proof since it is primitive. Since d and φ_0 are determined "up to units in R" (Exercise 10), this implies that φ has unique factorization in $R[x]$. //

XI

VECTOR SPACES

63. EXTERNAL COMPOSITIONS

Up to this point we have not given much consideration to compositions which are not binary. In this chapter we consider *sets of unary compositions*. We recall that a unary composition on the set S is just a function from S into S (or, strictly speaking, from S^1 into S, but we can, as usual, identify S^1 with S).

Let U be a set of unary compositions on the set S, and let F be the function from $U \times S$ into S defined by $F(u, x) = u(x)$ for all $u \in U$ and all $x \in S$. Evidently, specifying F is equivalent to specifying all the functions $u \in U$. Thus any *set* U of unary compositions on S can be defined by a *single* function F from $U \times S$ into S; this function can be thought of as a sort of generalized *binary* composition. We call such an F an **external composition** of U with S. [The word "external" can usually be omitted without danger of confusion. For purposes of contrast, a composition *on* S is sometimes referred to as "internal."] The concept of an external composition provides a concise vehicle for discussing sets of unary compositions.

> One could also consider the function G from $S \times U$ into S, defined by $G(x, u) = u(x)$, as an external composition of U with S "on the right." Under certain circumstances it is useful to work with both left-handed and right-handed external compositions, but we shall have no need to do so in this book.

Examples:

(a) Let S be a groupoid under the composition F; let S' be any subset of S; and let F' be obtained from F by restricting its first argument to S'—in other words, $F' = \{((x, y), z) \mid ((x, y), z) \in F; x \in S'\}$. Then F'

222

is a composition of S' with S. [Note in particular that F itself can be regarded as an "external" composition of S with itself.]

Familiar examples of external compositions of this type include multiplication of power series or polynomials by constants, and of matrices by scalars.

(b) More generally, let S be a groupoid under F, let T be any set, and let H be any function from T into S. Let F_H be the function from $T \times S$ into S defined by $F_H(t, s) = F(H(t), s)$; then F_H is a composition of T with S. [To see that this is a generalization of Example (a), take $T \subseteq S$, and let H be the "embedding" function of T into S.]

(c) Let S be a semigroup under a multiplicative composition; then $\{((n, x), x^n) \mid x \in S, n \in \mathbf{N}\}$ is a composition of $\mathbf{N}$ with S. Similarly, if S is a group, then $\{((n, x), x^n) \mid x \in S, n \in \mathbf{I}\}$ is a composition of $\mathbf{I}$ with S.

(d) Let F be a composition of T with S, and for any $m \in \mathbf{N}$, define the function $F^{(m)}$ from $T \times S^m$ into S^m by

$$F^{(m)}(t, (s_1, \ldots, s_m)) = (F(t, s_1), \ldots, F(t, s_m));$$

then $F^{(m)}$ is a composition of T with $S^{(m)}$.

In particular, we can take $T = S$. This example generalizes the familiar multiplication of "vectors"—regarded as m-tuples of "scalars"—by "scalars."

(e) Let F be a composition of T with S, and define the function F^* from $T \times \mathscr{P}_S$ into $\mathscr{P}_S$ by $F^*(t, A) = \{F(t, a) \mid a \in A\}$ for all $t \in T$ and all $A \subseteq S$; then F^* is a composition of T with $\mathscr{P}_S$. [Here too we can have $T = S$.] Similarly, define the function $\bar{F}$ from $\mathscr{P}_T \times \mathscr{P}_S$ into $\mathscr{P}_S$ by $\bar{F}(V, A) = \{F(v, a) \mid v \in V, a \in A\}$ for all $V \subseteq T$ and all $A \subseteq S$; then $\bar{F}$ is a composition of $\mathscr{P}_T$ with $\mathscr{P}_S$.

Let F be a composition of T with S. We say that S is a **set with operators** under F, and call T the **set of operators** of F. In what follows we shall denote F multiplicatively.

Since F can be regarded as a set of unary compositions on S, a set with operators is a special type of universal algebra. We can thus speak about subalgebras, homomorphisms, quotient algebras, and direct products of sets with operators. For convenience, we state the key definitions in external composition terminology:

(1) $A \subseteq S$ is **stable** under F provided that $ta \in A$ for all $t \in T$ and all $a \in A$ —in other words, provided that $\bar{F}(T, A) \subseteq A$ [Example (e) above].

(2) The equivalence E on S is a **congruence** for F provided that $(x, y) \in E$ implies $(tx, ty) \in E$ for all $t \in T$ and all x, y in S.

(3) Let F, G be compositions of T with A, B, respectively, both denoted multiplicatively. Then the function H from A into B is an (F, G)-**homomorphism** provided that $H(ta) = tH(a)$ for all $t \in T$ and all $a \in A$. [One can also define a homomorphism concept for the general case where the sets of operators are not the same, but we shall not need this concept here.]

(4) If $(S_i)_I$ is an I-tuple of sets, and F_i is a composition of T with S_i, then F defined by $F(t, (x_i)_I) = (F_i(t, x_i))_I$ for all $t \in T$ and all $(x_i)_I \in \prod_I S_i$ is a composition of T with $\prod_I S_i$ (compare Example (d) above).

Let F be a composition of T with S. We call $t \in T$ an **identity** for F if $ts = s$ for all $s \in S$—in other words, if the unary composition t is the identity function I_S. [Note that for an external composition, this "left" identity is the only possible type; there is no way for an element of s to be a "right" identity for F. Analogous remarks apply to the definitions which follow.] We call $s \in S$ **absorbent** for F if $ts = s$ for all $t \in T$—in other words, if it is left fixed by every unary composition in T. We call $t \in T$ **cancellable** for F if $tx = ty$ implies $x = y$ for all x, y in S—in other words, if the unary composition t is one-to-one; and we call $s \in S$ cancellable for F if $us = vs$ implies $u = v$ for all u, v in T. Evidently an identity is cancellable, and an absorbent element can be cancellable only if T is trivial. There is little else that we can say about these concepts unless we introduce additional assumptions about S or T, which we proceed to do in the next two sections.

64. DISTRIBUTIVITY AND RELATED PROPERTIES

In Chapter X, when we studied algebraic structures involving two compositions on a set S, we assumed that the compositions were related by the property of distributivity. In this section we introduce some useful relationships which can hold between an external composition of T with S and internal compositions on T and on S. We begin by considering three examples, based on our standard examples of external compositions (Section 63), in which most or all of the relationships to be defined below are satisfied:

(a) Let S be a ringoid under the additive composition F and *associative* multiplicative composition G which distributes over F. Let T be a subringoid of S; let f, g be the restrictions of F, G to T; and let G' be the composition of T with S derived from G as in Example (a), Section 63. [Familiar special cases: (1) Let S be the ring of n-by-n matrices over a ring R, and let T be its subring of scalar matrices, so that $T \cong R$. Then F and G are addition and multiplication of matrices; f and g can be regarded as the addition and multiplication on R; and G' is multiplication of matrices by scalars. (2) Similarly, if S is the ring of polynomials over R, and $T \simeq R$ is the subring of constant poly-nomials.] Then the following relationships hold between the external composition G' and the internal compositions F, G, f, g:

(α) $t(x + y) = tx + ty$
(β) $t(xy) = (tx)y$
(γ) $(u + v)x = ux + vx$
(δ) $(uv)x = u(vx)$

for all t, u, v in T and all x, y in S. In fact, these properties are just special cases of the distributivity of G over F and the associativity of G. [If every $t \in T$ commutes under G with every $x \in S$, as is true in the cases of polynomials and matrices if R is commutative, we also have

(β′) $(tx)y = x(ty)$

for all $t \in T$ and all x, y in S.]

(b) Let S be as in Example (c), Section 63; then the laws of exponents (Exercises 33.3–4) hold:

(α) $(xy)^n = x^n y^n$, provided that the composition on S is com-mutative
(γ) $x^{m+n} = x^m x^n$
(δ) $x^{mn} = (x^n)^m$

for all m, n in $\mathbf{N}$ and all x, y in S. These laws are evidently just (α, γ, δ) of Example (a), rewritten in multiplicative notation.

(c) Let T be a ringoid under F and G, where G is associative; let $S = T^m$; let F_m, G_m be the mth direct power compositions of F, G, respectively, on T^m; and let $G^{(m)}$ be the composition of T with S defined from G as in Example (d), Section 63. Then (α − δ) hold for $G^{(m)}$ and the internal compositions F_m, G_m, F, G; and (β′) also holds if G is commutative.

We now give the general definitions suggested by these examples. In what follows, F, G are compositions on S; f, g are compositions on T; and H is a composition of T with S. We denote F and f additively, and G, g, and H multiplicatively; there need be no confusion as long as we know which arguments are elements of S and which are elements of T.

We say that H *distributes over* F if (α) holds. [Note that this is equivalent to saying that each unary composition t is an endomorphism of the groupoid S under F.]

Exercise 1. *Verify that the analog of Proposition 57.3 holds for F and H.*

We say that H *associates with* G if (β) holds, and that H *commutes with* G, if (β′) holds.

Exercise 2. *If H associates with G, an element of S which is absorbent for G is absorbent for H.*

Exercise 3. *If H associates with G, and there is a left identity for G, then each unary composition t is a "left G-translation"—in other words, for each $t \in T$ there exists an $x_t \in S$ such that $ty = x_t y$ for all $y \in S$.*

[This exercise shows that if there is a left identity for G, Example (a) of "associates with" is actually quite general, since H must be the same as G with its first argument restricted to a subset of S.]

Exercise 4. *If G is commutative and H associates with G, then H commutes with G.*

Exercise 5. *If H associates and commutes with G, and e is an identity for G, then every $t \in T$ is a left G-translation by an element which commutes (under G) with every element of S.*

We say that H *distributes over* (f, F) if (γ) holds.

Exercise 6. *Prove analogs of Propositions 57.5–6 for H distributing over F and over (f, F).*

Exercise 7. *Let H distribute over (f, F); let every element of S be right cancellable for F; let d be idempotent for f, and let e be a left identity for F. Then $dx = e$ for all $x \in S$; in particular, e is unique.*

Finally, we say that H *associates over g* if (δ) holds. [Note that this is equivalent to saying that g is composition of functions—*in reverse order*—on the set of unary compositions T.]

Exercise 8. *A composition associates over or with itself if and only if it is associative. Need an associative composition which commutes with itself be commutative?*

Exercise 9. *State and prove general associative, commutative, or distributive laws, as appropriate, for the relationships among compositions defined in this section.*

Exercise 10. *Let H associate over g, and let $a \in T$ be right absorbent for g; then for all $x \in S$, ax is absorbent for H.*

Note that if H associates over g, and $e \in T$ is a left identity for g, then $ex = x$ for all $x \in \overline{H}(T, S)$, since $e(ts) = (et)s = ts$, but this does not make e an identity for H, since H may not be onto. If an identity for g *is* an identity for H, we say that H is g-**unitary**. It may be verified that this property holds for the second and third examples considered at the beginning of this section.

65. GROUPOIDS AND GROUPS WITH OPERATORS

If H is a composition of T with S, where S and T are groupoids or bigroupoids, one could define many different special types of algebraic structures by assuming that various combinations of $(\alpha-\delta)$ hold, in conjunction with various combinations of properties of the internal compositions on S and T. However, only a few of these possible special types have received special names or have been studied to any extent. In the following paragraphs we introduce the nomenclature used for some of the particularly interesting cases.

GROUPOIDS WITH OPERATORS

Let S be a groupoid under F, and let H be a composition of the set T with S which distributes over F. In this situation we say that S is a **groupoid with operators** under F and H. The groupoid S is called the **underlying groupoid**, and the set T the **set of operators**, of the groupoid with operators S. If the groupoid S has special properties, we speak of the groupoid with operators as having the properties; for examples, if S is a group under F, we call it a **group with operators** under F and H.

Examples:

(a) Let S be a ringoid under F and G, and let T be any subset of S; then S is a groupoid with operators under F and G', where G' is as defined at the beginning of Section 64.

(b) Let S be a groupoid under F, let T be any set, and define the composition H of T with S by $tx = x$ for all $t \in T$ and all $x \in S$; then S is a groupoid with operators under F and H.

(c) Let S be a groupoid under F with idempotent element e; let T be any set; and define the composition H of T with S by $tx = e$ for all $t \in T$ and all $x \in S$. Then S is a groupoid with operators under F and H.

The trivial examples (b–c) are of interest because they illustrate how any groupoid can be regarded as the underlying groupoid of a groupoid with operators.

MODULOIDS

Let S be a groupoid under F, and T a bigroupoid under f and g; let H be a composition of T with S which distributes over F and over (f, F) and associates over g. In these circumstances we say that S is a T-**moduloid** ("under . . ." omitted unless there is danger of confusion as to which compositions are meant). In particular, if S is an Abelian group and T a ring, the moduloid is called a **module**. (One often speaks of S as being a module "over" the ring T.) If H is also g-unitary, the module is said to be unitary. A unitary T-module in which T is a division ring is called a **vector space**.

Examples:

   (a) In Example (a) at the beginning of Section 64, S is a T-moduloid; and if S is a ring and T a subring of S, then S is a T-module. In particular, taking $T = S$, we see that any ring can be regarded as a unitary module over itself, and any division ring as a vector space over itself.

   (b) Let S be an Abelian group under F; let T be any subring of the ring of endomorphisms of S (Section 59, Example (e)). Then T is also a ring under $+$ and composition of functions *in reverse order*. If we denote this latter ring by T^*, and define the composition H of T^* with S by $H(t, x) = t(x)$ for all $t \in T^*$ and all $x \in S$, then this composition makes S a T^*-module.

   (c) Let S be an Abelian group under F, and let H be as in the second part of Example (c), Section 63; then S is a unitary **I**-module.

ALGEBROIDS

Finally, let S be a bigroupoid under F and G, and T a bigroupoid under f and g, and let H be a composition of T with S which distributes over F and over (f, F), associates and commutes with G, and associates over g; then we call S a T-**algebroid** ("under . . ." understood). In particular, if S is a ring and T a commutative ring, and H is g-unitary, the algebroid is called an **algebra**. Note that if we ignore G, a T-algebra is a unitary T-module.

Examples:

   (a) In Example (a) at the beginning of Section 64, let S be a ring, and T a subring of S, every element of which commutes with every element of S; then S is a T-algebra (provided it is unitary). In particular, for any $n \in \mathbf{N}$, the set of n-by-n matrices over any commutative ring R is an R-algebra, and similarly for the polynomials or power series over R.

   (b) In Example (c) at the beginning of Section 64, if T is a commutative ring, then $S = T^m$ is a T-algebra. [Similarly, S is a unitary T-module, even if the ring T is not commutative.]

   (c) Let A be an R-module, where R is commutative, and let $E(A)$ be the ring of endomorphisms of A (defined as for Abelian groups). Given $c \in R$ and $t \in E(A)$, define the function ct from A into A by $(ct)(x) = ct(x)$ for all $x \in A$; then ct is an endomorphism of A, so that

$\{((c, t), ct) \mid c \in R, t \in E(A)\}$ is a composition of R with $E(A)$. If the R-module A is unitary, this composition makes $E(A)$ an R-algebra.

We shall study modules and vector spaces in the next section. In the remainder of this section we outline how to generalize the results of Chapter VII from groups to groups with operators.

Let S be a group with operators, A a subset of S. Readily A is a "sub group-with-operators" of S if and only if it is a subgroup of the group S and stable under the external composition H. By Exercise 64.1, the identity 0 of S is absorbent for H, so that $\{0\}$ is stable under H. Thus the complete lattice of stable subgroups of S has least element $\{0\}$ and greatest element S.

Exercise 1. *Describe the stable subgroup generated by a given subset of S; by a single element of S.*

Let A be a normal subgroup of the group S, so that $\{(x, y) \mid y - x \in A\} = R_A$ is a congruence for the group composition F. Then R_A is also a congruence for H provided that $y - x \in A$ implies $ty - tx \in A$ for all x, y in S and all $t \in T$. By distributivity, this is equivalent to $t(y - x) \in A$—in other words, to the requirement that A is stable under H. We thus have

Proposition 1. *If E is a congruence on the group with operators S, then $E = R_{E_0} = L_{E_0}$, where E_0 is a normal subgroup of the group S and is stable under H. Conversely, if A is such a stable normal subgroup, then $R_A = L_A$ is a congruence.*

Finally, let A, B be stable normal subgroups of S; then sup $\{A, B\}$, regarding A and B only as normal subgroups of the group S, is $A + B$. But by distributivity, we have $t(a + b) = ta + tb \in A + B$ for all $t \in T$, $a \in A$, $b \in B$, since A and B are stable. Thus the sup of A and B as stable normal subgroups is the same as their sup as normal subgroups. It follows that the results of Sections 38 and 40 remain true for factor groups and direct sums of groups with operators, provided that the word "stable" is added at the appropriate places.

66. MODULES AND VECTOR SPACES

Let S be a unitary module over the ring R with identity 1.

Proposition 1. *The submodule (x) generated by $x \in S$ is $\{cx \mid c \in R\}$.*

Proof: By $(\gamma - \delta)$, this set is stable under the internal and external compositions. Moreover, $0x = 0$ (Exercise 64.7) and $ax + (-a)x = (a + (-a))x = 0x$, so that this set is a subgroup. Finally, since S is unitary, this set contains $1x = x$, while conversely, any subset of S which contains x and is stable under the external composition must contain it. $/\!/$

Exercise 1. *The submodule* (A) *generated by* $A \subseteq S$ *is*

$$\left\{ \sum_{i=1}^{k} c_i x_i \mid k \in \mathbf{N};\ c_i \in R,\ x_i \in A,\ 1 \le i \le k \right\}.$$

Corollary. *The submodule* $(x_1, \ldots, x_n)$ *is*

$$\left\{ \sum_{i=1}^{n} c_i x_i \mid c_i \in R,\ 1 \le i \le n \right\}.$$

Exercise 2. *In any T-module S, we have* $0x = 0$ *for all* $x \in S$ *and* $a0 = 0$ *for all* $a \in T$. *If S is a vector space, then conversely,* $ax = 0$ *implies* $a = 0$ *or* $x = 0$.

It was pointed out in Section 65 (Example (a) of a module) that any division ring K can be regarded as a vector space, call it V_K, over itself. In terms of V_K, we can give a complete description of *any* vector space over K and, in particular, complete descriptions of the vector spaces over K which satisfy the various finiteness conditions. We begin with

Theorem 1. *A vector space over* K *is monogenic if and only if it is trivial or isomorphic to* V_K.

Proof: The trivial vector space $\{0\}$ is certainly monogenic, while $V_K = K$ is generated by $1 \in K$, since $(1) = \{c1 \mid c \in K\} = K$. Conversely, let $V = (x)$ be a monogenic vector space over K, where $x \ne 0$, and define the function F from V_K into V by $F(c) = cx$; thus by Proposition 1, F is onto. If $F(a) = F(b)$ we have $ax = bx$, that is, $(a - b)x = 0$, and since $x \ne 0$, by Exercise 2 this implies $a - b = 0$, so that $a = b$, proving F one-to-one. Finally, $F(a + b) = (a + b)x = ax + bx = F(a) + F(b)$, and $F(ca) = (ca)x = c(ax) = cF(a)$, so that F is an isomorphism. //

Theorem 2. *A vector space is prime if and only if it is monogenic.*

Proof: If V is prime (that is, has no subspaces except $\{0\}$ and itself), then either $V = \{0\}$, or $V = (x)$ for any $x \ne 0$ in V. Conversely, if the monogenic vector space (x) had a proper subspace, it would have a proper monogenic subspace (y), where $y \ne 0$. Let $y = ax$; then $a^{-1}y = a^{-1}(ax) = (a^{-1}a)x = 1x = x$, so that $x \in (y)$, that is, $(y) = (x)$, contradiction. //

Note also that any Abelian group with operators—in particular, any module or vector space—is simple if and only if it is prime.

From the above description of the monogenic vector spaces over K we can now derive a description of any vector space over K.

Proposition 2. *Let* V *be a vector space over* K, *and let* A *be a subset of* V *not containing* 0. *Then* A *is independent if and only if* $\sum_{i=1}^{k} c_i y_i = 0$ *implies* $c_i = 0$, $1 \le i \le k$, *for all* $k \in \mathbf{N}$, *all distinct* $y_1, \ldots, y_k$ *in* A, *and all* $c_1, \ldots, c_k$ *in* K.

Proof: Independence means that $(x) \cap (A - \{x\}) = \{0\}$ for all $x \in A$—in other words (Exercise 1), that $bx = \sum_{i=1}^{k} b_i x_i$ implies $bx = 0$ for all $k \in \mathbf{N}$, all distinct $x, x_1, \ldots, x_k$ in A, and all $b, b_1, \ldots, b_k$ in K. Let $\sum_{i=1}^{k} c_i y_i = 0$; then for any $j \in \mathbf{N}_k$ we have $-c_j y_j = c_1 y_1 + \cdots + c_{j-1} y_{j-1} + c_{j+1} y_{j+1} + \cdots + c_k y_k$, so that by independence, we have $-c_j y_j = 0$, and since $y_j \neq 0$, by Exercise 2 we have $c_j = 0$ for each $j \in \mathbf{N}_k$. The proof of the converse is left to the reader. $\;\;/\!/$

Proposition 3. *A maximal independent subset of a vector space generates the space.*

Proof: If B is such a subset and $x \notin (B)$, the set $B \cup \{x\}$ cannot be independent, so that $ax + \sum_{i=1}^{k} a_i x_i = 0$ for some $k \in \mathbf{N}$, some $x_1, \ldots, x_k$ in B, and some $a, a_1, \ldots, a_k$ in K with $a \neq 0$; but then $x = \sum_{i=1}^{k} (-a^{-1} a_i) x_i \in (B)$. $\;\;/\!/$

[Conversely, an independent subset which generates the space is readily maximal (see Proposition 51.2).]

Since any nontrivial vector space has a maximal independent subset (Zorn), by Proposition 3 it has an independent subset which generates it. Such a subset is called a **basis** for the space. Moreover, since the subspace generated by an independent set A is isomorphic to the weak direct sum of the monogenic subspaces (x), where $x \in A$, we have

Theorem 3. *Any nontrivial vector space over K is isomorphic to a weak direct sum of V_K's.*

We can also prove

Theorem 4. *Any subspace of a vector space is supplemented.*

Proof: Let W be a subspace of V, and let C be a basis for W, so that $(C) = W$. Since C is an independent subset of V, it is contained in a maximal independent subset—i.e., a basis—B, where $(B) = V$. Let $W^* = (B - C)$; then W^* is a direct supplement of W. In fact, let $x \in W \cap W^*$, say $x = \sum_{i=1}^{m} r_i x_i = \sum_{i=1}^{n} s_i y_i$, where $x_1, \ldots, x_m$ are distinct elements of C and $y_1, \ldots, y_n$ are distinct elements of $B - C$. Since $C \cap (B - C) = \varnothing$, the x's and y's are also distinct from each other, so that by the independence of B, every r_i and s_i must be 0, proving $x = 0$. Thus $W \cap W^* = \{0\}$, while $(W \cup W^*) \supseteq (C \cup (B - C)) = (B) = V$. $\;\;/\!/$

Corollary. *A vector space is indecomposable if and only if it is prime.*

Thus prime, simple, indecomposable and monogenic are all equivalent for vector spaces.

Exercise 3. *A minimal set of generators of a vector space is either $\{0\}$ or a basis.* [Thus for vector spaces, "maximal independent set," "independent set which generates," and "nontrivial minimal set of generators" are all equivalent (see Proposition 16.4).]

Exercise 4. *Any set of generators of a nontrivial vector space contains a basis. More generally, let A be an independent subset of V and let S generate V; then there exists a subset S' of S such that A ∪ S' is a basis for V and A ∩ S' = ∅.*

67. RANK AND DIMENSION

In this section we prove that all bases of a given vector space V have the same cardinality, which we call the rank of V. (Compare Section 51, and note that since any monogenic subspace is indecomposable, unrefinability is automatic.) Moreover, we shall prove that if the rank of V is finite, it is equal to the dimension of the subspace lattice $\mathscr{S}_V$, that is, to the maximal length of a chain of subspaces of V.

To begin with, it is easily verified that the proofs of the lemma and its corollaries in Section 51 remains valid if "aperiodic Abelian group" is replaced by "vector space over K," and the coefficients are elements of K rather than integers. We thus have

Proposition 1. *No finite independent set can have cardinality greater than that of any basis.*

Corollary 1. *All finite bases have the same cardinality.*

Corollary 2. *If there is a finite basis, there cannot be an infinite basis.*

This immediately gives us uniqueness of rank in the case where there exists a finite basis. Unfortunately, however, we cannot prove the uniqueness of rank in the infinite case by the method used to prove Proposition 51.10, since that proof depends on the denumerability of the set of coefficients, and breaks down for a vector space in which K has cardinality greater than that of the given basis. Instead, we must use an analog of the lemma for infinite sets:

Lemma. *Let S be an independent subset of the vector space V, and let T be a subset of V which generates V. Then $K(S) \leq K(T)$, and in fact there exists a one-to-one correspondence G of S with an independent subset T_G of T.*

Proof: Let $\mathscr{F}$ be the set of one-to-one correspondences F between subsets T_F of T and subsets of S such that $S - F(T_F) \cup T_F$ is independent. For example, the identity function $I_{T \cap S}$ (or the empty function, if $T \cap S = \varnothing$) is in $\mathscr{F}$, since $S - I_{T \cap S}(T \cap S) \cup (T \cap S) = S$. Let R be the relation "is a restriction of" on $\mathscr{F}$—in other words, R is the set of pairs (F_1, F_2) of elements of $\mathscr{F}$ such that $T_{F_1} \subseteq T_{F_2}$, and F_1 is the restriction of F_2 to T_{F_1}. Readily, R is an order relation on $\mathscr{F}$; we shall show that $\mathscr{F}$, ordered by R, is inductive.

Let $\mathscr{F}^* \subseteq \mathscr{F}$ be a chain under R, and let $T^* = \bigcup_{\mathscr{F}^*} T_F$; then readily $F^* = \{(x, y) \mid x \in T^*; y = F(x) \text{ for some } F \in \mathscr{F}^* \text{ such that } x \in T_F\}$ is a one-to-one function from T^* into S. Let $y_1, \ldots, y_m$ be in $S - F^*(T^*) \cup T^*$; we must show that $\{y_1, \ldots, y_m\}$ is independent. Now each y_i is either in S or in T^*, and if it is in T^*, it is in some T_{F_i}, where $F_i \in \mathcal{F}^*$. Since these T_i's are totally ordered by inclusion, and there are at most m of them, there is a greatest one, call it $T_{F'}$, where $F' \in \mathcal{F}^*$. Then all of the y_i's are in $S - F^*(T^*) \cup T_{F'} \subseteq S - F'(T') \cup T_{F'}$, which is independent since $F' \in \mathcal{F}^* \subseteq \mathcal{F}$. Hence $\{y_1, \ldots, y_m\}$ is independent, so that $S - F^*(T^*) \cup T^*$ is independent, completing the proof that $\mathcal{F}$ is inductive.

By Zorn's lemma, it follows that $\mathcal{F}$ has a maximal element. In particular, if we consider the set of F's in $\mathcal{F}$ whose restrictions to $S \cap T$ are $I_{S \cap T}$ (this is all of $\mathcal{F}$ if $S \cap T = \varnothing$), it too is inductive and so has a maximal element G. If $G(T_G) = S$, then G^{-1} is a one-to-one correspondence between S and an independent subset $T_G = S - G(T_G) \cup T_G$ of T, and the proof is complete. If not, let z be in $S - G(T_G)$; since G extends the identity function on $S \cap T$, this implies $z \notin T_G$. Suppose that z were in the subspace generated by $S - G(T_G) - \{z\} \cup T_G$, say $z = \sum_{i=1}^m a_i u_i$; then we would have $\sum_{i=1}^m a_i u_i - z = 0$ with not every coefficient zero, contrary to the independence of $S - G(T_G) \cup T_G$. Thus $z \notin (S - G(T_G) - \{z\} \cup T_G)$, but $z \in (T)$ since $(T) = V$; let $z = \sum_{i=1}^n b_i v_i$ with the v's in T, and where some v_j not in $(S - G(T_G) - \{z\} \cup T_G)$ must have coefficient $b_j \neq 0$. Let $G^* = G \cup \{(v_j, z)\}$. Since $v_j \notin T_G$, G is a proper restriction of G^*, while since $z \notin G(T_G)$ and $v_j \notin T_G$, G^* is still one-to-one. We shall show that $S - G(T_G) - \{z\} \cup T_G \cup \{v_j\}$ is independent; this will contradict the maximality of G, thus proving $G(T_G) = S$, as desired. Let $\sum_{i=1}^r c_i w_i = 0$ with the w's in $S - G(T_G) \cup T_G - \{z\} \cup \{v_j\}$ and all distinct. If v_j is not present in this sum with a nonzero coefficient, the w's are all in $S - G(T_G) \cup T_G$, which is independent, and we are done. But if v_j is present with a nonzero coefficient, we can transpose to obtain $v_j \in (S - G(T_G) \cup T_G - \{z\})$, contrary to the original choice of v_j.   //

Corollary 1. *Let S be any independent set, and T any basis; then $K(S) \leq K(T)$.*

Corollary 2. *All bases have the same cardinality.*

As indicated at the beginning of the section, we call the cardinality of any basis of V the **rank** of V, and denote it by $r(V)$. If $V = \{0\}$, we define $r(V) = 0$. By the proof of Theorem 66.3, if V is nontrivial, it is isomorphic to the weak direct sum of an I-tuple of V_K's, where $K(I) = r(V)$.

Corollary 3. *If W is a subspace of V, then $r(W) \leq r(V)$.*

Proof: A basis for W is an independent subset of V.   //

Thus any nontrivial subspace of V is isomorphic to the weak direct sum of an I-tuple of V_K's, where $K(I) \leq r(V)$. Conversely, if $K(J) \leq r(V)$, then J is in one-to-one correspondence with a subset B' of a basis of V, so that V has a subspace (B') of rank $K(J)$.

Corollary 4. *Let $r(V)$ be finite, and let W be a subspace of V; then $r(W) = r(V)$ if and only if $W = V$.*

Proof: Any basis for W is contained in a basis for V, and if they have the same number of elements they must be equal, so that the spaces W and V which they generate are equal.   //

We can now prove

Theorem 1. *If the vector space V has finite rank n then its lattice of subspaces $\mathscr{S}_V$ has dimension n, and conversely.*

Proof: If $B = \{x_1, \ldots, x_n\}$ is a basis, then readily $\{0\} \subset (x_1) \subset (x_1, x_2) \subset \cdots \subset (B) = V$, so that $\mathscr{S}_V$ has dimension at least n. Conversely, if $\{0\} \subset V_1 \subset \cdots \subset V_n = V$, by the last corollary and induction we have $r(V_i) \geq i$, so that $r(V) \geq n$.   //

Thus in the finite dimensional (or equivalently, finite rank) case, rank and dimension are the same. We usually speak of the dimension of V, rather than of $\mathscr{S}_V$.

Theorem 2. *A nontrivial vector space over K is finite dimensional if and only if it is isomorphic to a finite direct sum of V_K's.*

Proof: If V is finite dimensional, it has finite rank, and so is isomorphic to a finite direct sum of monogenic vector spaces. Conversely, if $V \cong (x_1) \oplus \cdots \oplus (x_n)$, then the n-tuples $(x_1, 0, \ldots, 0), (0, x_2, 0, \ldots, 0), \ldots, (0, \ldots, 0, x_n)$ are readily independent and generate the direct sum, so that $r(V) = n$.   //

Theorem 3. *The following statements about the vector space V are all equivalent:*

(1) *V is finite dimensional*
(2) *$\mathscr{S}_V$ satisfies the maximum condition*
(3) *$\mathscr{S}_V$ satisfies the minimum condition*
(4) *V is finitely generated.*

Proof: (1) implies (2–3) in any ordered set with greatest and least elements, and (2) implies (4) in any I-lattice. Conversely, if V is generated by a d-element set, any independent subset of V has at most d elements by the lemma, so that $r(V) \leq d$ is finite, proving that (4) implies (1) and making (1), (2), and (4) equivalent. Finally, if V has infinite rank, let B be a basis for V, and let $(x_i)_\mathbf{N}$ be a one-to-one correspondence between $\mathbf{N}$ and a subset of B; then $V = (B) \supset (B - \{x_1\}) \supset (B - \{x_1, x_2\}) \supset \cdots$ is a descending chain, so that (3) implies (1).   //

Exercise 1. *A vector space is monogenic if and only if it has dimension 0 or 1.*

Theorem 4. *The nontrivial vector space V over K is finite if and only if it is finite dimensional and K is finite.*

Proof: If K has m elements and V has dimension d, then $V \cong V_K \oplus \cdots \oplus V_K$ (d direct summands) has m^d elements. Conversely, any nontrivial V is a weak direct sum of V_K's, so that if V is finite, there can only be finitely many summands and each of them must be finite. //

Theorem 5. *A vector space is lattice-finite if and only if it is monogenic or finite.*

Proof: Since monogenic implies prime, "if" is immediate. Conversely, if V is not monogenic it has rank ≥ 2; let $\{x, y) \subseteq V$ be independent. If $(x + ay) = (x + by)$, where a, b are in K, we have $x + ay = c(x + by)$ for some $c \in K$, so that $(c - 1)x + (cb - a)y = 0$. Since $\{x, y\}$ is independent, this implies $c = 1$ and $a = cb = b$; thus the subspaces $(x + ay)$ are distinct for all $a \in K$. If V is lattice-finite, K must thus be finite; and since V must certainly be finite dimensional, it too is finite as in Theorem 4. //

68. ENDOMORPHISMS OF VECTOR SPACES

In this section we establish some properties of the ring of endomorphisms of a vector space (Section 65, Example (c) of an algebra) which will be needed in Chapter XII.

Let V be a vector space over the division ring K, and let $E(V)$ be the ring of endomorphisms of V. Let $M_K^{(n)}$ be the ring of n-by-n matrices over K.

Theorem 1. *If $r(V) = n$, then $E(V) \cong M_K^{(n)}$.*

Proof: Let $\{x_1, \ldots, x_n\}$ be a basis of V. Given $f \in E(V)$, let $f(x_i) = \sum_{j=1}^n a_{ij}x_j$, $1 \leq i \leq n$. Let $F = \{(f, (a_{ij})) \mid f \in E(V), a_{ij}$ as just defined$\}$; thus F is a function from $E(V)$ into $M_K^{(n)}$. If $F(f) = F(g) = (a_{ij})$, f and g have the same effect on $x_1, \ldots, x_n$, and since $f(\sum_{i=1}^n c_ix_i) = \sum_{i=1}^n c_if(x_i)$, this implies that they have the same effect on any element of V, that is, $f = g$, so that F is one-to-one. Let (b_{ij}) be any element of $M_K^{(n)}$, and for any $x \in V$, let $x = \sum_{i=1}^n c_ix_i$, where the c's are uniquely determined by x. Then h, defined by $h(x) = \sum_{i=1}^n c_i(\sum_{j=1}^n b_{ij}x_j)$, is a function from V into V, and is easily verified to be an endomorphism of V. Since evidently $h(x_i) = \sum_{j=1}^n b_{ij}x_j$, we have thus proved that F is onto. Finally, it is readily verified that if $F(f) = (a_{ij})$ and $F(g) = (b_{ij})$, then $F(f + g) = (a_{ij}) + (b_{ij})$ and $F(f \circ g) = (a_{ij})(b_{ij})$ [matrix addition and multiplication], so that F is a homomorphism. //

If K is a field, the same proof shows that the K-*algebra* of endomorphisms of V is isomorphic to the K-algebra of n-by-n matrices over K, since readily $F(af) = aF(f)$ for all $a \in K$.

Theorem 2. *Let F be an endomorphism of the vector space V, and let $(E_F)_0 = F^{-1}(0)$ be the kernel of F; then $r(F^{-1}(0)) + r(F(V)) = r(V)$.*

Proof: Let B be a basis for the subspace $F^{-1}(0)$; let $C \supseteq B$ be a basis for V; let V' be the subspace generated by $C - B$, so that $C - B$ is a basis for V'; and let F' be the restriction of F to V'. For any $x \in V$, let $x = \sum_{i=1}^{n} a_i x_i$, where (say) $x_1, \ldots, x_m$ are in B and $x_{m+1}, \ldots, x_n$ in $C - B$: then

$$F(x) = \sum_{i=1}^{n} a_i F(x_i) = \sum_{i=m+1}^{n} a_i F(x_i) = F\left(\sum_{i=m+1}^{n} a_i x_i \right) \in F(V'),$$

so that $F'(V') = F(V)$. Moreover, if $F(\sum_{i=1}^{r} d_i x_i) = F(\sum_{i=1}^{r} e_i x_i)$, where the x's are in $C - B$, we have $\sum_{i=1}^{r} (d_i - e_i) x_i \in F^{-1}(0)$, say $= \sum_{i=r+1}^{s} h_i x_i$ where these new x's are in B; by the independence of B, this requires that every $d_i - e_i$ and every h_i be 0, so that $\sum_{i=1}^{r} d_i x_i = \sum_{i=1}^{r} e_i x_i$, proving that F' is one-to-one. Thus F' is an isomorphism of V' with $F(V)$, so that $r(F(V)) = r(V')$, and we have

$$r(V) = K(C) = K(B) + K(C - B) = r(F^{-1}(0)) + r(V')$$
$$= r(F^{-1}(0)) + r(F(V)). \quad /\!/$$

Corollary 1. *If V is finite dimensional, F is one-to-one if and only if it is onto.*

Proof: F is one-to-one if and only if $r(F^{-1}(0)) = r(\{0\}) = 0$; onto, if and only if $r(F(V)) = r(V)$. $\quad /\!/$

Corollary 2. *If V is finite dimensional, and F is either one-to-one or onto, it is an automorphism.*

Exercise 1. *Let G be a group, F an endomorphism of G. Prove that if F is onto, and $\mathscr{S}_G^*$ satisfies the maximum condition, then F is one-to-one.*

Let V be a vector space, and S a subring of $E(V)$. We call S *r-transitive* if for all $\{x_1, \ldots, x_r\} \subseteq V$, independent, and all $y_1, \ldots, y_r$ in V, there exists an $f \in S$ such that $f(x_i) = y_i$, $1 \le i \le r$. If S is r-transitive for all $r \in \mathbf{N}$, we call it **dense**. The following propositions describe some useful properties of these concepts.

Proposition 1. *Let V be a vector space, S a 1-transitive subring of $E(V)$, and suppose that for all independent $\{x_1, \ldots, x_r\} \subseteq V$ there exists $f \in S$ such that $f(x_1) = \cdots = f(x_{r-1}) = 0$, while $f(x_r) \ne 0$. Then S is r-transitive.*

Proof: Since we can renumber the x's to make any of them x_r, it follows that for all $j \in \mathbf{N}_r$ there exists an f_j in S such that $f_j(x_i) = 0$, $i \in \mathbf{N}_r - \{j\}$, while $f_j(x_j) \ne 0$. Given any $y_1, \ldots, y_r$ in V, by 1-transitivity there exist $g_1, \ldots, g_r$ in S such that $g_j(f_j(x_j)) = y_j$, $1 \le j \le r$. Let $f = \sum_{i=1}^{r} f_i \circ g_i$; then evidently $f(x_i) = y_i$, $1 \le i \le r$. $\quad /\!/$

Proposition 2. *A subring of $E(V)$ is dense if and only if it is 1-transitive and 2-transitive.*

Proof: It suffices to show that if a 1- and 2-transitive subring S is $(r-1)$-transitive, it is r-transitive. Let $\{x_1, \ldots, x_r\} \subseteq V$ be independent; by induction hypothesis, for each $j \in N_{r-1}$ there exists an $f_j \in S$ such that $f_j(x_i) = 0$, $i \in N_{r-1} - \{j\}$, while $f_j(x_j) = x_j$. Let $f = \sum_{j=1}^{r-1} f_j$, and suppose that $f(x_r) \neq x_r$. Let $g(f(x_r) - x_r) \neq 0$, and let $h = f \circ g - g$. Then $h(x_r) \neq 0$, but $h(x_i) = 0$, for each i in N_{r-1}, so that S is r-transitive by Proposition 1. On the other hand, suppose that $f(x_r) = x_r$. If for each $j \in N_{r-1}$ we had $f_j(x_r) = a_j x_j$, then $x_r = f(x_r) = \sum_{j=1}^{r-1} a_j x_j$, contradicting the independence of $\{x_1, \ldots, x_r\}$; hence for some $m \in N_{r-1}$, x_m and $f_m(x_r)$ must be independent. By 2-transitivity, there thus exists $g \in S$ such that $g(x_m) = 0$, $g(f_m(x_r)) \neq 0$. Let $h = f_m \circ g$; then $h(x_r) \neq 0$, but $h(x_m) = g(f_m(x_m))g(x_m) = 0$, while $h(x_j) = g(f_m(x_j)) = g(0) = 0$ for all $j \in N_{r-1} - \{m\}$, so that S is r-transitive by Proposition 1. $\;/\!/$

Proposition 3. *If V is finite dimensional and S is a dense subring of $E(V)$, then $S = E(V)$.*

Proof: Let $\{x_1, \ldots, x_r\}$ be a basis of V, and let $y_i = \sum_{i=1}^{r} a_{ij} x_j$, $1 \leq i \leq r$. As in the proof of Theorem 1, there exists exactly one endomorphism g of V such that $g(x_i) = y_i$, $1 \leq i \leq r$. If S is dense, this g must be in it, so that S is all of $E(V)$. $\;/\!/$

Conversely, by the proof of Theorem 1, $E(V)$ itself is dense. As a further converse result we have

Proposition 4. *If there exists a dense subring of $E(V)$ whose lattice of right ideals satisfies the minimum condition, then V is finite dimensional.*

Proof: Let S be such a subring, and for any subspace W of V, let $S_W = \{f \mid f \in S; f(x) = 0 \text{ for all } x \in W\}$. Clearly f, g in S_W implies $f - g \in S_W$, and $f \in S_W$ implies $f \circ h \in S_W$ for all $h \in S$, so that S_W is a right ideal of S. Let $S_{V'}$ be a minimal element of the set of S_W such that W is finite dimensional; we show that V' must be all of V, so that V is finite dimensional. In fact, if not, let $\{x_1, \ldots, x_{r-1}\}$ be a basis for V', and let $\{x_1, \ldots, x_r\}$ be independent, so that $V' \subset (x_1, \ldots, x_r) = V''$ (say), where V'' is still finite dimensional. Since S is dense, there exists an $f \in S$ such that $f(x_1) = \cdots = f(x_{r-1}) = 0$ but $f(x_r) \neq 0$; thus $f \in S_{V'}$ but $f \notin S_{V''}$, so that $S_{V''} \subset S_{V'}$, contradicting the minimality of $S_{V'}$. $\;/\!/$

If we regard $E(V)$ as a ring under $+$ and composition of functions *in reverse order*, Propositions 1–4 evidently continue to hold, except that we must replace "right" by "left" in Proposition 4. We shall denote this ring by $E^*(V)$.

We conclude by developing an application of Propositions 1–4 which will be used in our study of simple rings in Chapter XII. Let A be a group (with composition denoted additively), and let S be a set of endomorphisms of A. We call S **primitive** if for all a, b in A, where $a \neq 0$, there exists an $f \in S$ such that $f(a) = b$. [Note that if A were a vector space, "primitive" would be the same as "1-transitive," since $\{a\}$ is independent if and only if $a \neq 0$.] Let $C(S)$ be the set of endomorphisms of A which commute (under $\circ$) with every $g \in S$. Evidently the identity endomorphism, and the "zero endomorphism" h_0 defined by $h_0(a) = 0$ for all $a \in A$, commute with every endomorphism and so are always in $C(S)$.

Proposition 5 (Schur's lemma). *If S is primitive, any $h \neq h_0$ in $C(S)$ is an automorphism.*

Proof: Let $h(c) \neq 0$ (such a $c \in A$ exists since $h \neq h_0$). Then for any $b \in A$, there exists an $f \in S$ such that $f(h(c)) = b$; hence $h(f(c)) = b$, so that h is onto. On the other hand, let $h(a) = 0$ with $a \neq 0$, and for any $b \in A$, let $f \in S$ be such that $f(a) = b$; then $h(b) = h(f(a)) = f(h(a)) = f(0) = 0$, that is, $h = h_0$, contradiction. In other words, $h(a) = 0$ implies $a = 0$, so that $h(c) = h(d)$ implies $h(c - d) = 0$, that is, $c = d$, which proves that h is one-to-one.   //

Corollary. *If A is a nontrivial Abelian group and S is a primitive subring of the ring $E(A)$ of endomorphisms of A, then $C(S)$ is a division ring.*

Proof: Readily, for any subset S of $E(A)$, $C(S)$ is a ring with identity (compare Exercise 60.4). Moreover, if $h \in C(S)$ is an automorphism, then $h^{-1} \circ (f \circ h) \circ h^{-1} = h^{-1} \circ (h \circ f) \circ h^{-1}$, that is, $h^{-1} \circ f = f \circ h^{-1}$, for all $f \in S$, so that $h^{-1} \in C(S)$.   //

These results evidently continue to hold if we work in the ring $E^*(A)$ of endomorphisms of A under $+$ and composition of functions in reverse order. By Example (b) of a module in Section 65, A is a T^*-module for any subring T^* of $E^*(A)$. In particular, if S^* is a primitive subring, $C(S^*)$ is a division ring, so that A is a *vector space* over $C(S^*)$; we shall denote this vector space by A_{S^*}. Now any $f \in S^*$ is an endomorphism of A_{S^*}, since $f(hx) = f(h(x)) = h(f(x)) = hf(x)$ for all $h \in C(S^*)$; hence S^* is a ring of endomorphisms of A_{S^*}. We have thus shown that any primitive ring of endomorphisms S^* of an Abelian group A is a ring of endomorphisms of a vector space A_{S^*}.

Proposition 6. *Let A be an Abelian group, and S^* a primitive subring of $E^*(A)$; then S^* is a dense subring of $E^*(A_{S^*})$.*

Proof: Since S^* is primitive, it is 1-transitive; hence by Proposition 2, we need only show that S^* is 2-transitive. In fact, by Proposition 1 it suffices to show that for all $\{x, y\} \subseteq A$, independent over $C(S^*)$, there exists an $f \in S^*$ such that $f(x) = 0$, $f(y) \neq 0$. Suppose not; then $f(x) = 0$ implies $f(y) = 0$. Let $F = \{(g(x), g(y)) \mid g \in S^*\}$. Since S^* is primitive, $g(x)$ can be any element of A. Moreover, if $g(x) = h(x)$, then $(g - h)(x) = 0$, which implies $(g - h)(y) = 0$, that is, $g(y) = h(y)$; thus $g(y)$ is uniquely determined by $g(x)$, so that F is a function from A into A. Now

$$F(g(x) + h(x)) = F((g + h)(x)) = (g + h)(y) = g(y) + h(y)$$
$$= F(g(x)) + F(h(x))$$

for all g, h in S^*, so that F is an endomorphism of A. Furthermore, for all g, h in S^* we have

$$(h \circ F)(g(x)) = F((g \circ h)(x)) = (g \circ h)(y) = h(g(y))$$
$$= h(F(g(x))) = (F \circ h)(g(x)),$$

and since $g(x)$ is an arbitrary element of A, this implies that $h \circ F = F \circ h$ for all $h \in S^*$, so that $F \in C(S^*)$. But then for all $f \in S^*$ we have

$$f(y - F(x)) = f(y) - f(F(x)) = f(y) - F(f(x)) = f(y) - f(y) = 0,$$

and since S^* is primitive, this is impossible unless $y - F(x) = 0$, which contradicts the independence of $\{x, y\}$ over $C(S^*)$. $\parallel$

Corollary. *Let A, S^* be as in the proposition, and let the lattice of left ideals of S^* satisfy the minimum condition; then A_{S^*} is finite dimensional and $S^* = E^*(A_{S^*})$.*

Proof: Propositions 3, 4, and 6. $\parallel$

In Chapter XII (Section 74) we shall show that if R is a simple ring, not a zero-ring, whose lattice of left ideals satisfies the minimum condition, then there exists an Abelian group A (namely, a minimal left ideal of R) such that R is a primitive subring of $E^*(A)$. It follows by the last corollary that any such ring R is the ring of endomorphisms of a finite dimensional vector space—or equivalently, by Theorem 1 and Exercise 58.6, is isomorphic to a ring of n-by-n matrices over a division ring.

XII

FINITENESS CONDITIONS ON RINGS

In this final chapter we study rings and fields which have properties analogous to those studied in Chapter VIII for semigroups and groups. It will be recalled that, in the case of groups, such properties could be defined using either the lattice of subgroupoids (= subsemigroups) or the lattice of subgroups; similarly for rings, we can define such properties using either the lattice of subringoids (= subsemirings) or the lattice of subrings, while in the case of division rings we can also use the lattice of division subrings. To avoid confusion, when we refer to any but the weakest applicable property we will specify, for example, "the ring R is prime as a semiring," "the field K is lattice finite as a ring," and so on. [Exercise: Write out the definitions of all fourteen properties and determine what implications hold among them. Which of them pass to subrings? Which to residue rings?]

69. PRIME SEMIRINGS, RINGS, AND FIELDS

The semiring S will be called **prime** if any subsemiring of S is either $\varnothing$, S, or trivial. We can obtain a complete description of the prime semirings by applying the methods used in Section 44 to describe the prime semigroups. In what follows, by a left (right) ideal of S we mean a subsemigroup of the additive semigroup of S which is also a left (right) ideal of the multiplicative semigroup of S. Thus a left or right ideal is a subsemiring, and for any $x \in S$, Sx is a left ideal and xS a right ideal.

Theorem 1. *A semiring is prime if and only if its additive semigroup is prime.*

Proof: We consider several cases and subcases.

(a) If S has a unique multiplicatively absorbent element 0, then as in the proof of Theorem 44.1, the only trivial left or right ideal of S is $\{0\}$ (it is an

240

ideal, since by Proposition 57.2, 0 must be additively idempotent). Hence if S is prime, we have $xS = \{0\}$ or S, and $Sx = \{0\}$ or S, for all $x \in S$.

(a') If $xS = Sx = \{0\}$ for all $x \in S$, the multiplicative composition on S is defined by $xy = 0$ for all x, y in S. For this composition, a nonempty subset of S is a subsemiring if and only if it contains 0 and is an additive subsemigroup. Thus if every additive subsemigroup of S contains 0, we are done. If not, 0 must fail to be in some monogenic additive subsemigroup $A = \{na \mid n \in \mathbf{N}\}$, where $a \in S$. Hence the sup of A and $\{0\}$ in the lattice of additive subsemigroups must be all of S. Now readily this sup is $A \cup \{0\} \cup \{na + 0 \mid n \in \mathbf{N}\} = A \cup \{0\} \cup (A + \{0\})$, and this has $\{0\} \cup (A + \{0\})$, which is an additive subsemigroup containing 0, as a subsemiring; hence this subsemiring must be $\{0\}$ or all of S.

(a'$_1$) If $A + \{0\} = \{0\}$, we have $A \cup \{0\} = S$, and if A' is any subsemigroup of A, then $A' \cup \{0\}$ is a subsemiring of S. Hence for S to be prime, A can have no subsemigroups but itself and $\varnothing$, which implies (Corollary to Theorem 44.1) that $A = \{a\}$ is trivial, so that $S = \{0, a\}$.

(a'$_2$) If $(A + \{0\}) \cup \{0\} = S$, and $0 \notin A + \{0\}$, we can apply the argument of (a'$_1$) to $A + \{0\}$ to prove it trivial, so that $S = \{0, a + 0\}$.

(a'$_3$) Otherwise, we have $A + \{0\} = S$, so that $0 \in A + \{0\}$, say $0 = ma + 0$; but then $S = \{a + 0, 2a + 0, \ldots, (m - 1)a + 0, 0\}$ is an additive group with identity 0, and since it can have no proper subsemigroups which contain 0, in particular it can have no proper subgroups, making it a prime group.

(a'') If (a') does not hold, then just as in the proof of Theorem 44.1, $S - \{0\}$ is a multiplicative group. Let its identity be 1; then $N^* = \{n1 \mid n \in \mathbf{N}\}$ is a subsemiring, hence is trivial (that is, $= \{1\}$) or is all of S.

(a''$_1$) If N^* is trivial, 1 is additively idempotent, so that $\{0, 1 + 0\}$ is a subsemiring. Hence if $1 + 0 \neq 0$ we must have $S = \{0, 1 + 0\}$, while if $1 + 0 = 0$, then $\{0, 1\}$ is a subsemiring, so that in either case $S = \{0, 1\}$.

(a''$_2$) But if $N^* = S$, note that any additive subsemigroup of N^* is an ideal, so that the additive semigroup N^* must be prime.

(b) If (a) does not hold, then just as in the proof of Theorem 44.1, either (b') or (b'') must hold:

(b') S is a multiplicative group, say with identity 1, and as in (a''), we have $N^* = \{1\}$ or S.

(b'$_1$) If $N^* = \{1\}$, every element of S is additively idempotent (indeed, $x + x = x1 + x1 = x(1 + 1) = x1 = x$), but no $x \neq 1$ can be multiplicatively idempotent, so that for any $a \neq 1$ the subsemiring generated by either a or a^{-1} is all of S. Readily, for a^{-1} this subsemiring is

$$\left\{ \sum_{i=1}^{k} \delta_i a^{-i} \mid k \in \mathbf{N}; \ \delta_i = 0 \text{ or } 1, \ 1 \leq i \leq k \right\}$$

(where $\delta_i = 0$ means that a^{-i} is not a term of the sum), and since 1 must be in it, we have $1 = \sum_{i=1}^{n} \delta_i a^{-i}$ for some $n \in \mathbf{N}$ and some choice of δ's. Hence $a^n = \sum_{i=1}^{n} \delta_i a^{n-i}$ is a sum of lower nonnegative powers of a, so that any power of a is such a sum; and since a generates S, we have

$$S = \left\{ \sum_{i=0}^{n-1} \delta_i a^i \mid \delta_i = 0 \text{ or } 1, 1 \leq i \leq n \right\}.$$

It follows that $b = \sum_{i=0}^{n-1} a^i$ is additively absorbent. But then for all x, y in S we have $x + y = xy^{-1}bb^{-1}y + bb^{-1}y = (xy^{-1}b + b)b^{-1}y = bb^{-1}y = y$, so that any $y \in S$ is additively absorbent, and since an absorbent element must be unique, S is thus trivial.

  (b_2') If $N^* = S$, then as in (a_2''), the additive semigroup of S must be prime. [Note, however, that in this case if S is nontrivial, 1 is not additively idempotent, so that as in the first part of (b_1'), no element of S can be additively idempotent. But if the additive semigroup of S is prime, it is finite and hence does contain an idempotent (Proposition 45.4). Thus this case cannot arise unless S is trivial.]

  (b'') The composition on S is given by $xy = x$ (or by $xy = y$) for all x, y in S. In this case any subset is a multiplicative subsemigroup, so that any additive subsemigroup is a subsemiring; hence the additive semigroup of S must be prime. [Note, however, that in this case, if S has more than two elements, its additive semigroup is a prime group $\{0, a, \ldots, (p-1)a\}$, and since $(ma)(na) = (mn)a = (nm)a = (na)(ma)$, the multiplicative composition on S must be commutative, so that $x = xy = yx = y$ for all x, y in S, making S trivial, contradiction. Hence this case cannot arise if S has more than two elements.]   //

Corollary 1. *A semiring with more than two elements is prime if and only if it is isomorphic either to a zero-ring with additive group* $\mathbf{I}_p$ *or to a field* $\mathbf{I}_p$, *where* $p \in \mathbf{N}$ *is prime.*

  Proof: By the theorem, the additive group is a prime group, so is isomorphic to an additive group $\mathbf{I}_p$. Moreover, either $xy = 0$ for all x, y in S (case a′), or else $S - \{0\}$ is a multiplicative group, so that S is a field (case a″), and readily a field with additive group $\mathbf{I}_p$ must be isomorphic to the field $\mathbf{I}_p$. Conversely, the prime additive group $\mathbf{I}_p$ has no proper subsemigroups, so that any semiring with this additive group must be prime.   //

Corollary 2. *A ring is prime as a semiring if and only if it is isomorphic either to a zero-ring with additive group* $\mathbf{I}_p$, *where* $p = 1$ *or is prime, or to a field* $\mathbf{I}_p$, *where* p *is prime.*

  Proof: Readily, a ring with two elements is isomorphic either to the zero-ring $\mathbf{I}_2$ or to the field $\mathbf{I}_2$; for more than two elements, use Corollary 1.   //

In particular, a ring with identity is prime as a semiring if and only if it is trivial or isomorphic to a field $\mathbf{I}_p$, where p is prime.

Corollary 3. *A ring has no proper left or right ideals if and only if it is a division ring or is isomorphic to a zero-ring with additive group* $\mathbf{I}_p$, *where* $p = 1$ *or is prime.*

Proof: We need only consider cases (a) in the proof of the theorem, since a ring R has a multiplicatively absorbent element 0. In case (a″), $R - \{0\}$ is a multiplicative group, so that R is a division ring, and in case (a′) R is a zero-ring. Moreover, in case (a′) any additive subsemigroup of R which contains 0 is an ideal; in particular, any additive subgroup of R is an ideal, so that R must be a prime group. Conversely, a ring with prime additive group has no proper additive subgroups, and in particular no proper left or right ideals, while by Proposition 60.5, a division ring can never have proper left or right ideals.   //

It follows that a *commutative* ring has no proper ideals if and only if it is a field or is isomorphic to a zero-ring with additive group $\mathbf{I}_p$, where $p = 1$ or is prime. If, in analogy with Section 47, we call a ring **simple** if it has no proper ideals, we thus have a description of the simple commutative rings. In particular, a commutative ring with identity is simple if and only if it is trivial or a field.

We next consider prime division rings (that is, division rings which have no proper division subrings).

Theorem 2. *A division ring is prime if and only if it is isomorphic to* $\mathbf{R}$ *or to* $\mathbf{I}_p$ *for some prime p.*

Proof: Let D be a prime division ring, 1 its multiplicative identity. By Proposition 59.2, the characteristic of D is either 0 or prime (it cannot be 1 since $1 \neq 0$). If the characteristic is p, then the subring $\{n1 \mid n \in \mathbf{N}\}$ is readily isomorphic to $\mathbf{I}_p$, and since this is a field, it must be all of D. If the characteristic is 0, the subring $\{n1 \mid n \in \mathbf{I}\}$ is readily isomorphic to $\mathbf{I}$, and D must have a subfield isomorphic to $\mathbf{R}$, the field of quotients of $\mathbf{I}$, so that this subfield must be all of D. Conversely, $\mathbf{I}_p$ is prime even as a semiring; as for $\mathbf{R}$, any subfield must contain 1 and so must be all of $\mathbf{R}$, so that $\mathbf{R}$ is a prime division ring.   //

Note that in particular, a prime division ring is a field.

A prime division ring need not be prime as a ring, since $\mathbf{R}$ has proper subrings (for example, $\mathbf{I}$). In fact, the same example shows that a prime division ring need not even be finitely generated as a ring. However, we can now prove

Theorem 3. *A ring is prime if and only if it is prime as a semiring.*

Proof: If R has no proper subrings, it has no proper left or right ideals, so that by Corollary 3 to Theorem 1, it is prime as a semiring unless it is a division ring. But then R is certainly a prime division ring, so that by Theorem 2 it is prime as a semiring unless it is isomorphic to $\mathbf{R}$; but $\mathbf{R}$ is not prime as a ring.   //

70. MONOGENIC AND FINITELY GENERATED FIELDS

We have seen (Corollary 1 to Proposition 60.1) that in any semiring we have $(a) = \{\sum_{i=1}^{k} n_i a^i \mid k \in \mathbf{N}; n_i \in \mathbf{N}^\circ, 1 \le i \le k; \text{ not all } n_i = 0\}$. Let $\mathbf{N}^\circ[x]$ be the semiring of polynomials in one indeterminate over $\mathbf{N}^\circ$; we have seen in Section 58 that the elements of $\mathbf{N}^\circ[x]$ are of the form $\sum_{i=0}^{k} n_i x^i$, where k and the n_i's are in $\mathbf{N}^\circ$. Let (x) be the subsemiring of $\mathbf{N}^\circ[x]$ generated by x; readily, this is just the set of nonzero $\sum_{i=0}^{k} n_i x^i$ such that $n_0 = 0$—in other words, it is the set of $\sum_{i=1}^{k} n_i x^i$ with $k \in \mathbf{N}$ and each $n_i \in \mathbf{N}^\circ$, but not all $n_i = 0$. Thus $\{(\sum_{i=1}^{k} n_i x^i, \sum_{i=1}^{k} n_i a^i) \mid \sum_{i=1}^{k} n_i x^i \in (x)\}$ (compare Exercise 58.2) is a homomorphism of (x) onto (a), so that (a) is isomorphic to a quotient semiring of (x). Conversely, since (x) is monogenic, so are all its quotient semirings, so that we have proved

Theorem 1. *A semiring is monogenic if and only if it is isomorphic to a quotient semiring of the subsemiring (x) of $\mathbf{N}^\circ[x]$.*

Corollary. *A subsemiring of a monogenic semiring need not be monogenic.*

Proof: For example, it is not difficult to show (using Exercise 58.3) that the subsemiring of (x) generated by x^2 and x^3 is not monogenic.   //

In an exactly analogous manner we can prove

Theorem 2. *A ring is monogenic (as an element of its subring lattice) if and only if it is isomorphic to a residue ring of the subring of $\mathbf{I}[x]$ generated by (x).*

Corollary. *A subring of a monogenic ring need not be monogenic.*

Evidently a monogenic ring need not be monogenic as a semiring; for example, $\mathbf{I} = (1)$ as a ring, but is not monogenic as a semiring.

The descriptions of the monogenic semirings and rings provided by Theorems 1–2 are not very explicit, since we have no catalog of the quotient semirings or residue rings of (x). We can give a somewhat better description of the monogenic division rings. Note first that any division ring has a unique prime subfield, namely its division subring (1) (this can have no proper division subrings, since any division subring must contain 1). Let D be a division ring, K_0 its prime subfield; we prove

Theorem 3. *D is monogenic if and only if it is isomorphic either to the field of quotients of $K_0[x]$ or to a residue ring $K_0[x]/\varphi K_0[x]$, where φ is an irreducible polynomial of degree > 0.*

Proof: The division ring (a) must contain K_0, hence must contain the ring R_a generated by $K_0 \cup \{a\}$, which readily is $\{\sum_{i=0}^{k} c_i a^i \mid k \in \mathbf{N}^{\circ}; c_i \in K_0, 0 \leq i \leq k\}$. Now R_a is the image of $K_0[x]$ under the substitution homomorphism which takes x into a; hence it is isomorphic to a residue ring of $K_0[x]$, say $K_0[x]/A_a$, where A_a is an ideal, and since R_a is nontrivial, A_a cannot be all of $K_0[x]$. Since R_a, as a subring of a division ring, is a domain, the ideal A_a must be prime (Exercise 61.1). But $K_0[x]$ is Euclidean, so that every ideal of $K_0[x]$ is principal (Proposition 62.2). Hence if $A_a \neq \{0\}$, it is maximal (corollary to Proposition 35.6, applied to the multiplicative semigroup $K_0[x] - \{0\}$), and $A_a = \varphi K_0[x]$, where $\varphi \in K_0[x]$ is an irreducible nonunit. But if A_a is maximal, $R_a \cong K_0[x]/A_a$ has no proper ideals, making it a field by the remark preceding Theorem 69.2; thus in this case R_a must already be all of (a). On the other hand, if $A_a = \{0\}$, we have $R_a \cong K_0[x]$, a commutative domain, so that the subfield of (a) isomorphic to the field of quotients of R_a must be all of (a). //

> Note that if $(a) \cong K_0[x]/\varphi K_0[x]$, we can regard (a) as the set of polynomials in a over K_0 of degrees less than that of φ, under addition and multiplication of polynomials "modulo φ."

In proving Theorem 3, we made no use of the fact that K_0 is a prime field, but only of the fact that every element of K_0 commutes with a. We thus have the following immediate generalization:

Theorem 4. *Let D be a division ring, K a subfield of D, and a an element of D which commutes with every element of K. Then the division subring of D generated by $K \cup \{a\}$ is isomorphic either to the field of quotients of $K[x]$ or to a residue ring $K[x]/\varphi K[x]$, where φ is irreducible.*

In the former case we say that a is **transcendental** over K; in the latter case, that a is **algebraic** over K. Note that in the former case there are no polynomials over K which have a as a root, while in the latter case there are such polynomials, namely those in A_a.

Exercise 1. *If $\varphi \in K[x]$ is an irreducible nonunit and $a \in D$ is a root of φ, then $A_a = \varphi K[x]$.*

If a is algebraic over K, the polynomial φ evidently has lowest degree of all nonzero polynomials in $A_a = \varphi K[x]$. Moreover, if we also have $A_a = \psi K[x]$, then φ and ψ must both be irreducible and must divide each other, so that either of them is a multiple of the other by a polynomial of degree 0; hence there is a unique one having any given leading coefficient. The polynomial $\varphi_{a,K}$ with leading coefficient 1 such that $A_a = \varphi_{a,K}K[x]$ is called the **minimal polynomial** of a over K. Readily $a \in K$ if and only if $\varphi_{a,K}$ has degree 1.

By repeatedly applying Theorem 4, we can extend the description of the monogenic division rings ($=$ fields) provided by Theorem 3 into a description of the finitely generated fields. In fact, let $L = (a_1, \ldots, a_n)$, and let $L_i = (a_1, \ldots, a_i)$, $1 \leq i \leq n$; then L_1 is monogenic, while Theorem 4 describes L_{i+1} in terms of L_i, $1 \leq i \leq n$. The next two propositions state some further consequences of the proof of Theorem 4:

Proposition 1. *Let K_1, a_1 and K_2, a_2 each be as in Theorem 4, and let F be an isomorphism of K_1 with K_2. Let a_1 and a_2 both be transcendental (over K_1 and K_2, respectively), or let them both be algebraic and have minimal polynomials whose coefficients correspond under F. Then there exists an isomorphism of $(K_1 \cup \{a_1\})$ with $(K_2 \cup \{a_2\})$ which takes a_1 into a_2 and whose restriction to K_1 is F.*

Proof: The fields of quotients of $K_1[x]$ and $K_2[x]$, or the residue rings $K_1[x]/\varphi_{a_1,K_1}K_1[x]$ and $K_2[x]/\varphi_{a_2,K_2}K_2[x]$, are evidently isomorphic in the desired manner. //

Proposition 2. *Let $K \subseteq L$ be fields; then every element of L is algebraic over K if and only if every subring of L which contains K is a field.*

Proof: If every $a \in L$ is algebraic over K, the subring R_a generated by $K \cup \{a\}$ is a field; hence any ring R "between" K and L contains the inverse of any $a \in R$, since it must contain R_a. Conversely, if any such R is a field, in particular R_a is a field for any $a \in L$; hence $a^{-1} \in R_a$, that is, $a^{-1} = \sum_{i=0}^{k} c_i a^i$ where the c's are in K, so that $\sum_{i=0}^{k} c_i a^{i+1} - 1 = 0$, proving a algebraic over K. //

> Note that L need not be a field; it suffices that every element of K commute with every element of L—in other words, that K be contained in the *center* of L. The same remark applies to many of the results which follow.

DIVISION RINGS AS VECTOR SPACES

A very useful technique for studying division rings is to regard them as vector spaces over division subrings (Section 65, Example (a) of a module).

Proposition 3. *Let K, a be as in Theorem 4, and let $\varphi_{a,K}$ have degree d; then $\{1, a, \ldots, a^{d-1}\}$ is a basis for $(K \cup \{a\})$ as a vector space over K.*

Proof: Given $\varphi \in K[x]$, let $\varphi = q\varphi_{a,K} + r$, where q, r are in $K[x]$ and r has degree $< d$. Then since $\varphi_{a,K}(a) = 0$, we have $\varphi(a) = r(a)$, so that $R_a = \{\sum_{i=0}^{d-1} c_i a^i \mid c_i \in K, 0 \leq i < d\}$ is generated by $\{1, a, \ldots, a^{d-1}\}$ as a vector space over K. On the other hand, if we had $\sum_{i=0}^{d-1} c_i a^i = 0$, a would be a root of a polynomial of degree $< d$, contradicting the minimality of $\varphi_{a,K}$ unless every $c_i = 0$; thus $\{1, a, \ldots, a^{d-1}\}$ is an independent subset of the vector space R_a over K. //

Proposition 4. *Let $K \subseteq L$ be fields, and let L be finite dimensional as a vector space over K; then every element of L is algebraic over K.*

Proof: Let the dimension of the vector space be d; then for any $b \in L$, the $(d + 1)$-element set $\{1, b, \ldots, b^d\}$ cannot be independent, so that b must be a root of a nonzero polynomial in $K[x]$ of degree $\leq d$. //

Corollary. *Every element of $(K \cup \{a\})$ is algebraic over K.*

From now on, if L is a division ring and K a division subring of L, we shall refer to the dimension of L as a vector space over K as the *degree* of L over K, and shall abbreviate it by $\deg(L:K)$.

Exercise 2. *If $K \subseteq L \subseteq M$, then $\deg(M:K) = \deg(M:L)\deg(L:K)$.*

Proposition 5. *Let $K \subseteq L$ be fields; then L is finite dimensional as a vector space over K if and only if $L = (K \cup \{a_1, \ldots, a_n\})$ for some $n \in \mathbf{N}$, where each a_i is algebraic over K.*

Proof: If L is finite dimensional as a vector space over K, let $\{b_1, \ldots, b_m\}$ be a basis for this vector space; then evidently $L = (K \cup \{b_1, \ldots, b_m\})$, while any element of L must be algebraic over K by Proposition 4. Conversely, let $(K \cup \{a_1, \ldots, a_i\}) = L_i$, $1 \leq i \leq n$, and let $\varphi_{a_i,K}$ have degree d_i. Then as in Proposition 3, L_i is generated as a vector space over K—and so certainly as a vector space over L_{i-1}—by $\{1, a_i, \ldots, a_i^{d_i-1}\}$, so that $\deg(L_i:L_{i-1}) \leq d_i$. Hence by Exercise 2 and induction we have $\deg(L:K) \leq \prod_{i=1}^n d_i$. //

Corollary 1. *Let $K \subseteq L$ be fields, and let $L = (K \cup S)$, where every element of S is algebraic over K; then every element of L is algebraic over K.*

Proof: Any $a \in L$ is contained in some $(K \cup \{s_1, \ldots, s_m\})$, where the s's are in S. //

Corollary 2. *Let $K \subseteq M$ be fields; then the set L of elements of M which are algebraic over K is a subfield of M and contains K.*

Proof: If a and b are algebraic over K, so are $a - b$ and ab^{-1} (where $b \neq 0$), since they are elements of $(K \cup \{a, b\})$. //

This subfield is called the **algebraic closure** of K in M.

Corollary 3. *Let $K \subseteq L \subseteq M$ be fields such that every element of L is algebraic over K; then any element of M which is algebraic over L is algebraic over K.*

Proof: Let a be such an element, and let $\varphi_{a,L} = \sum_{i=0}^n c_i x^i$; then

$(K \cup \{c_0, \ldots, c_n, a\})$ is finite dimensional as a vector space over $(K \cup \{c_0, \ldots, c_n\})$, which in turn is finite dimensional as a vector space over K. Hence by Exercise 2, $(K \cup \{c_0, \ldots, c_n, a\})$ is finite dimensional as a vector space over K, so that its element a is algebraic over K.   //

Corollary 4. *Let K, L, M be as in Corollary 2; then any element of M which is algebraic over L is in L.*

If $L \subseteq M$ are fields for which Corollary 4 holds, L is called **algebraically closed** in M.

> Exercise 2 can also be applied to prove that a root of an irreducible cubic polynomial cannot be constructed by straightedge and compass. To prove this, one first shows that constructions by straightedge and compass can produce only lengths which are sums, differences, products, quotients, or square roots of given or previously constructed lengths. Readily, this implies that if a unit length is given, one can construct from it, in a finite number of steps, only lengths which are in a field
>
> $$K = (\mathbf{R} \cup \{a_1, \ldots, a_n\})$$
>
> for some $n \in \mathbf{N}$, where a_i is the square root of an element of $(\mathbf{R} \cup \{a_1, \ldots, a_{i-1}\})$, $1 \le i \le n$. Thus the degree of the minimal polynomial of a_i over $(\mathbf{R} \cup \{a_1, \ldots, a_{i-1}\})$ is either 1 or 2, $1 \le i \le n$. By Exercise 2 and induction, it follows that $\deg(K:\mathbf{R})$ is a power of 2. Let $\varphi \in \mathbf{R}[x]$ be an irreducible polynomial of degree 3, and suppose that K contained a root b of φ; then by Exercise 2,
>
> $$\deg((\mathbf{R} \cup \{b\}):\mathbf{R}) = 3$$
>
> would divide $\deg(K:\mathbf{R})$, which is impossible. In particular, this shows that it is in general impossible to "duplicate a cube" or trisect an angle using only straightedge and compass. In fact, since 2 has no cube root in $\mathbf{R}$, the polynomial $x^3 - 2 \in \mathbf{R}[x]$ is readily irreducible; while $\cos(\theta/3)$ is a root of $4x^3 - 3x - \cos\theta$, which in general is irreducible.

Exercise 3. *Let K be a field; let a_1 be transcendental over K; and let a_i be transcendental over $(K \cup \{a_1, \ldots, a_{i-1}\})$, $2 \le i \le n$. Then $(K \cup \{a_1, \ldots, a_n\})$ is isomorphic to the field of quotients of the polynomial ring $K[x_1, \ldots, x_n]$ in n indeterminates over K.* [This field is called the field of **rational functions** in n indeterminates over K, and is denoted by $K(x_1, \ldots, x_n)$.]

Exercise 4. *Let* $K \subseteq L$ *be fields, and let* S *be a subset of* L. *We say that* S *is* **algebraically independent** *over* K *if for all* $n \in \mathbf{N}$ *and all* $\varphi \in K[x_1, \ldots, x_n]$, $\varphi \neq 0$, *there exist no distinct elements* $s_1, \ldots, s_n$ *of* S *which take* φ *into* 0 *when they are substituted for* $x_1, \ldots, x_n$, *respectively. Prove that:* (a) $\varnothing$ *is algebraically independent over* K; (b) $\{s\}$ *is algebraically independent over* K *if and only if* s *is transcendental over* K; (c) S *is algebraically independent over* K *if and only if* s *is transcendental over* $(K \cup S - \{s\})$ *for all* $s \in S$; (d) *If* $\{s_1, \ldots, s_n\}$ *is algebraically independent over* K, *then* $(K \cup \{s_1, \ldots, s_n\}) \cong K(x_1, \ldots, x_n)$.

Exercise 5. *Let* $K \subseteq L$ *be fields. Prove that there exists a subset* B *of* L *which is algebraically independent over* K, *and such that every element of* L *is algebraic over* $(K \cup B)$. [Hint: Let B be a *maximal* algebraically independent (over K) subset of L. (Why must such exist?)] Such a B is called a **transcendence base** for L over K. Note that $B = \varnothing$ if and only if every element of L is algebraic over K.

Exercise 6. *Let* $K \subseteq L$ *be fields; let* S *be a subset of* L *such that every element of* L *is algebraic over* $(K \cup S)$; *and let* B *be a maximal algebraically independent* (*over* K) *subset of* S. *Prove that* B *is a transcendence base for* L *over* K. [Hint: Use Corollaries 1 and 3 to Proposition 5.]

Corollary. *Let* A *be a subset of* L *which is algebraically independent over* K; *then there exists a subset* S' *of* S *such that* $A \cup S'$ *is a transcendence base for* L *over* K, *and* $A \cap S' = \varnothing$. [Hint: Let B be a maximal algebraically independent subset of $S \cup A$ which contains A; let $S' = B - A$.]

Exercise 7. *Let* B *be a transcendence base for* L *over* K *which has* n *elements. Prove that every algebraically independent* (*over* K) *subset of* L *has at most* n *elements, and that every transcendence base for* L *over* K *has exactly* n *elements.* [Hint: Let B, C be transcendence bases for L over K, let $c \in C$, and let B' be a subset of B such that $c \notin B'$ and $B' \cup \{c\}$ is a transcendence base for L over K (corollary to Exercise 6). Then B' and $C - \{c\}$ are transcendence bases for L over $(K \cup \{c\})$, so that by induction hypothesis they have the same number of elements.] We call n the **transcendence degree** of L over K.

71. FINITE FIELDS

We can say little about finite semirings or rings, but we can give a complete description of the finite domains (and, in particular, of the finite division rings), which in fact turn out to be the same as the finite fields. We begin with

Theorem 1. *Any finite field has* p^k *elements for some* p *and* k *in* $\mathbf{N}$, *where* p *is prime; its additive group is isomorphic to the direct sum of* k $\mathbf{I}_p$'s, *and its multiplicative group is isomorphic to* $\mathbf{I}_{p^k - 1}$.

Proof: If the field K is finite, its prime field K_0 must be $\cong \mathbf{I}_p$ for some prime $p \in \mathbf{N}$. Let the dimension of K as a vector space over K_0 be k; then K has p^k elements, and its additive group is isomorphic to that of the k-dimensional vector space over $\mathbf{I}_p$. Let $a \in K - \{0\}$ have maximal multiplicative order m; then m divides $p^k - 1$, the order of the multiplicative group $K - \{0\}$. By Corollary 2 to Proposition 46.5 we have $b^m = 1$ for all $b \in K - \{0\}$. Hence every such b is a root of $x^m - 1$, which must thus (Exercise 62.5, corollary) have degree $\geq$ the number of b's, that is, $m \geq p^k - 1$. Hence $m = p^k - 1 = o(K - \{0\})$, so that $K - \{0\} = (a)$ is cyclic. //

Exercise 1. *Generalize the last part of the proof of Theorem 1 to prove that any finite multiplicative subgroup of a field is cyclic.*

We next prove that, conversely, for every such k and p there exists a unique field with p^k elements. To do this, we first show that given any field K and any polynomial in $K[x]$ of degree > 0, there exists a field containing an isomorphic image K^* of K and also containing a root of the corresponding polynomial in $K^*[x]$.

Proposition 1. *Let K be a field, and let $\psi = \sum_{i=0}^n c_i x^i \in K[x]$ have degree > 0. Then there exist a field L, a subfield K^* of L isomorphic to K, and an element a of L, such that $L = (K^* \cup \{a\})$ and $\sum_{i=0}^n c_i^* a^i = 0$, where $c_i^* \in K^*$ corresponds to $c_i \in K$ under the isomorphism.*

Proof: Let $\varphi = \sum_{i=0}^m b_i x^i$ be an irreducible nonunit factor of ψ, say $\psi = \varphi\theta$, and let $L = K[x]/\varphi K[x]$; since φ is an irreducible nonunit, L is a field. Let F be the canonical homomorphism of $K[x]$ onto L, and let F' be its restriction to the set K' of constant polynomials. Since φ has degree > 0, constant polynomials cannot differ by a multiple of φ unless they are equal; thus F' is an isomorphism of K' with $F'(K') = K^*$ (say), and since $K \cong K'$, this proves $K \cong K^*$. Moreover, we have $0 = F(\varphi) = F(\varphi)F(\theta) = F(\psi) = F(\sum_{i=0}^n c_i x^i) = \sum_{i=0}^n F'(c_i)(F(x))^i$; set $a = F(x)$ to give $\sum_{i=0}^n c_i^* a^i = 0$. To see that $(K^* \cup \{a\}) = L$, use the fact that a homomorphic image of a set of generators is a set of generators.

As a generalization of Proposition 1 we have

Proposition 2. *Let K and ψ be as in Proposition 1; then there exist a field L_ψ, a subfield K_ψ of L_ψ, and elements $a_1, \ldots, a_n$ of L_ψ, such that $K \cong K_\psi$; $L_\psi = (K_\psi \cup \{a_1, \ldots, a_n\})$; and $\sum_{i=0}^n c_i^\psi x^i = c_n^\psi \prod_{i=1}^n (x - a_i)$, where the $c_i^\psi \in K_\psi$ correspond to the $c_i \in K$. Moreover, L_ψ is unique up to isomorphism.*

Proof: If $n = 1$, say $\psi = c_1 x + c_0$, take $L_\psi = K_\psi = K$; $a_1 = -c_1^{-1} c_0$. Furthermore, for any K_ψ, L_ψ, a_1 which are as in the proposition we must have $c_1^\psi a_1 + c_0^\psi = c_1^\psi (a_1 - a_1) = 0$, so that $a_1 = -(c_1^\psi)^{-1} c_0^\psi \in K_\psi$, whence $L_\psi = K_\psi \cong K$, proving uniqueness. We proceed by induction on n; let L,

K^*, φ, a be as in Proposition 1 and its proof. Now (Exercise 62.5) $x - a$ divides $\sum_{i=0}^{n} c_i^* x^i$ in $L[x]$, say $\sum_{i=0}^{n} c_i^* x^i = q(x - a)$, where $q = \sum_{i=0}^{n-1} d_i x^i$ has degree $n - 1$. Hence by induction hypothesis there exist $L^{\#} \subseteq L_\psi = (L^{\#} \cup \{a_2, \ldots, a_n\})$ such that $L \simeq L^{\#}$ and $\sum_{i=0}^{n-1} d_i^{\#} x^i = d_{n-1}^{\#} \prod_{i=2}^{n} (x - a_i)$. Let F be this isomorphism of L with $L^{\#}$, and let $K_\psi = F(K^*)$, $a_1 = F(a)$; then $K_\psi \simeq K^* \simeq K$ and $L^{\#} = F((K^* \cup \{a\})) = (K_\psi \cup \{a_1\})$, so that $L_\psi = (K_\psi \cup \{a_1, \ldots, a_n\})$. Moreover,

$$\sum_{i=0}^{n} c_i^\psi x^i = \sum_{i=0}^{n} F(c_i^*) x^i = \left(\sum_{i=0}^{n-1} F(d_i) x^i \right)(x - F(a)) = \left(\sum_{i=0}^{n-1} d_i^{\#} x^i \right)(x - a_1)$$
$$= d_{n-1}^{\#} \prod_{i=1}^{n} (x - a_i),$$

and since the left member has leading coefficient c_n^ψ, we must have $d_{n-1}^{\#} = c_n^\psi$. Finally, by Proposition 70.1, $L^{\#}$ is unique up to isomorphism, and by induction hypothesis this makes L_ψ unique up to isomorphism. //

L_ψ is called the **splitting field** of ψ over K (we can use "the" since L_ψ is unique). We can similarly speak of the splitting field of a finite set of polynomials over K. The uniqueness of the splitting field can be restated as follows: Let $K \subseteq L$ be fields such that $L = (K \cup \{a_1, \ldots, a_n\})$, where each a_i is algebraic over K, and suppose that in $L[x]$, each $\varphi_{a_i, K}$ "splits"—in other words, is a product of polynomials of degrees ≤ 1; then L is (isomorphic to) the splitting field of $\{\varphi_{a_i, K} \mid i \in \mathbf{N}_n\}$. Note that by Exercise 62.5 and unique factorization, if L contains n_i roots of $\varphi_{a_i, K}$, where n_i is the degree of $\varphi_{a_i, K}$, then $\varphi_{a_i, K}$ must "split" in $L[x]$.

We can now prove

Theorem 2. *For any p, k in $\mathbf{N}$, where p is prime, there exists a field with p^k elements, and any two such fields are isomorphic.*

Proof: For the uniqueness, note that if K is such a field, then for any $a \in K - \{0\}$ we have $a^{p^k - 1} = 1$, so that every element of K is a root of $x^{p^k} - x$, which implies that K must be its splitting field over $\mathbf{I}_p$. Conversely, let L be this splitting field; we shall show that the set $L' \subseteq L$ of roots of $x^{p^k} - x$ is a field, so must be all of L, and that there are p^k roots, so that L has p^k elements. Note first that $L' - \{0\}$ is a multiplicative group, since $a^{p^k} = a$ and $b^{p^k} = b$ evidently imply $(ab^{-1})^{p^k} = (a^{p^k})(b^{p^k})^{-1} = ab^{-1}$. Moreover, by Exercise 59.3 we have $(a - b)^{p^k} = a^{p^k} + (-b)^{p^k} = a - b$ (if $p = 2$, the last step is still valid since $-b = b$); thus L' is also an additive group, hence a field, so that $L' = L$. Finally, let $x^{p^k} - x = \prod_{i=1}^{p^k} (x - a_i)$, where the a's are in L. If any two a's were equal, by Exercise 62.6 the repeated one would have to be a root of $p^k x^{p^k - 1} - 1 = -1$. But this has no roots; hence there are p^k distinct a's. //

Corollary. *Any subfield of the finite field with p^k elements has p^d elements, where d divides k; conversely, for any such d there is such a subfield.*

Proof: Let the subfield have n elements; since the given field is a vector space over it, p^k must be a power of n. Conversely, the splitting field of $x^{p^k} - x$ contains that of its factor $x^{p^d} - x$.   //

Exercise 2. *If K is a finite field of characteristic p, then for any $n \in \mathbf{N}$, the function $\{(a, a^{p^n}) \mid a \in K\}$ is an automorphism of K.* [Hint: By the proof of Theorem 2, every element of K is a pth power, hence a p^nth power.]

Exercise 3. *If K is the finite field with p^k elements, then for any $a \in K$ we have $g_a{}^{p^k} = g_a$ (see Exercise 59.5).*

FINITE DIVISION RINGS AND DOMAINS

In the remainder of this section we prove that any finite division ring, and in fact any finite domain, is a field. Thus Theorem 1 actually gives a complete description of the finite domains.

Lemma 1. *Let K be a finite field; then for all a, b, c in K, none of them 0, there exist u, v in K such that $au^2 + bv^2 = c$.*

Proof: If K has characteristic 2, every element of K is a square, and we can take $u = 0$, $v^2 = b^{-1}c$. Otherwise, K has odd prime characteristic p, and has (say) p^n elements. Now if $z \neq 0$ we have $aw^2 = az^2$ if and only if $(wz^{-1})^2 = 1$, so that $wz^{-1} = \pm 1$, that is, $w = \pm z$, where the two values are distinct since $p \neq 2$. Thus $A = \{aw^2 \mid w \in K - \{0\}\}$ has $(p^n - 1)/2$ nonzero elements. Similarly $c - bw^2 = c - bz^2$ (where $z \neq 0$) if and only if $w = \pm z$, so that $B = \{c - bw^2 \mid w \in K - \{0\}\}$ also has $(p^n - 1)/2$ elements, all different from c. Hence $\{aw^2 \mid w \in K\} = A \cup \{0\}$ and $\{c - bw^2 \mid w \in K\} = B \cup \{c\}$ each has $(p^n - 1)/2 + 1 = (p^n + 1)/2$ elements. If these subsets of K were disjoint, their union would thus have $p^n + 1$ elements, which is impossible since K has only p^n elements. Hence their intersection is nonempty, say $ax^2 = c - by^2$, which is what we want.   //

Lemma 2. *Let D be a division ring, K its center (see Exercise 60.4). Let $a \in D - K$ be such that the monogenic field (a) is finite. Then some positive power of a other than itself is a conjugate of a in the multiplicative group of D.*

Proof: (1) $\subset (a)$ must be finite, so that D has prime characteristic p, and by the proof of Theorem 2 there exists $k \in \mathbf{N}$ such that (a) is the set of roots of $x^{p^k} - x$, that is, $x^{p^k} - x = \prod_{i=1}^{p^k} (x - a_i)$, where the a's are the elements of (a).

Let $E(D)$ be the ring of endomorphisms of the additive group of D. Let $f_i = \{(u, a_i u) \mid u \in D\}$; thus $f_i \in E(D)$, $1 \leq i \leq p^k$. Let $F = \{(a_i, f_i) \mid a_i \in (a)\}$; readily F is an isomorphism of (a) with a subfield A of $E(D)$. Thus in the polynomial ring $E(D)[x]$ we have $x^{p^k} - x = \prod_{i=1}^{p^k} (x - f_i)$, where the coefficient 1 now denotes the identity function on D, and multiplication means composition of functions.

Let $g_a = \{(u, ua - au) \mid u \in D\}$. Readily g_a is in $E(D)$ and commutes with every element of A. Hence the subring $A^* = (A \cup \{g_a\})$ of $E(D)$ is commutative, so that if we regard $x^{p^k} - x$ and $\prod_{i=1}^{p^k} (x - f_i)$ as polynomials in $A^*[x]$, we have $g_a^{p^k} - g_a = \prod_{i=1}^{p^k} (g_a - f_i)$.

Now by Exercise 3, $g_a^{p^k} = g_a$ for all $k \in \mathbf{N}°$; hence $\prod_{i=1}^{p^k} (g_a - f_i) = 0$, that is, the composite of the functions $g_a - f_i$ takes every $u \in D$ into 0. Suppose that $g_a - f_i$ were one-to-one for every i such that $a_i \neq 0$; then the remaining factor, g_a, would have to take every $u \in D$ into 0, that is, $ua - au = 0$ for all $u \in D$. But then a would commute with every $u \in D$, so that $a \in K$, contrary to the choice of a. Hence there exist $a_j \neq 0$, and $b \neq 0$ in D, such that $(g_a - f_j)(b) = 0$, that is, $ba - ab - a_jb = 0$, so that $bab^{-1} = a + a_j$ is in (a), and is not a itself, since $a_j \neq 0$.

Let a have multiplicative order r; then $1, a, \ldots, a^{r-1}$ are distinct elements of (a) and are all roots of $x^r - 1 \in (a)[x]$. It can thus have no other roots in (a); but $(bab^{-1})^r = ba^r b^{-1} = bb^{-1} = 1$, so that bab^{-1}, which is in (a), is also a root. Hence $a \neq bab^{-1} = a^i$ for some $i \neq 1$. Moreover, we cannot have $i = 0$ since then $bab^{-1} = 1$, so that $a = 1$ is in K, contradiction; thus $i \geq 2$, as desired. $\quad //$

We can now prove

Theorem 3. *A finite division ring is a field.*

Proof: If not, let D be a finite noncommutative division ring with the fewest possible elements, and let $K \subset D$ be the center of D. We break the proof up into six steps:

(1) Let $ab \neq ba$ but $ab^k = b^k a$ for some $k \in \mathbf{N}$; then $b^k \in K$—in fact, the set of elements of D which commute with b^k is a division subring of D and contains a and b, hence is not commutative and so must be all of D.

(2) Since $D - \{0\}$ is a finite group, any element of D has finite multiplicative order, and in particular has a power in K. Let r be the smallest natural number such that $a^r \in K$ for any $a \in D - K$; then r is prime—indeed, if $r = st$ with $1 < s < r$, $1 < t < r$, we would have $a^s \notin K$ but $(a^s)^t \in K$ with $t < r$, contradiction.

(3) Let $a \in D - K$ be such that $a^r \in K$, and let $bab^{-1} = a^k \neq a$ as in Lemma 2, where evidently $b \notin K$. Then $b^2ab^{-2} = ba^kb^{-1} = (bab^{-1})^k = a^{k^2}$, and similarly $b^{r-1}ab^{1-r} = a^{k^{r-1}}$. But since r is prime, by the corollary to Exercise 46.5 we have $k^{r-1} = qr + 1$ for some $q \in \mathbf{N}$; thus $b^{r-1}ab^{1-r} = ca$, where $c = a^{qr}$ is in K. By the minimality of r, we have $b^{r-1} \notin K$; by step (1), we thus cannot have $b^{r-1}a = ab^{r-1}$, so that c cannot be 1. On the other hand, $c^r a^r = (ca)^r = (b^{r-1}ab^{1-r})^r = b^{r-1}a^r b^{1-r} = a^r$, since $a^r \in K$; hence $c^r = 1$, and since $c \neq 1$ and r is prime, the multiplicative order of c must be exactly r.

Let t be any element of D such that $t^r = 1$; then in the field $(K \cup \{t\})$, the polynomial $x^r - 1$ has the root t. But since c has order r, this polynomial has the r distinct roots $1, c, \ldots, c^{r-1}$; hence t must be a power of c.

(4) Let $b^{r-1} = d$; then $dad^{-1} = ca = ac$, so that $a^{-1}da = cd$. Hence $d^r = c^r d^r = (cd)^r = (a^{-1}da)^r = a^{-1}d^r a$, that is, $ad^r = d^r a$, so that by step (1) we have $d^r \in K$. Let w generate the multiplicative group of K, and let $a^r = w^i$, $d^r = w^j$. If r divided i, we would have $(a/w^{i/r})^r = 1$, so that by the last part of step (3), $a/w^{i/r} = c^h$ (say), that is, $a = w^{i/r}c^h \in K$, contradiction; hence r does not divide i, and similarly it does not divide j. Let $a^* = a^j$, $d^* = d^i$; thus $a^* \notin K$, $d^* \notin K$, but $a^{*r} = d^{*r} = w^{ij} \in K$. Moreover, by Lemma 55.2, since $dad^{-1}a^{-1} = c$ commutes with d and a, we have $d^i a^j d^{-i} a^{-j} = (dad^{-1}a^{-1})^{ij} = c^{ij}$, that is, $d^* a^* = c^{ij} a^* d^*$. Since r is prime and divides neither i nor j, it cannot divide ij, and since c has order r, we thus have $c^{ij} \neq 1$. Let $c^{ij} = c^*$; thus $c^* \neq 1$ but evidently $c^{*r} = 1$.

(5) By Lemma 55.3 we have $(a^{*-1}d^*)^k = a^{*-k}d^{*k}c^{*k(k-1)/2}$ for all $k \in \mathbb{N}$. [To see this, note that $d^*a^*d^{*-1}a^{*-1} = c^*$, so that $d^*a^*d^{*-1} = c^*a^* = a^*c^*$; hence $[a^{*-1}, d^*] = a^{*-1}d^*a^*d^{*-1} = c^*$.] Let $k = r$; if r is odd, it divides $r(r-1)/2$, so that $(a^{*-1}d^*)^r = 1$. Thus $a^{*-1}d^* = c^h$ (say), that is, $d^* = c^h a^*$, so that a^* and d^* commute, contradicting the fact that $c^* \neq 1$. This contradiction proves the theorem unless $r = 2$.

(6) If $r = 2$, we have $a^{*2} = d^{*2} \in K$, and $d^*a^* = c^*a^*d^*$, where $c^* \in K$, $c^* \neq 1$, and $c^{*2} = 1$. Thus $c^* = -1$, and $(a^*d^*)^2 = a^*(d^*a^*)d^* = -a^*(a^*d^*)d^* = -a^{*4}$. (Note that the characteristic of K cannot be 2, since $-1 = c^* \neq 1$.) Let u, v in K be such that $a^{*2}u^2 - v^2 = 1$ (Lemma 1). Then readily $(a^* + vd^* + ua^*d^*)^2 = a^{*2}(1 + v^2 - u^2a^{*2}) + ua^*(a^*d^* + d^*a^*) + v(a^*d^* + d^*a^*) + uv(a^*d^* + d^*a^*)d^* = 0$, so that $a^* + vd^{*2} + ua^*d^* = 0$. We thus have $0 = a^*(a^* + vd^* + ua^*d^*) + (a^* + vd^* + ua^*d^*)a^* = 2a^* + v(a^*d^* + d^*a^*) + ua^*(a^*d^* + d^*a^*) = 2a^{*2} \neq 0$, a contradiction, which completes the proof. //

Corollary. *A finite domain is empty, trivial, or a field.*

Proof: If D has more than one element, the multiplicative semigroup $D - \{0\}$ is a nonempty finite cancellation semigroup, whence a group (Proposition 45.5), making D a division ring. //

Exercise 4. *A domain whose set of principal left ideals, ordered by inclusion, satisfies the minimum condition is empty, trivial, or a division ring.* [Hint: Proposition 45.6.]

Proposition 3. *A domain which is finite dimensional as a vector space over a subfield of its center is a division ring.*

Proof: Let R be the domain, K the subfield; then the identity of K is a cancellable idempotent, hence is an identity for R (Proposition 34.1). Moreover, for any $x \in R$, the function $L_x = \{(x, xy) \mid y \in R\}$ is an endomorphism of the vector space R. Since R is a domain, L_x is one-to-one provided that $x \neq 0$; hence (Corollary 1 to Theorem 68.2) L_x is onto, so that in particular x has a multiplicative inverse.   //

A much shorter proof of Theorem 3 can be given if we assume some simple facts about complex numbers. Let D be any division ring, K its center; readily $K - \{0\}$ is the center of the multiplicative group $D - \{0\}$. If D is finite, its dimension as a vector space over K must be finite, say $= k$; thus if K has m elements, D has m^k elements. Similarly, the centralizer $C(a)$ of any $a \in D$ is a division subring of D containing K, and so has m^d elements for some d dividing k. The class equation of $D - \{0\}$ is thus $m^k - 1 = m - 1 + \sum (m^k - 1)/(m^d - 1)$, where the d's divide k and are not equal to k. Let ψ_k be the least common multiple in $K_0[x]$ (where K_0 is the prime field of K) of the set of polynomials $\{x^d - 1 \mid d \mid k, d \in \mathbf{N}_{k-1}\}$. Since each $x^d - 1$ divides $x^k - 1$, so does ψ_k; let $x^k - 1 = \psi_k \Phi_k$. [Φ_k is called the kth **cyclotomic polynomial**.] Thus Φ_k divides $x^k - 1$ and also divides every $(x^k - 1)/(x^d - 1)$, so that $\Phi_k(m)$ (which we can regard as an integer) divides $m^k - 1$ and every term $(m^k - 1)/(m^d - 1)$ of the class equation, and so must divide $m - 1$.

Let Φ_k, regarded as a polynomial over the field of complex numbers, be equal to $\prod_{i=1}^{k'} (x - \zeta_i)$, where k' is the degree of Φ_k and the ζ's are the roots of $x^k - 1$ which are not roots of $x^d - 1$ for any $d < k$. Then $\Phi_k(m) = |\Phi_k(m)| = \prod_{i=1}^{k'} |m - \zeta_i|$, where the bars denote absolute value. If $k > 1$, none of the ζ's is 1, so that (using the fact that the $m - \zeta_i$ lie on a circle of radius 1 about $(m, 0)$ in the complex plane) we have $|m - \zeta_i| > |m - 1|$ $= m - 1 \geq 1$ for each i; thus $\Phi_k(m) > m - 1$, contradicting the fact that $\Phi_k(m)$ divides $m - 1$. Hence we must have $k = 1$, so that $D = K$ is a field.

72. SUBFIELDS OF MONOGENIC AND FINITELY GENERATED FIELDS

In this section we prove that any subfield of a monogenic algebraic field is monogenic algebraic, and that any subfield of a monogenic transcendental field is either prime or monogenic transcendental. At the same time, we show that the monogenic algebraic fields are the same as the lattice-finite fields. We also prove that any subfield of a finitely generated field is finitely generated.

SUBFIELDS OF MONOGENIC ALGEBRAIC FIELDS

Theorem 1. *The following statements about the field K are equivalent:*

(1) *K is lattice-finite*
(2) *K is monogenic algebraic—that is, $K = (a)$, where a is algebraic over the prime field K_0*
(3) *K is finitely generated algebraic—that is, $K = (a_1, \ldots, a_n)$, where each a_i is algebraic over K_0.*

Proof: If (1) holds, and any $a \in K$ were transcendental over K_0, the monogenic subfield (a) would have infinitely many subfields, for example, (a^2), $(a^3), \ldots$; hence every $a \in K$ is algebraic over K_0, and evidently K must be finitely generated, proving (3).

If (2) holds, let K' be a subfield of K, so that $K_0 \subseteq K' \subseteq K = (a)$; let $\varphi_{a,K'} = \sum_{i=0}^{m} c_i x^i$, and let $K^* = (K_0 \cup \{c_0, \ldots, c_m\})$, so that $K^* \subseteq K'$. Since $\varphi_{a,K'}$ is irreducible in $K'[x]$, it is certainly irreducible in $K^*[x]$, and so must be φ_{a,K^*}. Hence deg $((a):K') = $ deg $((a):K^*)$, so that $K' = K^*$. Now $\varphi_{a,K'}$ divides φ_{a,K_0} in $K'[x]$, hence in $K[x]$; thus any subfield K' is generated by the set of coefficients of a factor of φ_{a,K_0} in $K[x]$ which has leading coefficient 1. Since by unique factorization there are only finitely many such factors, there can be only finitely many subfields, proving (1).

If (3) holds and K_0 is finite, so is K, so that by Theorem 71.1, the multiplicative group $K - \{0\}$ is cyclic. Let a generate this group; then clearly a generates K as a field, proving (2). It thus remains only to show that (3) implies (2) in the case $K_0 \cong \mathbf{R}$; and by induction on n, it suffices to show that if b, c are algebraic over $\mathbf{R}$, then (b, c) is monogenic.

To this end, note first that if $\varphi = \sum_{i=0}^{k} a_i x^i \in \mathbf{R}[x]$ is irreducible, and is equal to $a_k \prod_{i=1}^{k} (x - x_i)$ in the ring of polynomials over its splitting field L, then the x_i must be distinct—for if any x_i occurred twice, it would also be a root of $\varphi' = \sum_{i=0}^{k} i a_i x^{i-1}$, a nonzero polynomial (for example, $k a_k \neq 0$ since $a_k \neq 0$); hence φ and φ' would have a common divisor in $L[x]$ of degree ≥ 1, so that (Proposition 62.1) their greatest common divisor in $\mathbf{R}[x]$ would also have degree ≥ 1, which is impossible since φ is irreducible.

Let the roots of $\varphi_{b,\mathbf{R}} = \sum_{i=0}^{r} b_i x^i$ and $\varphi_{c,\mathbf{R}} = \sum_{i=0}^{s} c_i x^i$ [in a splitting field, which we may regard as containing (b, c)] be $b, u_2, \ldots, u_r$ and $c, v_2, \ldots, v_s$, respectively. Let $d \in \mathbf{R}$ be different from 0 and from every $-(u_i - b)/(v_j - c)$, $2 \leq i \leq r$, $2 \leq j \leq s$; let $a = b + dc$, so that $(a) \subseteq (b, c)$. Now c is the only common root of $\sum_{i=0}^{s} c_i x^i$ and $\sum_{i=0}^{r} b_i(a - dx)^i$; indeed, clearly it is a root of both, while if v_j $(2 \leq j \leq s)$ is also a root of both, say $a - dv_j = u_i$, then $b + dc = a = u_i + dv_j$, contrary to the choice of d. Since the v's are all distinct from each other and from c, this means that these polynomials, which are in $(a)[x]$, have $x - c$ as their greatest common divisor. Hence $x - c$ is in $(a)[x]$, so that c is in (a), whence $b = a - dc$ is in (a), proving $(b, c) \subseteq (a)$.   //

Corollary 1. *Any subfield of a monogenic algebraic field is monogenic algebraic.*

In most of the proof of the theorem, no use was made of the fact that K_0 is a prime field. In fact, we have as an easy generalization:

Corollary 2. *The following statements about the fields $K \subseteq L$ are equivalent:*
  (1') *There are only finitely many fields K' such that $K \subseteq K' \subseteq L$*
  (2') $L = (K \cup \{a\})$, *where a is algebraic over K*
  (3') $L = (K \cup \{a_1, \ldots, a_n\})$, *where each a_i is algebraic over K, say of degree d_i, $1 \leq i \leq n$, and $\varphi_{a_i, K}$ has d_i distinct roots in its splitting field, $2 \leq i \leq n$.*

Proof: Analogous to that of the theorem; for example, the last part of that proof used only the fact that $\varphi_{c, \mathbf{R}}$ had s distinct roots.   //

If a is algebraic over K, say of degree d, and $\varphi_{a, K}$ has d distinct roots in its splitting field, we say that a is **separable** over K. The field K is called **perfect** if, in any field containing K, any element which is algebraic over K is separable over K.

Exercise 1. *K is perfect if and only if no irreducible polynomial φ of degree ≥ 1 in $K[x]$ has a divisor of degree ≥ 1 in common with φ'.*

Corollary. *Any field isomorphic to a perfect field is perfect.*

By the fourth paragraph of the proof of Theorem 1, $\mathbf{R}$ is perfect; the same argument can be used to prove

Proposition 1. *Any field whose prime field $\cong \mathbf{R}$ is perfect.*

We also have

Proposition 2. *A field whose prime field $\cong \mathbf{I}_p$ is perfect if and only if every element of it is a pth power.*

Proof: An irreducible $\varphi = \sum_{i=0}^{k} a_i x^i \in K[x]$ can have a divisor of degree ≥ 1 in common with $\varphi' = \sum_{i=0}^{k} i a_i x^{i-1}$ if and only if $\varphi' = 0$, that is, $i a_i = 0$ for all $i \in \mathbf{N}_k^\circ$, so that either $a_i = 0$ or p divides i; thus $\varphi = \sum_{j=0}^{h} a_{jp} x^{jp}$ for some $h \leq k/p$. Let $a_{jp} = b_{jp}^p$, $1 \leq j \leq h$; then $\varphi = \sum_{j=0}^{h} (b_{jp} x^j)^p = (\sum_{j=0}^{h} b_{jp} x^j)^p$ is not irreducible, contradiction. Conversely, if $a \in K$ is not a pth power, let ψ be an irreducible factor in $K[x]$ of $x^p - a$, and let $L = (K^* \cup \{b\})$, where $K^* \cong K$ and b is a root of the polynomial $\psi^* \in K^*[x]$

which corresponds (under the isomorphism) to ψ; then in $L[x]$ we have $x^p - b^p = (x - a)^p$, so that ψ^* does not have p distinct roots.   ∥

Corollary. *Any finite field is perfect.*

Exercise 2. *If K is perfect and $K \subseteq L$, where every element of L is algebraic over K, then L is perfect.*

Exercise 3. *If $K \subseteq L \subseteq M$ are fields, any element of M which is separable over K is also separable over L.*

SUBFIELDS OF MONOGENIC TRANSCENDENTAL FIELDS

We have seen above (corollaries to Theorem 1) that any subfield of a monogenic algebraic field is monogenic algebraic—or, more generally, that if L is monogenic algebraic over K, so is any subfield of L which contains K. We now prove that any subfield of a monogenic transcendental field is either prime or monogenic transcendental; in fact, we have the more general

Theorem 2 (Lüroth). *Let $L = (K \cup \{a\})$, where a is transcendental over K, and let $K \subseteq L' \subseteq L$; then $L' = K$ or $L' = (K \cup \{b\})$, where b is transcendental over K.*

To prove Lüroth's theorem we first establish

Proposition 3. *Let $L = (K \cup \{a\})$, where a is transcendental over K, and let $c \in L - K$; then c is transcendental over K and a is algebraic over $(K \cup \{c\})$.*

Proof: Let $c = (\sum_{i=0}^r a_i a^i)/(\sum_{i=0}^s b_i a^i)$, where the a_i's and b_i's are in K. We can assume $r = s$ (add terms with coefficients $= 0$ as necessary); hence a is a root of $\varphi = \sum_{i=0}^r (a_i - cb_i)x^i \in (K \cup \{c\})[x]$. Now $b_i \neq 0$ implies $a_i - cb_i \neq 0$, since $c \notin K$; hence $\varphi \neq 0$, so that a is algebraic over $(K \cup \{c\})$. If c were algebraic over K, this would make a algebraic over K, contradiction; hence c is transcendental over K.   ∥

We next show that in the proof of Proposition 3, if $\sum_{i=0}^r a_i x^i$ and $\sum_{i=0}^s b_i x^i$ are relatively prime in $K[x]$, then φ is irreducible. Indeed, since c is transcendental over K, the field $(K \cup \{c\})$ is isomorphic to the field $K(y)$ of rational functions in one indeterminate over K. Thus by Proposition 62.5, if φ were not irreducible in $(K \cup \{c\})[x]$, the polynomial

$$\varphi^* = \sum_{i=0}^r (a_i - b_i y)x^i \in (K[y])[x]$$

would also not be irreducible. But φ^* has degree 1 in y (that is, as a polynomial in $(K[x])[y]$, so that it would thus have a factor ψ free of y (that is, $\psi \in K[x]$) and of degree > 0 (in x). Readily, since ψ divides

$$\varphi^* = \left(\sum_{i=0}^r a_i x^i\right) - y\left(\sum_{i=0}^s b_i x^i\right),$$

it must divide both $\sum_{i=0}^{r} a_i x^i$ and $\sum_{i=0}^{s} b_i x^i$, contrary to their relative primeness.

We can now prove Lüroth's theorem. By Proposition 3, any $c \in L' - K$ is transcendental over K, and a is algebraic over $(K \cup \{c\})$, so that a is algebraic over L'. Let $\varphi_{a,L'} = \sum_{i=0}^{m} (u_i/v_i) x^i$ have degree m, where $u_i = \sum_{j=0}^{r_i} a_{ij} a^j$, $v_i = \sum_{j=0}^{s_i} b_{ij} a^j$ with the a_{ij}'s and b_{ij}'s in K. Let $\varphi_i = \sum_{j=0}^{r_i} a_{ij} x^j$, $\psi_i = \sum_{j=0}^{s_i} b_{ij} x^j$, where we can assume for each $i \in \mathbf{N}_m$ that φ_i and ψ_i are relatively prime in $K[x]$. Let $\psi = \sum_{i=0}^{s} b_i x^i$ be the least common multiple of the ψ_i's in $K[x]$, and let $v = \sum_{i=0}^{s} b_i a^i$; let $\varphi^* = v \varphi_{a,L'}$.

Since a is not algebraic over K, not every u_i/v_i can be in K; let $b = u_h/v_h$ not be in K, so that φ_h or ψ_h has degree > 0—let the greater of their degrees be n. Since $\varphi_h - b\psi_h \in L'[x]$ has a as a root, it must be divisible by $\varphi_{a,L'}$. Hence (see the proof of Proposition 62.5) $v_h \varphi_h - u_h \psi_h$ must be divisible by φ^*, say $= \varphi^* \psi^*$. Now the highest power of a in $v_h \varphi_h - u_h \psi_h$ is at most n, while that in φ^* is at least n, since its leading coefficient v is a multiple of v_h, while its coefficient of x^h is a multiple of u_h; hence both are exactly n, and ψ^* is free of a. But as in the paragraph following Proposition 3, since φ_h and ψ_h are relatively prime, $v_h \varphi_h - u_h \psi_h$ cannot be divisible by such a ψ^* unless ψ^* has degree 0. Hence the degree of $v_h \varphi_h - u_h \psi_h$, which by symmetry is the same as its highest power of a, namely n, is the same as that of φ^*, namely m. Thus by the usual dimension argument we must have $L' = (K \cup \{b\})$, where $b \in L'$ is transcendental over K. $/\!/$

SUBFIELDS OF FINITELY GENERATED FIELDS

We conclude this section by proving that any subfield of a finitely generated field is finitely generated. In fact, we shall show that if the field M is finitely generated over its subfield K (that is, $M = (K \cup S)$ where S is finite), so is any subfield of M which contains K.

Let $K \subseteq L \subseteq N$ be fields, and let E be a subring of N which contains K. We say that E is **linearly disjoint** from L over K if every subset of E which is independent in the vector space N over K is still independent in the vector space N over L. [Evidently it suffices that this be true for finite subsets.]

Proposition 4. *If E is a field and is linearly disjoint from L over K, then L is linearly disjoint from E over K.*

Proof: Let $\{x_1, \ldots, x_n\} \subseteq L$ be independent as a subset of the vector space N over K, and let $\sum_{i=1}^{n} a_i x_i = 0$, where the a's are in E. Let $\{b_1, \ldots, b_m\}$ be a basis of the subspace of E (regarded as a vector space over K) generated by $\{a_1, \ldots, a_n\}$. Then $a_i = \sum_{j=1}^{m} c_{ij} b_j$ (say), $1 \le i \le n$, so that

$$0 = \sum_{i=1}^{n} \left(\sum_{j=1}^{m} c_{ij} b_j \right) x_i = \sum_{j=1}^{m} \left(\sum_{i=1}^{n} c_{ij} x_i \right) b_j.$$

Since E is linearly disjoint from L over K, the set of b's is still independent over L. Hence $\sum_{i=1}^{n} c_{ij} x_i = 0$ for each j; and since the x's are independent over K, it follows that every c_{ij}, whence every a_i, is 0, proving that the x's are independent over E. $\parallel$

Exercise 4. *If E is linearly disjoint from L over K, so is its field of quotients.*

Proposition 5. *If there exists a basis for E (as a vector space over K) which is independent over L, then E is linearly disjoint from L over K.*

Proof: Let B be such a basis, and let $\{x_1, \ldots, x_n\}$ be a subset of E which is independent over K. There exist $b_1, \ldots, b_r$ in B such that each x_i is in the subspace S generated by $b_1, \ldots, b_r$. Since the x's are independent, there exist $x_{n+1}, \ldots, x_r$ such that $\{x_1, \ldots, x_r\}$ is a basis for S. But since the b's are still independent over L, S has dimension r over L; hence the x's must still be independent over L. $\parallel$

Corollary. *Let $\{u_1, \ldots, u_n\} \subseteq N$ be algebraically independent over L (Exercise 70.4); then the subring of N generated by $K \cup \{u_1, \ldots, u_n\}$ is linearly disjoint from L over K.*

Proof: The multiplicative semigroup generated by $\{1, u_1, \ldots, u_n\}$ is readily a basis for this subring as a vector space over K, and is still an independent set over L since $\{u_1, \ldots, u_n\}$ is algebraically independent over L. $\parallel$

[By Exercise 4, the field $(K \cup \{u_1, \ldots, u_n\})$ is thus also linearly disjoint from L over K.]

We can now prove

Theorem 3. *If the field M is finitely generated over K (that is, there exist $a_1, \ldots, a_n$ in M such that $M = (K \cup \{a_1, \ldots, a_n\})$) then so is any subfield L of M which contains K.*

Proof: Let B be a transcendence base (Exercise 70.5) for L over K, and C a transcendence base for M over L. Since M has finite transcendence degree over K (Exercise 70.7), and since B and C are subsets of M which are algebraically independent over K, they are finite. In the corollary to Proposition 5, take C for $\{u_1, \ldots, u_n\}$, and $(K \cup B)$ for K; then L is linearly disjoint from $(K \cup B \cup C)$ over $(K \cup B)$. Thus (Proposition 4) any subset of L which is independent over $(K \cup B)$ is still independent over $(K \cup B \cup C)$. It follows that if L were not finite dimensional as a vector space over $(K \cup B)$, M would not be finite dimensional as a vector space over $(K \cup B \cup C)$. But every element of M is algebraic over $(L \cup C)$, and every element of $(L \cup C) = (K \cup B \cup C \cup L)$ is algebraic over $(K \cup B \cup C)$, so that every element of M is algebraic over $(K \cup B \cup C)$; and since $M = (K \cup B \cup C \cup \{a_1, \ldots, a_n\})$, it *is* finite dimensional as a vector space over $(K \cup B \cup C)$ by Proposition 70.5. $\parallel$

Corollary. *Any subfield of a finitely generated field is finitely generated.*

Proof: Take $K = K_0$ in the theorem.   ∥

Note that a sub(semi)ring of a finitely generated (semi)ring need not be finitely generated. For example, let S be the semiring of polynomials in two indeterminates $\mathbf{N}[x, y]$; it is not difficult to show that the subsemiring of S generated by $\{xy^i \mid i \in \mathbf{N}\}$ is not finitely generated. [Another example is the subsemiring $\mathbf{N} \oplus \mathbf{N}$ of $\mathbf{N}^\circ \oplus \mathbf{N}^\circ$, in which readily any set of generators must contain $\{(1, p) \mid p \text{ prime}\}$.] Analogously for rings, one can use as an example the same subset of the polynomial ring $\mathbf{I}[x, y]$.

73. GALOIS THEORY

By Lüroth's theorem, if L is a monogenic transcendental field, any subfield of L is isomorphic to either L or its prime field. We have also seen that if L is a monogenic algebraic field, so is any subfield L' of L, and (Exercise 70.2) the degree of L' over K_0 divides that of L, where K_0 is the prime field. However, this is certainly not a complete description of L', since we have no way of constructing the minimal polynomial of a generator of L' in terms of that of L.

In this section we prove the "fundamental theorem of Galois theory," which establishes a close relationship between the subfields of a given monogenic algebraic field L and the subgroups of a certain finite group. [This theorem can thus be thought of as reducing the problem of describing the subfields of a monogenic algebraic field to the problem of describing the subgroups of the corresponding finite group.] More generally, let $K \subseteq L$ be fields, and let $L = (K \cup \{a\})$, where a is algebraic over K; then we can establish a relationship between the subfields of L which contain K and the subgroups of a certain finite group.

We know (Proposition 70.1) that if $K \subseteq L$ are fields, if a, b in L have the same minimal polynomial over K, and if F is any automorphism of K, then there exists an isomorphism of $(K \cup \{a\})$ with $(K \cup \{b\})$ whose restriction to K is F. In particular, taking F as the identity function on K, there exists an isomorphism of $(K \cup \{a\})$ with $(K \cup \{b\})$ which leaves every element of K fixed. Conversely, if G is any isomorphism of $(K \cup \{a\})$ into a field $M \supseteq K$ which leaves every element of K fixed, then $G(a)$ is algebraic over K and has the same minimal polynomial over K as a, since $\sum_{i=1}^{n} c_i a^i = 0$ implies $\sum_{i=1}^{n} c_i G(a)^i = G(\sum_{i=1}^{n} c_i a^i) = G(0) = 0$. An isomorphism of a field L which leaves every element of a subfield K fixed will be called a *K-isomorphism* of L.

Proposition 1. *The following statements about the fields $K \subseteq L$, where* $\deg (L:K)$ *is defined, are equivalent:*

(1) *Every element of L is algebraic over K, and every K-isomorphism of L is an automorphism*
(2) *Every element of L is algebraic over K, and if a polynomial in K[x] is irreducible and has a root in L, it "splits" in L*
(3) *L is the splitting field of a finite set of polynomials in K[x].*

Proof: By the remarks just above, (1) implies (2). If (2) holds, let $L = (K \cup \{a_1, \ldots, a_n\})$, where each a_i is algebraic over K; then L is evidently the splitting field of $\{\varphi_{a_1,K}, \ldots, \varphi_{a_n,K}\}$. Conversely, let L be the splitting field of $\{\varphi_1, \ldots, \varphi_n\}$; then L is generated by K together with the roots b_{ij} of the φ_i's, and since any K-isomorphism takes b_{ij}'s into (other) b_{ij}'s, it must be an automorphism. //

If $L \supseteq K$ is as in Proposition 1, it is called **normal** over K.

Corollary. *If L is normal over K, and $K \subseteq L' \subseteq L$, then L is normal over L'.*
[Proof: Use (3).]

Let $L = (K \cup \{a_1, \ldots, a_k\})$ be normal over K, say $\deg(L:K) = n$, and let every element of L be separable over K. Let $G_{L/K}$ be the group of all K-automorphisms of L under composition of functions; this group is called the **Galois group** of L over K. By Corollary 2 to Theorem 72.1, we have $L = (K \cup \{a\})$; thus any K-automorphism of L is completely determined if we specify its effect on a. Now a K-automorphism must take a into a root of its minimal polynomial, and since a is separable over K, there are n roots, so that $o(G_{L/K}) = n$.

Theorem 1. *Let L be normal over K, let $\deg(L:K)$ be defined, and let every element of L be separable over K. Then $\{(L', G_{L/L'}) \mid K \subseteq L' \subseteq L\}$ is an order isomorphism of the lattice of subfields of L which contain K, ordered by $\subseteq$, with the lattice of subgroups of $G_{L/K}$, ordered by $\supseteq$; moreover,*

$$\deg(L:L') = o(G_{L/L'}).$$

Proof: Let K' be the set of elements of L left fixed by every automorphism in $G_{L/K}$; clearly K' is a subfield of L and contains K. Now since L is normal over K, any K-isomorphism of L is an automorphism. Hence any $b \in K'$ is left fixed by every K-isomorphism of L, so that b is the only root of $\varphi_{b,K}$. But b is separable over K, so that the number of roots of $\varphi_{b,K}$ is equal to its degree; hence it must have degree 1, that is, $b \in K$, so that $K' = K$.

Let $K \subseteq L' \subseteq L$. By the corollary to Proposition 1, L is normal over L', and by Exercise 72.3, every element of L is separable over L'. The group $G_{L/L'}$ is clearly a subgroup of $G_{L/K}$, and by the first paragraph of the proof, the set of elements of L left fixed by every automorphism in $G_{L/L'}$ is just L'. Hence $\{(L', G_{L/L'}) \mid K \subseteq L' \subseteq L\}$ is a one-to-one function.

Let H be a subgroup of $G_{L/K}$, and let L_H be the subset of L consisting of the elements left fixed by the automorphisms in H; clearly L_H is a field and contains K. Let H' be the group of all L_H-automorphisms of L, so that H' is a subgroup of G and contains H. By the remarks just preceding the theorem, $\deg(L{:}L_H) = o(H')$. Let $L = (L_H \cup \{c\})$, and let the distinct images of c under the automorphisms in H be $c = c_1, c_2, \ldots, c_h$; then the coefficients of $\psi = \prod_{i=1}^{h}(x - c_i)$ are left fixed by any automorphism in H, so are in L_H. But ψ has degree $\leq o(H)$; hence the degree of $L = (L_H \cup \{c\})$ over L_H, which is equal to the degree of an irreducible divisor of ψ, can be at most $o(H)$, so that $o(H') \leq o(H)$. Since $H' \supseteq H$, this proves that $H' = H$, so that $\{(L', G_{L/L'}) \mid K \subseteq L' \subseteq L\}$ is onto; and evidently this function and its inverse are both $\subseteq$-reversing. $\ /\!/$

Corollary 1. $\deg(L'{:}K) = i_{G_{L/K}}(G_{L/L'}).$

Corollary 2. *Let $K \subseteq L$ be fields, K perfect, and let $L = (K \cup \{a\})$, where a is algebraic over K; let $L^* \supseteq L$ be a splitting field of $\varphi_{a,K}$. Then $\{(L', G_{L^*/L'}) \mid K \subseteq L' \subseteq L\}$ is an order isomorphism of the lattice of subfields of L which contain K, ordered by $\subseteq$, with the lattice of subgroups of $G_{L^*/K}$ which contain $G_{L^*/L}$, ordered by $\supseteq$; and $\deg(L'{:}K) = i_{G_{L^*/K}}(G_{L^*/L'}).$*

Proposition 2. $G_{L/g(L')} = g^{-1} \circ G_{L/L'} \circ g$ *for all* $g \in G_{L/K}$ *and all* $K \subseteq L' \subseteq L$.

Proof: Evidently any element of $g^{-1} \circ G_{L/L'} \circ g$ does leave every element of $g(L')$ fixed. Conversely, if h is in $G_{L/g(L')}$, clearly $g \circ h \circ g^{-1}$ is in $G_{L/L'}$, so that h is in $g^{-1} \circ G_{L/L'} \circ g$. $\ /\!/$

Proposition 3. *The set of $h \in G_{L/K}$ such that $h(b) = g(b)$ for all $b \in L'$ is the coset $G_{L/L'} \circ g$.*

Proof: Clearly any $h \in G_{L/L'} \circ g$ does so; conversely, if h does so, evidently $h \circ g^{-1}$ is in $G_{L/L'}$, so that $h \in G_{L/L'} \circ g$. $\ /\!/$

Theorem 2. *Under the order isomorphism of Theorem 1, subfields of L which are normal over K correspond to normal subgroups of $G_{L/K}$; moreover, if L' is normal over K, we have $G_{L'/K} \cong (G_{L/K})/(G_{L/L'})$.*

Proof: By Proposition 2, if $G_{L/L'}$ is normal we have $G_{L/g(L')} = G_{L/L'}$ for all $g \in G_{L/K}$. Since $\{(L', G_{L/L'}) \mid K \subseteq L' \subseteq L\}$ is a one-to-one correspondence, this implies that $g(L') = L'$ for all $g \in G_{L/K}$. Now any K-isomorphism of L' can be "extended," as in Proposition 70.1, to a K-isomorphism of L, and since L is normal over K, this "extension" must be an automorphism; hence any K-isomorphism of L' is the restriction to L' of a K-automorphism of L. We thus have $h(L') = L'$ for all K-isomorphisms h of L', so that every K-isomorphism of L' is an automorphism, proving L' normal over K.

Conversely, if L' is normal over K, every K-isomorphism of L' is an automorphism, so that in particular $g(L') = L'$ for all $g \in G_{L/K}$. Hence $g^{-1} \circ G_{L/L'} \circ g = G_{L/g(L')} = G_{L/L'}$ for all $g \in G_{L/K}$, proving $G_{L/L'}$ normal in $G_{L/K}$.

Finally, by Proposition 3, the set of those $h \in G_{L/K}$ which have the same restriction g' to L' as g does is just the coset $G_{L/L'} \circ g$. Now every K-automorphism of L' is the restriction to L' of some K-automorphism of L. Hence $\{(g', G_{L/L'} \circ g) \mid g' \in G_{L'/K}\}$ is a one-to-one correspondence of $G_{L'/K}$ with $G_{L/K}/G_{L/L'}$, and readily the restriction of a composite is the composite of the restrictions, so that this correspondence is an isomorphism.   //

Theorems 1–2 constitute the **fundamental theorem of Galois theory**.

SOLVABILITY BY RADICALS

We conclude this section by applying Theorem 2 to prove that a polynomial equation of degree > 4 over a field K is not in general "solvable by radicals." For simplicity, we assume that the prime field K_0 is isomorphic to **R**; by Proposition 72.1, this implies that every element of every field considered below is separable over K.

Proposition 4. *Let ζ be a root of $x^n - 1$, but not of $x^d - 1$ for any $d < n$; then $(K \cup \{\zeta\})$ is normal over K, and $G_{(K \cup \{\zeta\})/K}$ is Abelian.*

Proof: $\zeta, \zeta^2, \ldots, \zeta^n = 1$ must all be distinct, since no lower power of ζ is 1; hence they are all of the roots of $x^n - 1$, so that $(K \cup \{\zeta\})$ is normal over K. Moreover, any K-automorphism f of $(K \cup \{\zeta\})$ is determined by specifying $f(\zeta) = \zeta^r$ (where r must evidently be relatively prime to n). Let g be any other such K-automorphism, say $g(\zeta) = \zeta^s$; then $(f \circ g)(\zeta) = \zeta^{rs} = \zeta^{sr} = (g \circ f)(\zeta)$. Thus any f and g in $G_{(K \cup \{\zeta\})/K}$ commute on ζ and on K (since they leave any $a \in K$ fixed), whence on all of $(K \cup \{\zeta\})$.   //

A root of $x^n - 1$ which is not a root of $x^d - 1$ for any $d < n$ is called **primitive**.

Proposition 5. *Let K contain a primitive root of $x^n - 1$, and let $\alpha \notin K$ be a root of $x^n - a$; then $(K \cup \{\alpha\})$ is normal over K and $G_{(K \cup \{\alpha\})/K} \cong \mathbf{I}_n$.*

Proof: The roots of $x^n - a$ are evidently just $\alpha, \zeta\alpha, \ldots, \zeta^{n-1}\alpha$, where ζ is the given primitive root of $x^n - 1$, so that $(K \cup \{\alpha\})$ is normal over K. Moreover, any K-automorphism h_i of $(K \cup \{\alpha\})$ is determined by specifying $h_i(\alpha) = \zeta^i\alpha$; thus h_1 generates $G_{(K \cup \{\alpha\})/K}$, making it the cyclic group of order n.   //

In order for $\psi \in K[x]$ to be "solvable by radicals," its splitting field must be contained in a field of the form $L = (K \cup \{\alpha_1, \ldots, \alpha_n\})$, where for each $i \in \mathbf{N}_n$ there exist $k_i \in \mathbf{N}$ and $a_{i-1} \in (K \cup \{\alpha_1, \ldots, \alpha_{i-1}\}) = L_{i-1}$ such that α_i

is a root of $x^{k_i} - a_{i-1} \in L_{i-1}[x]$. Such an L is called an *extension of K by radicals*.

Proposition 6. *Any extension of K by radicals has a K-isomorphic image which is contained in a normal extension of K by radicals.*

Proof: Suppose that we have constructed a normal L^*_{i-1} which contains a K-isomorphic image of L_{i-1} (for $i = 1$, this is K itself). Let L^*_i be constructed by the method of Proposition 71.1 to contain a K-isomorphic image of L^*_{i-1} and also to contain $\{\zeta_i, \alpha_{i1}, \ldots, \alpha_{im_i}\}$, where ζ_i is a primitive root of $x^{k_i} - 1$, and α_{ij} is a root of $x^{k_i} - f_j(a^*_{i-1})$. [Here a^*_{i-1} is the element of L^*_{i-1} corresponding to $a_{i-1} \in L_{i-1}$, and the f_j's are the K-automorphisms of L^*_{i-1}.] By the proof of Proposition 5, L^*_i contains all of the roots of these latter polynomials; hence L^*_i is the splitting field $\prod_{j=1}^{m_i} (x^{k_i} - f_j(a^*_{i-1})) = \varphi_i$ (say). But the coefficients of φ_i are evidently left fixed by all the f_j's; thus φ_i is in $K[x]$, proving L^*_i normal over K. $\quad /\!/$

Corollary. *If $\psi \in K[x]$ has a root in an extension L of K by radicals, then ψ is solvable by radicals.*

Proof: We can assume that L is normal, so that all of the roots of ψ are in L. $\quad /\!/$

Using Propositions 4–6 we can now prove

Proposition 7. *If the splitting field M_ψ of $\psi \in K[x]$ is contained in a normal extension of K by radicals, then the Galois group $G_{M_\psi/K}$ is solvable.*

> This relationship between the solvability of a polynomial equation by radicals and the solvability of the Galois group of its splitting field is, in fact, the reason for the terminology "solvable group."

Proof: Let M be a normal extension of K by radicals which contains M_ψ. By the proof of Proposition 6 and by Propositions 4–5, there exist $\beta_1, \ldots, \beta_m$ in M such that if we let $M_i = (K \cup \{\beta_1, \ldots, \beta_i\})$, $0 \le i \le m$, then $M_m = M$; M_i is normal over M_{i-1}, $1 \le i \le m$; and $G_{M_i/M_{i-1}}$ is Abelian. Hence by Theorem 2, G_{M/M_i} is normal in $G_{M/M_{i-1}}$ and $G_{M/M_{i-1}}/G_{M/M_i} \cong G_{M_i/M_{i-1}}$ is Abelian. Thus $G_{M/K}$ has a normal series $\{e\} = G_{M/M} \subseteq G_{M/M_{m-1}} \subseteq \cdots \subseteq G_{M/M_1} \subseteq G_{M/K}$ with Abelian factors, and so is solvable. It follows that $G_{M_\psi/K} \cong G_{M/K}/G_{M/M_\psi}$, as a factor group of a solvable group, is also solvable. $\quad /\!/$

Finally, we show that if the coefficients of $\varphi \in K[x]$ are "arbitrary," the Galois group of its splitting field cannot be solvable:

Proposition 8. *Let K^* be the field of rational functions in n indeterminates*

$y_1, \ldots, y_n$ over K. Let $\varphi = x^n - y_1 x^{n-1} + \cdots + (-1)^n y_n \in K^*[x]$, and let L be the splitting field of φ; then $G_{L/K^*} \cong S_n$, the symmetric group.

Proof: Let M be the field of rational functions in n indeterminates $u_1, \ldots, u_n$ over K; let $\psi = \prod_{i=1}^n (x - u_i) = x^n - v_1 x^{n-1} + \cdots + (-1)^n v_n$ (say), and let $N = (K \cup \{v_1, \ldots, v_n\}) \subseteq M$. Evidently M is the splitting field of $\psi \in N[x]$, and since any permutation of the u's leaves the v's and K fixed and defines an automorphism of M, we have $G_{M/N} \cong S_n$. Moreover, N is K-isomorphic to K^*. [To see this, suppose that we had $\psi(v_1, \ldots, v_n) = 0$, where ψ is a polynomial in n indeterminates over K; say $\psi = \sum_{i=1}^k a_i \bar{x}_i$, where each $\bar{x}_i$ is in the multiplicative semigroup generated by $\{1, x_1, \ldots, x_n\}$. Since the v's are sums of products of u's, we can write $\sum_{i=1}^k a_i \bar{v}_i$ as a linear combination C of elements of the multiplicative semigroup generated by the u's and 1. Let the roots of φ in L be $z_1, \ldots, z_n$; evidently the y's are the same functions of the z's as the v's are of the u's. Hence if we substitute the z's for the u's in C we get $\sum_{i=1}^k a_i \bar{y}_i = 0$, which implies that each $a_i = 0$—in other words, that $\psi = 0$—since the y's are algebraically independent over K.] Thus by Proposition 71.2, M is K-isomorphic to L, so that $G_{L/K^*} \cong G_{M/N} \cong S_n$.   //

Corollary. φ *is not solvable by radicals if* $n > 4$.

Proof: By Proposition 7, if it were solvable by radicals, G_{L/K^*} would be a solvable group, contrary to Proposition 49.6.   //

74. SIMPLE RINGS

A simple ring R is one on which there are no congruences but I_R and $R \times R$ —or, equivalently, in which there are no two-sided ideals but $\{0\}$ and R. Thus in particular, a division ring is simple—in fact, it cannot even have proper left or right ideals. We recall also that by Corollary 3 to Theorem 69.1, a *commutative* ring is simple if and only if it is a field or is a zero-ring with additive group $\cong I_p$, where $p = 1$ or is prime. Our goal in this section is to prove

Theorem 1 (Wedderburn–Artin). *A simple ring whose lattice of left ideals satisfies the minimum condition is either prime or isomorphic to the ring of m-by-m matrices over a division ring for some* $m \in N$. *Conversely, any such ring is simple, and its lattice of left ideals satisfies the minimum condition.*

Corollary. *A finite simple ring is either prime or isomorphic to a ring of matrices over a finite field.*

We first establish the converse part.

Proposition 1. *Let* $A_1, \ldots, A_n$ *be submodules of the module A, and let the*

lattice of submodules of each A_i satisfy the minimum condition; then so does that of $A_1 + \cdots + A_n$.

Proof: Proposition 13.2 and induction.   //

Proposition 2. *Let R' be a subring of the ring R such that the lattice of submodules of R (regarded as an R'-module) satisfies the minimum condition; then the lattice of left ideals of R satisfies the minimum condition. Conversely, if the lattice of left ideals of R satisfies the minimum condition, and we regard R as a module over itself, its lattice of submodules satisfies the minimum condition.*

Proof: A left ideal of R is an R'-submodule for any subring R'. Conversely, a subset of R (regarded as a module over itself) is a submodule if and only if it is a left ideal.   //

Proposition 3. *If the lattice of left ideals of the ring R satisfies the minimum condition, so does that of $M_R^{(n)}$ for all $n \in \mathbf{N}$.*

Proof: Let R_{ij} denote the set of n-by-n matrices over R whose entries are all 0 except possibly for the (i, j)th; thus R_{ij} is isomorphic to R as an R-module, so that (Proposition 2) its lattice of R-submodules satisfies the minimum condition. Since $M_R^{(n)} = \sup \{R_{ij} \mid 1 \le i \le n, 1 \le j \le n\}$, by Proposition 1 its lattice of R-submodules, hence (Proposition 2) its lattice of left ideals, also satisfies the minimum condition.   //

Corollary. *If D is a division ring, the lattice of left ideals of $M_D^{(n)}$ satisfies the minimum condition for all $n \in \mathbf{N}$.*

Proposition 4. *If D is a division ring, $M_D^{(n)}$ is simple for all $n \in \mathbf{N}$.*

Proof: Let M_{rs} denote the matrix (a_{ij}) in which $a_{rs} = 1$, while $a_{ij} = 0$ for all $(i, j) \ne (r, s)$. Let I be a nontrivial ideal of $M_D^{(n)}$, and let $(c_{ij}) \in I - \{0\}$, say $c_{hk} \ne 0$. Then I contains $bc_{hk}{}^{-1}M_{ih}(c_{ij})M_{kj} = bM_{ij}$ for all $1 \le i \le n$, $1 \le j \le n$ and all $b \in D$. It follows that I contains any $\sum_{i=1}^n \sum_{j=1}^n b_{ij}M_{ij} = (b_{ij})$, that is, I is all of $M_D^{(n)}$.   //

To prove the direct part of the theorem, we need only show, as remarked at the end of Chapter XI, that there exists an Abelian group A such that the given ring R is a primitive subring of $E^*(A)$. We shall show this below provided that R is not a zero-ring; but if it is a zero-ring, every additive subgroup is an ideal, so that in this case R is prime. We break the proof up into four steps:

(1) If R is any ring and A any left ideal of R, then for each $x \in R$, the function $L_x = \{(a, xa) \mid a \in A\}$ is an endomorphism of the additive group A. Moreover, we have $L_{x+y} = L_x + L_y$ and $L_{xy} = L_y \circ L_x$, so that the function $F = \{(x, L_x) \mid x \in R\}$ is a homomorphism of R into $E^*(A)$.

(2) Let R be a simple ring and not a zero-ring. By Exercise 34.6, the set $T = \{y \mid y \in R; Ry = \{0\}\}$ is an ideal of R; since R is simple, it must be $\{0\}$ or R, and it cannot be R since then R would be a zero-ring.

(3) Let A be a minimal element of the set of nonzero left ideals of R. Then the set $B = \{x \mid x \in R;\ xA = \{0\}\}$ is an ideal of R, and since R is simple, it must be $\{0\}$ or R. If it were R, we would have $RA = \{0\}$, so that $\{0\} \subset A \subseteq T$, contradicting step (2). Hence $B = \{0\}$, and we see that if $x \neq 0$, L_x does not take every element of A into 0, that is, it is not the zero element of $E^*(A)$; thus F is an isomorphism.

(4) It remains only to show that $F(R) \subseteq E^*(A)$ is primitive, or equivalently, that for all $a \neq 0$ in A we have $Ra = A$. Now Ra is a left ideal of R, and since a is in the left ideal A, we have $Ra \subseteq A$; thus by the minimality of A we have $Ra = \{0\}$ or A. But if $Ra = \{0\}$, we would have $a \in T$, contradicting step (2); hence $Ra = A$, as desired. $/\!/$

75. A STRUCTURE THEOREM: SEMISIMPLE RINGS

Just as we did for groups, we can attempt to characterize rings which are isomorphic to direct sums of rings of known types, or which have "normal series" (that is, finite chains of subrings from $\{0\}$ to R, each an ideal of the next larger) whose residue rings are of known types. [Note that we can have no such theorems for division rings, since they cannot have nontrivial normal series nor be nontrivial direct sums.]

In this section we prove one such nontrivial "structure theorem"—analogous to the main result of Section 48—concerning rings which are finite direct sums of simple rings. [Exercise: Which of the other results of Sections 48–49 have straightforward ring analogs?]

Exercise 1. *If R is a commutative ring with identity, prove that R/I is a field if and only if I is maximal (that is, a maximal element of the set of ideals of R other than R itself).*

Corollary 1. *In a commutative ring with identity, every maximal ideal is prime.*

Corollary 2. *In a commutative ring R whose lattice of ideals satisfies the minimum condition, every prime ideal other than R is maximal.*

We first need some results about nilpotent ideals.

Lemma. *Let R be a ring whose lattice $\mathcal{L}_R$ of left ideals, ordered by inclusion, satisfies the minimum condition; then a left ideal of R is nilpotent if and only if every element of it is nilpotent.*

Proof: It suffices to prove "if," or equivalently, that if $L \in \mathcal{L}_R$ is nonnilpotent, it contains a nonnilpotent element. Now the set of nonnilpotent left ideals of R which are contained in L is nonempty, hence has a minimal element M. Since the left ideal $\overline{M}^2$ generated by M^2 is contained in M, by the minimality of M it must either $= M$ or be nilpotent; but its subset M^2 cannot be nilpotent since M is not, so that we must have $\overline{M}^2 = M$. Thus the set $\{I \mid I \in \mathscr{L}_R; I \subseteq M; MI \neq \{0\}\}$ is nonempty (it contains M, since if $M^2 = \{0\}$ we would have $\overline{M}^2 = \{0\}$), hence has a minimal element N. Since $MN \neq \{0\}$, there exists an $x \in N$ such that $Mx \neq \{0\}$. Now Mx is a left ideal and $\subseteq N$, and the left ideal generated by $M(Mx) = M^2x$ is readily $\overline{M}^2x = Mx \neq \{0\}$; hence $M(Mx) \neq \{0\}$, and by the minimality of N we must have $Mx = N$. In particular, there exists a $y \in M$ such that $yx = x$, whence (induction) $y^kx = x$ for all $k \in \mathbf{N}$, and since $x \neq 0$, this proves that y cannot be nilpotent.   //

Corollary. *The sup in $\mathscr{L}_R$ of any set of nilpotent left ideals of R is nilpotent.*

Proof: Corollary 2 to Proposition 60.6.   //

The sup of all the nilpotent left ideals of R is called the **radical** of R, and is denoted by $\langle R \rangle$.

Exercise 2. *If R is commutative, and its lattice of ideals satisfies the minimum condition, then $\langle R \rangle$ is the set of nilpotent elements of R.*

Proposition 1. *If $\mathscr{L}_R$ satisfies the minimum condition, then $\langle R \rangle$ is a nilpotent two-sided ideal and contains every nilpotent right ideal of R.*

Proof: By Exercise 34.9 and Proposition 60.7, the ideal generated by $\langle R \rangle R$ is nilpotent, so that it must be contained in $\langle R \rangle$; but $\langle R \rangle R \subseteq \langle R \rangle$ means that $\langle R \rangle$ is a right ideal too. Similarly, if I is a nilpotent right ideal, then the ideal $\overline{RI}$ generated by RI is a nilpotent two-sided ideal, so that (Proposition 60.6) $I + \overline{RI}$ is nilpotent. But readily $I + \overline{RI}$ is a left ideal; hence we have $I + \overline{RI} \subseteq \langle R \rangle$, and since $\overline{RI}$, as a nilpotent left ideal, is contained in $\langle R \rangle$, so is I.   //

A ring whose lattice of left ideals satisfies the minimum condition, and in which $\langle R \rangle = \{0\}$, is called **semisimple**. By Proposition 1, the requirement $\langle R \rangle = \{0\}$ is equivalent to assuming that $\{0\}$ is the only nilpotent ideal of R. Note that, in particular, this condition is satisfied if R has no nilpotent elements except 0.

Proposition 2. *If $\langle R \rangle$ is a two-sided ideal, $R/\langle R \rangle$ has trivial radical.*

Proof: If $R/\langle R \rangle$ has a nontrivial nilpotent left ideal, it has a nontrivial nilpotent principal left ideal $R(x + \langle R \rangle) = Rx + \langle R \rangle$, say $(Rx + \langle R \rangle)^n \subseteq \langle R \rangle$. Since $\langle R \rangle$ is a two-sided ideal, we have $(Rx + \langle R \rangle)^n = (Rx)^n + \langle R \rangle$; hence $(Rx)^n \subseteq \langle R \rangle$, so that $(Rx)^n$ is nilpotent. But this makes Rx nilpotent, and since Rx is a left ideal we thus have $Rx \subseteq \langle R \rangle$, so that $Rx + \langle R \rangle = \langle R \rangle$, contradiction.   //

Corollary. *If $\mathscr{L}_R$ satisfies the minimum condition, $R/\langle R \rangle$ is semisimple.*

Proof: To see that $\mathscr{L}_{R/\langle R \rangle}$ must satisfy the minimum condition, use Proposition 74.2.   ∥

Proposition 3. *A simple ring R in which $\mathscr{L}_R$ satisfies the minimum condition and $\langle R \rangle$ is a two-sided ideal is either prime or semisimple.*

Proof: If R is simple, the ideal $\langle R \rangle$ must be either R or $\{0\}$. If $\langle R \rangle = R \supset \{0\}$, note that since $\langle R \rangle$ is nilpotent, the ideal $\bar{R}^2$ generated by $R^2 = \langle R \rangle^2$ cannot be all of R (otherwise we would readily have the ideal $\bar{R}^n$ generated by R^n equal to R for all $n \in \mathbf{N}$, so that $\langle R \rangle = R$ could not be nilpotent). Hence $R^2 = \bar{R}^2$ must be $\{0\}$, so that R is a zero-ring. Since any additive subgroup of a zero-ring is an ideal, R can thus be simple only if it is prime.   ∥

Our goal in this section is to prove

Theorem 1 (Wedderburn–Artin). *Any semisimple ring is isomorphic to a finite direct sum of simple rings.*

We first prove a series of propositions about semisimple rings.

Proposition 4. *If R is semisimple, any nontrivial left ideal of R contains a multiplicatively idempotent element other than 0.*

Proof: By the minimum condition, any nontrivial left ideal contains a minimal nontrivial left ideal M, and it suffices to show that any such M contains a nonzero idempotent. Now for any $x \in M$, Mx is a left ideal and $Mx \subseteq M$; hence by the minimality of M, we have $Mx = \{0\}$ or M. If $Mx = \{0\}$ for all $x \in M$, we have $M^2 = \{0\}$, so that M is nilpotent, contrary to the semisimplicity of R; hence $My = M$ for some $y \neq 0$ in M, and in particular there exists an $e \neq 0$ in M such that $ey = y$. Now $A_y = \{z \mid z \in M; zy = 0\}$ is a left ideal, and is not all of M since $ey = y \neq 0$; hence by the minimality of M it must be $\{0\}$. But $e^2 - e$ is in A_y, since $(e^2 - e)y = e(ey) - ey = ey - y = 0$; thus we must have $e^2 - e = 0$, proving e idempotent.   ∥

> It can in fact be shown, more generally, that if $\mathscr{L}_R$ satisfies the minimum condition, then any nonnilpotent left ideal of R contains a nonzero idempotent. [Since no nonzero element of the additive group R can be additively idempotent, we can omit the "multiplicatively" when speaking about nonzero idempotents in R.]

Proposition 5. *If R is semisimple, every left ideal of R is principal; in fact, every left ideal L has a right identity e, and $L = Re$.*

Proof: If $L = \{0\}$, take $e = 0$. Otherwise, there is a nonzero idempotent in L by Proposition 4; let e be such an idempotent for which $A_e = \{z \mid z \in L; ze = 0\}$ is minimal. If $A_e \neq \{0\}$, it contains a nonzero idempotent e', and

$e'e = 0$ since $e' \in A_e$. Let $e'' = e - ee' + e'$; then $e'' \in L$, and readily we have $e''^2 = e''$ and $e'e'' = e'$, while $e = e''e$, so that $A_{e''} \subseteq A_e$. But $e'e = 0$, whereas $e'e'' = e' \neq 0$, so that $A_{e''} \subset A_e$, contradicting the minimality of A_e; hence we must have $A_e = \{0\}$. Now for all $x \in L$ we have $(x - xe)e = 0$, so that $x - xe$ is in A_e; hence $x = xe$, making e a right identity. Finally, $L \supseteq Re \supseteq Le = L$. $\parallel$

Proposition 6. *Any ideal of a semisimple ring has identity.*

Proof: Let I be an ideal, and let e be as in Proposition 5. Let $B_e = \{z \mid z \in I;\ ez = 0\}$; then B_e is a right ideal since I is. Now since e is a right identity in I, we have $B_e e = B_e$; hence $B_e{}^2 = (B_e e)B_e = B_e(eB_e) = \{0\}$, so that B_e is nilpotent. But by Proposition 1, there are no nontrivial nilpotent right ideals; thus $B_e = \{0\}$, and it follows as in the last part of the proof of Proposition 5 that e is also a left identity in I. $\parallel$

Corollary. *A semisimple ring has identity.*

Evidently we have $I = eR = Re$. Note that since e is a two-sided identity. it is unique; we denote it by e_I.

Exercise 3. e_I *is in the center of* R. *Moreover,* $\{(e_I, Re_I)\}$ *is a one-to-one correspondence between the set of idempotents in the center of* R *and the set of two-sided ideals of* R.

Proposition 7. *Any ideal of a semisimple ring is supplemented.*

Proof: Given $I = Re$, let $I' = R(1 - e)$. Since $x = xe + x(1 - e)$ for all $x \in R$, we have $R = I + I'$. On the other hand, if $xe = y(1 - e)$, then $xe = (xe)e = (y(1 - e))e = y(e - e^2) = 0$, so that $I \cap I' = \{0\}$. $\parallel$

This result corresponds to (3) of Theorem 48.2.

Corollary 1. *If* R *is semisimple and* I *is a two-sided ideal of* R, *then any left ideal of* I *is a left ideal of* R.

Proof: Exercise 61.2. $\parallel$

Corollary 2. *A two-sided ideal of a semisimple ring is a semisimple ring.*

Corollary 3. *A minimal nontrivial two-sided ideal of a semisimple ring is a simple ring.*

Proposition 8. *If* $S_1, \ldots, S_n$ *are distinct minimal nontrivial two-sided ideals of a semisimple ring, then their sup is isomorphic to their direct sum.*

Proof: Let x be in $S_i \cap \sup \{S_j \mid j \in \mathbf{N}_n - \{i\}\}$, say

$$x = x_i = x_1 + \cdots + x_{i-1} + x_{i+1} + \cdots + x_n$$
$$= x_1 e_1 + \cdots + x_{i-1}e_{i-1} + x_{i+1}e_{i+1} + \cdots + x_n e_n,$$

where e_j is the identity of S_j; then

$$x = x_i e_i = x_1(e_1 e_i) + \cdots + x_{i-1}(e_{i-1} e_i) + x_{i+1}(e_{i+1} e_i) + \cdots + x_n(e_n e_i).$$

But $e_j e_i$ is in $S_j \cap S_i$, which is a two-sided ideal and properly contained in the minimal ideal S_i; hence $S_j \cap S_i = \{0\}$, so that $e_j e_i = 0$ for each $j \in N_n - \{i\}$, proving that $x = 0$.   ‖

We can now finally prove Theorem 1. Let R be semisimple, and let $\mathscr{S}$ be the set of sups of finite sets of minimal nontrivial two-sided ideals of R; thus $\mathscr{S}$ is a set of two-sided ideals of R. Let $\mathscr{S}'$ be the set of direct supplements of the ideals in $\mathscr{S}$, and let S' be a minimal element of $\mathscr{S}'$, say $S_1 \oplus \cdots \oplus S_n \oplus S' \cong R$. If $S' \neq \{0\}$, it contains a nontrivial minimal two-sided ideal $S = Re$, which is an ideal of R, and $S' \cong S \oplus R(e' - e)$, where e' is the identity of S'. But then $(S_1 \oplus \cdots \oplus S_n \oplus S) \oplus R(e' - e) \cong R$ with $R(e' - e) \subset S'$, contrary to the minimality of S'; hence $S' = \{0\}$, and $R \cong S_1 \oplus \cdots \oplus S_n$ is a finite direct sum of simple rings by Corollary 3 to Proposition 7.   ‖

Corollary. *A commutative semisimple ring is isomorphic to a finite direct sum of fields.*

76. LATTICE-FINITE RINGS

In this section we apply the results of Sections 74–5 to prove

Theorem 1. *A ring with identity is lattice-finite if and only if it is finite.*

We break the proof of "only if" down into steps as follows:

(1) The subring generated by 1 is finite.

Proof: If R had characteristic 0, the subring I generated by 1 would be isomorphic to **I**, which has infinitely many subrings. Hence R has characteristic k for some $k \in N$, and readily $I = \{0, \ldots, k - 1\}$, where the integers denote sums of corresponding numbers of 1's.

(2) There are only finitely many nilpotent elements.

Proof: If $a^n = 0$, the subring (a) is the set of $\sum_{i=1}^{n-1} k_i a^i$, where the k_i are in I. Since I is finite, (a) is finite, and since there can only be finitely many (a)'s, we are done.

(3) There are only finitely many units.

Proof: Let u be a unit, v its inverse. Since the subrings (v^2), (v^4), $\ldots$ cannot all be distinct, we must have $v^{2^m} \in (v^{2^{m+1}})$ for some $m \in N$, say $v^{2^m} = \sum_{i=1}^r k_i v^{2^{m+1}i}$. Hence $u^{2^{m+1}r} = \sum_{i=1}^r k_i u^{2^{m+1}(r-i)+2^m}$, where the highest exponent in the right member is $2^{m+1}r - 2^m$; thus

$$(u) = \left\{ \sum_{i=1}^{2^{m+1}r-1} k_i u^i \mid \text{the } k_i\text{'s in } I \right\}$$

is finite, and the desired conclusion follows as in step (2).

(4) If the ring is simple, it is finite.

Proof: Since a left ideal is a subring, $\mathscr{L}_R$ certainly satisfies the minimum condition; hence R is either prime (and so finite) or isomorphic to the ring of (say) n-by-n matrices over a division ring D. Since D is isomorphic to a subring of R (the scalar matrices), it can have only finitely many subrings, hence is finite by step (3). Let D have N elements; then $R \cong M_D^{(n)}$ has N^{n^2} elements.

(5) If the ring is semisimple, it is finite.

Proof: Let $R \cong R_1 \oplus \cdots \oplus R_n$, where each R_i is simple. Since each R_i is isomorphic to a subring of R, it can have only finitely many subrings, hence is finite by step (4). Let R_i have N_i elements; then R has $\prod_{i=1}^n N_i$ elements.

(6) The ring is finite in any case.

Proof: Since $\mathscr{L}_R$ satisfies the minimum condition, $R/\langle R \rangle$ is semisimple. Since the subring lattice of $R/\langle R \rangle$ is order isomorphic to a sublattice of that of R, it is finite, making $R/\langle R \rangle$ finite by step (5). On the other hand, every element of $\langle R \rangle$ is nilpotent, so that $\langle R \rangle$ is finite by step (2). Since $\langle R \rangle$ and $R/\langle R \rangle$ are finite, so is R.   //

Corollary. *A lattice-finite ring which has a cancellable element must be finite.*

Proof: Corollary 1 to Proposition 45.6.   //

The analogous statement about division rings is false; an infinite field can have a finite subfield lattice, as we see from the example of the prime field **R**. However, we can prove

Theorem 2. *A lattice-finite division ring is a field.*

Proof: Let D be such a ring, K_0 its prime field. As in the first part of the proof of Theorem 72.1, every $a \in D$ is algebraic over K_0, so that $(a) = (K_0 \cup \{a\})$ is finite dimensional as a vector space over K_0. Let the monogenic subfields of D be $(a_1), \ldots, (a_n)$, and let deg $((a_i):K_0) = d_i$, $1 \le i \le n$; then since D is their union, we have deg $(D:K_0) \le d_1 + \cdots + d_n$. Thus if $K_0 \cong \mathbf{I}_p$ is finite, so is D, making D a field; it remains only to consider the case $K_0 \cong \mathbf{R}$. Since $D = (a_1, \ldots, a_n)$, it suffices to show that the a's commute with one another. To this end, note that for any i, j in $\mathbf{N}_n$ the subfields $(a_i + ca_j)$ cannot be distinct for all $c \in K_0$. Let $(a_i + aa_j) = (a_i + ba_j)$, where $a \ne b$; then this field contains $(a_i + aa_j) - (a_i + ba_j) = (a - b)a_j$, hence contains $(a - b)^{-1}(a - b)a_j = a_j$, and so contains also $(a_i + aa_j) - aa_j = a_i$. Since a_i and a_j are thus both in a subfield of D, they commute.   //

Note that we have actually proved a somewhat stronger assertion, namely that a division ring which has only finitely many subfields must be a field. Thus these division rings are the same as the lattice-finite fields, that is, the same as the monogenic algebraic fields.

Corollary 1. *A lattice-finite domain is empty, trivial, or a finite field.*

Proof: It is finite by the corollary to Theorem 1; now use the corollary to Theorem 71.3.   ‖

Corollary 2. *A lattice-finite division ring of characteristic $\neq 0$ is a finite field.*

Exercise 1. *Let D be a division ring, and K a subfield of the center of D such that D has only finitely many subfields which contain K; then D is a field.*

SPECIAL SYMBOLS

SYMBOL	MEANING	DEFINED IN SECTION
$\{\cdots\}$	the set whose elements are...	1
$\{x\|\cdots\}$	the set of x such that...	1
$\in$	is an element of	1
$=$	is equal to	1
$\subseteq$	is contained in	1
$\subset$	is properly contained in	1
$\subseteq_{\mathscr{S}}$	the inclusion relation on $\mathscr{S}$	2
$\sim$	is in one-to-one correspondence with	3
$\leq$	is not greater than	4
	order relation	6
$<$	is less than	4
	strict order relation	6
$\cong$	is isomorphic to	24
$\cup$	union	1
$\cap$	intersection	1
$\circ$	composition of relations	2
inf, $\wedge$	greatest lower bound	7, 11
sup, $\vee$	least upper bound	7, 11
$x + y$	sum (of x and y)	
	natural numbers	4
	cardinal numbers	21
	additive composition	22

275

SYMBOL	MEANING	DEFINED IN SECTION
$\underset{m}{+}$	sum modulo m	38
$\oplus$	direct sum	50
$\sum_{i=1}^{k} x_i$	sum of $(x_1, \ldots, x_k)$	4
	composite of $(x_1, \ldots, x_k)$ (additive composition)	33, 50
$\sum_{i=1}^{k} S_i$	direct sum of $(S_1, \ldots, S_k)$	50
$\sum_I S_i$	direct sum of $(S_i)_I$	50
$\sum_I^* S_i$	weak direct sum of $(S_i)_I$	50
$-$	relative complement	1
	difference	4
	inverse (with respect to an additive composition)	36
$\times$	Cartesian product	2, 19
	direct product	29
xy	product (of x and y)	
	natural numbers	5
	cardinal numbers	21
	multiplicative composition	22
nx	$x + \cdots + x$ (n terms; additive composition)	33
AB	$\{ab \mid a \in A, b \in B\}$	22
$\underset{m}{\cdot}$	product modulo m	38
$\prod_{i=1}^{k} x_i$	composite of $(x_1, \ldots, x_k)$ (multiplicative composition)	33
$\prod_{i=1}^{k} S_i$	Cartesian product of $(S_1, \ldots, S_k)$	19
	direct product of $(S_1, \ldots, S_k)$	29
$\prod_I S_i$	Cartesian product of $(S_i)_I$	19
	direct product of $(S_i)_I$	29
$\prod_I^* S_i$	weak direct product of $(S_i)_I$	39
$(\cdots)^{-1}$	inverse	
	of a relation	2
	of an element with respect to a multiplicative composition	34
	ordered set under the inverse order relation	19, 29

SYMBOL	MEANING	DEFINED IN SECTION
$x \mid y$	x divides y	
	natural numbers	5
	multiplicative composition	35
$x/y, \dfrac{x}{y}$	quotient of x by y	
	natural numbers	5
	rational numbers	36
$n!$	n factorial	5
$\dbinom{n}{m}$	$\dfrac{n!}{m!(n-m)!}$	5
x^y	x to the yth power	
	natural numbers	5
	cardinal numbers	21
x^n	$x \cdots x$ (n factors; multiplicative composition)	33
(a, b)	the ordered pair with first term a and second term b	1
$[a, b]$	the interval $\{x \mid a \le x \le b\}$	7
	the commutator of a and b	41
$(a_1, \ldots, a_n)$	the n-tuple whose ith term is a_i	4
$(a_i)_{\mathbf{N}}$	the sequence whose ith term is a_i	4
$(a_i)_I$	the I-tuple whose ith term is a_i	19
$\deg(L:K)$	the degree of L over K	70
$\dim(b:a)$	the dimension of b over a	10
$i_G(x)$	the index of x in G	46
$o(x)$	the order of x	46
$r(x)$	the rank of x	12, 51
$r_0(G)$	the 0-rank of G	51
$r_p(G)$	the p-rank of G	51
$A(S)$	the set of automorphisms of S	24
$E(S)$	the set of endomorphisms of S	24
E_x	the E-class containing x	17
EA	$\{x \mid (x, a) \in E \text{ for some } a \in A\}$	18
E_A	the smallest congruence on S such that A is contained in an E-class	27
E_F	$F \circ F^{-1}$	18

SYMBOL	MEANING	DEFINED IN SECTION
F_E	the canonical function of E	18
F/E	the quotient of F by E	24
$F(a)$	the value of the function F for the argument a	3
$F(A)$	$\{F(a) \mid a \in A\}$; same as $\tilde{F}(A)$	3
$F^{-1}(b)$	the preimage of b under the function F	3
$F^{-1}(B)$	$\{F^{-1}(b) \mid b \in B\}$	3
$\tilde{F}$	$\{(A, \{F(a) \mid a \in A\}) \mid A \subseteq S\}$, where F is a function defined on S	3
$\bar{F}$	$\{((A, B), \{F(a, b) \mid a \in A, b \in B\}) \mid A, B \subseteq S\}$, where F is a composition on S	22
G_P	the set of elements of finite order of G	51
G_p	the set of elements of G whose orders are powers of p	51
$G_{L/K}$	the Galois group of L over K	73
I_S	the equality relation on S	2
	the identity function on S	3
$K(x)$	the rational functions in one indeterminate over K	60
$K(x_1, \ldots, x_n)$	the rational functions in n indeterminates over K	70
$K(S)$	the cardinality of S	20
L_x	left multiplication by x	31
L_A	$\{(x, y) \mid y \in xA\}$	38
$M_S^{(n)}$	the n by n matrices over S	58
$\varnothing$	the empty set	1
Q	the quaternion group	55
$\langle R \rangle$	the radical of R	75
R_A	$\{(x, y) \mid y \in Ax\}$	38
(S)	element of an I-lattice generated by S	16
S^n	the nth Cartesian power of S	4
	the nth direct power of S	29
S^I	the set of functions from I into S; the Ith Cartesian power of S	19
	the Ith direct power of S	29
S^{N°	the power series in one indeterminate over S	58

SYMBOL	MEANING	DEFINED IN SECTION
$S[x]$	the polynomials in one indeterminate over S	58
$S[x, y]$	the polynomials in two indeterminates over S	58
$S[x_1, \ldots, x_n]$	the polynomials in n indeterminates over S	70
S/E	the quotient of S by E	17
0	the integer "zero"	4
	least element of an ordered set	7
	identity element for an additive composition	50
1	the natural number "one"	4
	greatest element of an ordered set	7
	multiplicative identity element in a ring or field	59
$\mathbf{I}$	the integers	36
$\mathbf{I}_m$	N°_{m-1}; the integers modulo m	38
$\mathbf{N}$	the natural numbers	4
$\mathbf{N}^\circ$	the nonnegative integers	4
$\mathbf{N}_m$	the natural numbers through m	4
$\mathbf{N}^\circ_m$	the nonnegative integers through m	4
$\mathbf{R}$	the rational numbers	36
$\mathbf{R}^+$	the positive rational numbers	36
$\mathbf{R}/\mathbf{I}$	the rational numbers modulo 1	53
$\mathscr{C}_S$	the set of all congruences on S	25
$\mathscr{C}_{S,E}$	the set of all congruences on S which contain E	26
$\mathscr{E}_S$	the set of all equivalences on S	17
$\mathscr{E}_{S,E}$	the set of all equivalences on S which contain E	18
$\mathscr{F}_S$	the set of all functions defined on S	18
$\mathscr{I}_S$	the set of principal ideals of S	35
$\mathscr{I}'_S$	$\mathscr{I}_S - \{S\}$	35
$\mathscr{J}_R$	the set of all ideals of R	60
$\mathscr{L}_R$	the set of left ideals of R	75
$\mathscr{M}_S$	the set of all normal subsets of S	27
$\mathscr{M}_{S,E}$	the set of all normal subsets of S which either $= \varnothing$ or are classes of congruences containing E	27

SYMBOL	MEANING	DEFINED IN SECTION
$\mathcal{N}_S$	the set of all normal subgroupoids of S	28
$\mathcal{N}_G^*$	the set of all normal subgroups of G	38
$\mathcal{N}_{G,H}^*$	the set of all normal subgroups of G which contain H	38
$\mathcal{P}_S$	the set of all subsets of S	1
$\mathcal{P}_S^{(E)}$	the set of all E-invariant subsets of S	18
$\mathcal{Q}_S$	the set of all quotient sets of S	17
$\mathcal{S}_S$	the set of all subgroupoids of S	23
$\mathcal{S}_S^{(E)}$	the set of all E-invariant subgroupoids of S	26
$\mathcal{S}_G^*$	the set of all subgroups of the group G	37
$\mathcal{S}_{G,H}^*$	the set of all subgroups of the group G which contain H	38
$\mathcal{S}_V$	the set of all subspaces of the vector space V	67
$\varphi_{a,K}$	the minimal polynomial of a over K	70
φ'	$\sum_{i=0}^{n} i a_i x^{i-1}$ (where $\varphi = \sum_{i=0}^{n} a_i x^i$)	62

INDEX

Gaussian, 219
principal, 219
residue, 216
semisimple, 269, 270–272
simple, 243, 266–268
zero-, 210
Ringoid, 206
Root, 209

Schreier refinement theorem, 53, 103
Schur's lemma, 238
Segment, 30
Semigroup, 117
cancellation, 120
commutative, 117
Gaussian, 126
GCD, 127
with identity, 117
LCM, 129
PL-, 129
Semiring, 207
zero-, 207
Separable element, 257
Sequence, 18
Set, 1, 2
denumerable, 25
empty, 2
finite, 21
inductive, 35
infinite, 21
of operators, 223, 227
with operators, 223
ordered, 26
underlying, 90
well ordered, 34
Solvability by radicals, 264–266
Straightedge and compass constructions, 248
Subalgebra, 203
Subfield, 214
Subgroup, 135
normal, 138–143
stable, 229
supplemented, 149
Sylow p-, 166
Subgroupoid, 90
normal, 101
subnormal, 102
supplemented, 145
Sublattice, 42
Submodule, 229
Subring, 213

division, 214
Subsemigroup, 117
Subsemiring, 212
Subset, 2
invariant, 74
normal, 98
proper, 3
stable, 90, 203, 223
Subspace, 230
Subtractions, of integers, 131
of natural numbers, 15
Sum, of cardinal numbers, 84
direct, 146, 178
of natural numbers, 15, 19
weak direct, 179
Supplement, of a congruence, 105
of an equivalence, 79
of a supplemented subgroup, 149
Supplemented congruence, 105
Supplemented equivalence, 79
Supplemented subgroup, 149
Supplemented subgroupoid, 145
Sylow's theorem, 165

Term, constant, 208
of an I-tuple, 74
of an n-tuple, 18
of an ordered pair, 5
of a sequence, 18
of a sum, 15
Transcendence base, 249
Transcendence degree, 249
Transcendental element, 245
Transposition, 169
Type, 188

Union, 3, 4
Unit, 122
Universal algebra, 203
Unrefinable chain, 39
Unrefinable independent set, 48
Unrefinable normal series, 102

Value, 9
Vector space, 228

Wedderburn–Artin theorems, 266, 270
Well ordered set, 34

Zassenhaus' lemma, 102
Zorn's lemma, 35